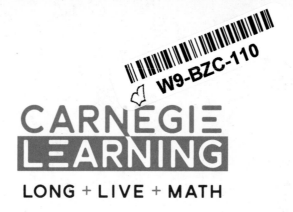

High School Math Solution
Geometry

Student Edition
Volume 1

Sandy Bartle Finocchi and Amy Jones Lewis

with Josh Fisher, Janet Sinopoli, and Victoria Fisher

501 Grant St., Suite 1075
Pittsburgh, PA 15219
Phone 888.851.7094
Customer Service Phone 412.690.2444
Fax 412.690.2444

www.carnegielearning.com

Cover Design by Anne Milliron

ISBN: 978-1-60972-415-3
Student Edition, Volume 1

Printed in the United States of America
3 4 5 6 7 8 9 BB 21

LONG + LIVE + MATH

ACKNOWLEDGMENTS

High School Math Solution Authors
- Sandy Bartle Finocchi, Senior Academic Officer
- Amy Jones Lewis, Director of Instructional Design
- Josh Fisher, Instructional Designer
- Victoria Fisher, Instructional Designer
- Janet Sinopoli, Instructional Designer

Foundational Authors
- William S. Hadley, Co-Founder
- David Dengler
- Mary Lou Metz

Vendors
- Lumina Datamatics, Ltd.
- Mathematical Expressions, LLC

Images
www.pixabay.com

Special Thanks

- Alison Huettner for project management and editorial review.
- Jacyln Snyder for her contributions to the Teacher's Implementation Guide facilitation notes.
- Harry Lynch for his contributions and review of the Statistics and Probability strand.
- The members of Carnegie Learning Cognitive Scientist Team—Brendon Towle, John Connelly, Bob Hausmann, Chas Murray, and Martina Pavelko—for their insight in learning science and collaboration on MATHia® Software.
- John Jorgenson, Chief Marketing Officer, for all his insight and messaging.
- Carnegie Learning Education Services Team for content review and providing customer feedback.
- The entire Carnegie Learning staff for their hard work and dedication to transforming math education.
- The families of the authoring team for their continued support.

" Mathematics is so much more than memorizing rules. It is learning to reason, to make connections, and to make sense of the world. We believe in Learning by Doing(TM)—you need to actively engage with the content if you are to benefi t from it. The lessons were designed to take you from your intuitive understanding of the world and build on your prior experiences to then learn new concepts. My hope is that these instructional materials help you build a deep understanding of math. "

Sandy Bartle Finocchi, Senior Academic Officer

" You have been learning math for a very long time—both in school and in your interactions in the world. You know a lot of math! In this course, there's nothing brand new. It all builds on what you already know. So, as you approach each activity, use all of your knowledge to solve problems, to ask questions, to fix mistakes, and to think creatively. "

Amy Jones Lewis, Director of Instructional Design

" At Carnegie Learning we have created an organization whose mission and culture is defined by your success. Our passion is creating products that make sense of the world of mathematics and ignite a passion in you. Our hope is that you will enjoy our resources as much as we enjoyed creating them. "

Barry Malkin, CEO, Carnegie Learning

Volume 1 Student Edition

Module 1: Reasoning with Shapes

Topic 1: Using a Rectangular Coordinate System

1.1 The Squariest Square
From Informal to Formal Geometric Thinking M1-7

1.2 Hip to Be Square
Constructing a Coordinate Plane... M1-17

1.3 Ts and Train Tracks
Parallel and Perpendicular Lines M1-33

1.4 Where Has Polly Gone?
Classifying Shapes on the Coordinate Plane.. M1-51

1.5 In and Out and All About
Area and Perimeter on the Coordinate Plane... M1-69

Topic 2: Composing and Decomposing Shapes

2.1 Running Circles Around Geometry
Using Circles to Make Conjectures M1-111

2.2 The Quad Squad
Conjectures About Quadrilaterals.. M1-127

2.3 Into the Ring
Constructing an Inscribed Regular Polygon M1-145

2.4 Tri- Tri- Tri- and Separate Them
Conjectures About Triangles M1-161

2.5 What's the Point?
Points of Concurrency.. M1-175

Topic 3: Rigid Motions on a Plane

3.1 Put Your Input In, Take Your Output Out
Geometric Components of Rigid Motions M1-205

3.2 Bow Thai
Translations as Functions M1-217

3.3 Staring Back at Me
Reflections as Functions M1-229

3.4 Turn Yourself Around
Rotations as Functions.. M1-243

3.5 OKEECHOBEE
Reflectional and Rotational Symmetry M1-257

Module 2: Establishing Congruence

Topic 1: Congruence Through Transformations

1.1 The Elements
Formal Reasoning in Euclidean Geometry M2-7

1.2 ASA, SAS, and SSS
Proving Triangle Congruence Theorems.. M2-23

1.3 I Never Forget a Face
Using Triangle Congruence to Solve Problems M2-39

Topic 2: Justifying Line and Angle Relationships

2.1 Proof Positive
Forms of Proof M2-61

2.2 A Parallel Universe
Proving Parallel Line Theorems M2-83

2.3 Ins and Outs
Interior and Exterior Angles of Polygons... M2-103

2.4 Identical Twins
Perpendicular Bisector and Isosceles Triangle Theorems................................. M2-119

2.5 Corners in a Round Room
Angle Relationships Inside and Outside Circles.................................... M2-141

Topic 3: Using Congruence Theorems

3.1 SSS, SAS, AAS, . . . S.O.S!
Using Triangle Congruence to Determine Relationships Between Segments.... M2-185

3.2 Props To You
Properties of Quadrilaterals... M2-197

3.3 Three-Chord Song
Relationships Between Chords M2-225

Volume 2 Student Edition

Module 3: Investigating Proportionality

Topic 1: Similarity

1.1 Big, Little, Big, Little
Dilating Figures to Create Similar Figures...M3-7

1.2 Similar Triangles or Not?
Establishing Triangle Similarity Criteria M3-23

1.3 Keep It in Proportion
Theorems About Proportionality... M3-37

1.4 This Isn't Your Average Mean
More Similar Triangles M3-65

1.5 Run It Up the Flagpole
Application of Similar Triangles M3-79

1.6 Jack's Spare Key
Partitioning Segments in Given Ratios.. M3-95

Topic 2: Trigonometry

2.1 Three Angle Measure
Introduction to Trigonometry M3-121

2.2 The Tangent Ratio
Tangent Ratio, Cotangent Ratio, and Inverse Tangent M3-137

2.3 The Sine Ratio
Sine Ratio, Cosecant Ratio, and Inverse Sine M3-155

2.4 The Cosine Ratio
Cosine Ratio, Secant Ratio, and Inverse Cosine.. M3-171

2.5 We Complement Each Other
Complement Angle Relationships M3-187

2.6 A Deriving Force
Deriving the Triangle Area Formula, the Law of Sines,
and the Law of Cosines.. M3-199

Module 4: Connecting Geometric and Algebraic Descriptions

Topic 1: Circles and Volume

1.1   All Circles Great and Small
       Similarity Relationships in Circles M4-7

1.2   A Slice of Pi
       Sectors and Segments of a Circle M4-25

1.3   Do Me a Solid
       Building Three-Dimensional Figures M4-45

1.4   Get to the Point
       Building Volume and Surface Area Formulas for Pyramids,
       Cones, and Spheres... M4-65

Topic 2: Conic Sections

2.1   Any Way You Slice It
       Cross-Sections M4-101

2.2 X^2 Plus Y^2 Equals Radius^2
       Deriving the Equation for a Circle... M4-119

2.3   A Blip on the Radar
       Determining Points on a Circle M4-133

2.4   Sin^2 θ Plus Cos^2 θ Equals 1^2
       The Pythagorean Identity M4-149

2.5   Going the Equidistance
       Equation of a Parabola.. M4-159

2.6   It's a Stretch
       Ellipses M4-187

2.7   More Asymptotes
       Hyperbolas M4-211

Module 5: Making Informed Decisions

Topic 1: Independence and Conditional Probability

1.1   What Are the Chances?
Compound Sample Spaces..M5-7

1.2   And?
Compound Probability with *And* M5-27

1.3   Or?
Compound Probability with *Or* M5-41

1.4   And, Or, and More!
Calculating Compound Probability.. M5-57

Topic 2: Computing Probabilities

2.1   Table Talk
Compound Probability for Data Displayed in Two-Way Tables.......................... M5-81

2.2   It All Depends
Conditional Probability M5-99

2.3   Give Me 5!
Permutations and Combinations M5-113

2.4   A Different Kind of Court Trial
Independent Trials.. M5-135

2.5   What Do You Expect?
Expected Value.. M5-149

Glossary G-1

Index I-1

Each lesson has the same structure. Key features are noted.

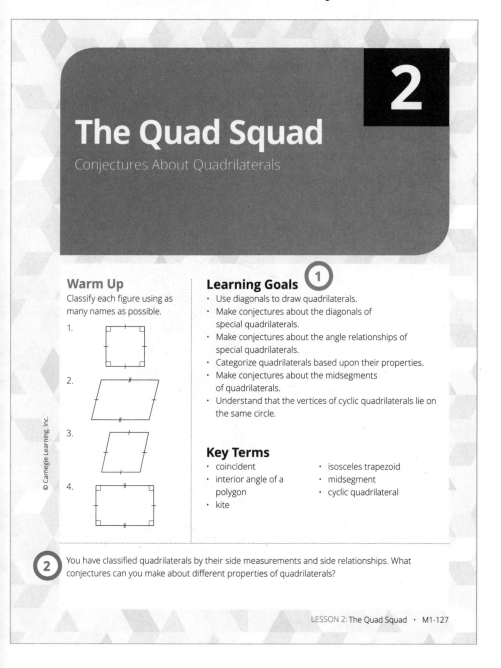

Warm Up

Classify each figure using as many names as possible.

1.

2.

3.

4.

Learning Goals ①

- Use diagonals to draw quadrilaterals.
- Make conjectures about the diagonals of special quadrilaterals.
- Make conjectures about the angle relationships of special quadrilaterals.
- Categorize quadrilaterals based upon their properties.
- Make conjectures about the midsegments of quadrilaterals.
- Understand that the vertices of cyclic quadrilaterals lie on the same circle.

Key Terms

- coincident
- interior angle of a polygon
- kite
- isosceles trapezoid
- midsegment
- cyclic quadrilateral

② You have classified quadrilaterals by their side measurements and side relationships. What conjectures can you make about different properties of quadrilaterals?

The Quad Squad

Conjectures About Quadrilaterals

2

© Carnegie Learning, Inc.

LESSON 2: The Quad Squad • M1-127

1. Learning Goals
Learning goals are stated for each lesson to help you take ownership of the learning objectives.

2. Connection
Each lesson begins with a statement connecting what you have learned with a question to ponder.

Return to this question at the end of this lesson to gauge your understanding.

3. Getting Started

Each lesson begins with a Getting Started. When working on the Getting Started, use what you know about the world, what you have learned previously, or your intuition. The goal is just to get you thinking and ready for what's to come.

GETTING STARTED

Cattywampus

A quadrilateral may be convex or concave. The quadrilaterals you are most familiar with—trapezoids, parallelograms, rectangles, rhombi, and squares—are convex. For a polygon to be convex it contains all of the line segments connecting any pair of points. It is concave if and only if at least one of its interior angles is greater than 180°.

Why can a concave quadrilateral have only one angle greater than 180°?

Consider the two quadrilaterals shown. A quadrilateral has exactly two diagonals.

Convex   Concave

1. Draw the diagonals in the two quadrilaterals shown. What do you notice?

2. Make a conjecture about the diagonals of a convex quadrilateral and about the diagonals of a concave quadrilateral.

The diagonals of any convex quadrilateral create two pairs of vertical angles and four linear pairs of angles.

3. Label the vertices of the convex quadrilateral as well as the point of intersection of the diagonals. Identify each pair of vertical angles and each linear pair of angles.

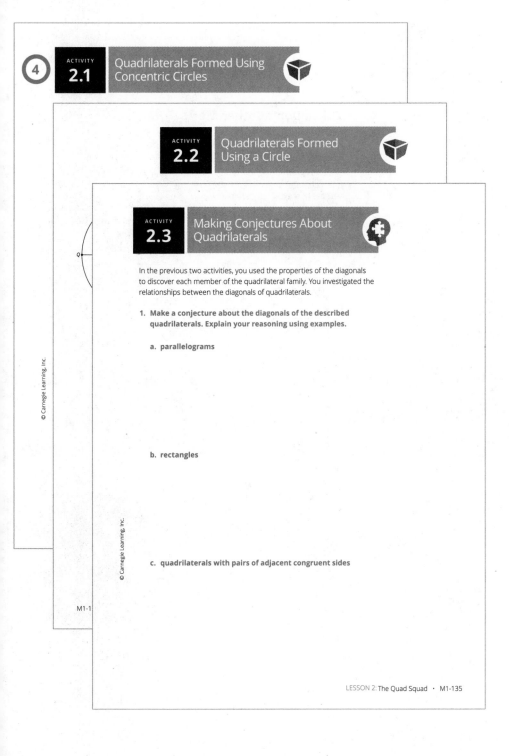

ACTIVITY 4

ACTIVITY 2.1 Quadrilaterals Formed Using Concentric Circles

ACTIVITY 2.2 Quadrilaterals Formed Using a Circle

ACTIVITY 2.3 Making Conjectures About Quadrilaterals

In the previous two activities, you used the properties of the diagonals to discover each member of the quadrilateral family. You investigated the relationships between the diagonals of quadrilaterals.

1. **Make a conjecture about the diagonals of the described quadrilaterals. Explain your reasoning using examples.**

   a. parallelograms

   b. rectangles

   c. quadrilaterals with pairs of adjacent congruent sides

M1-1

4. Activities

You are going to build a deep understanding of mathematics through a variety of activities in an environment where collaboration and conversations are important and expected.

You will learn how to solve new problems, but you will also learn why those strategies work and how they are connected to other strategies you already know.

Remember:

- It's not just about answer-getting. The process is important.

- Making mistakes are a critical part of learning, so take risks.

- There is often more than one way to solve a problem.

Activities may include real-world problems, sorting activities, worked examples, or analyzing sample student work.

Be prepared to share your solutions and methods with your classmates.

5. Talk the Talk

Talk the Talk gives you an opportunity to reflect on the main ideas of the lesson.

- Be honest with yourself.
- Ask questions to clarify anything you don't understand.
- Show what you know!

Don't forget to revisit the question posed on the lesson opening page to gauge your understanding.

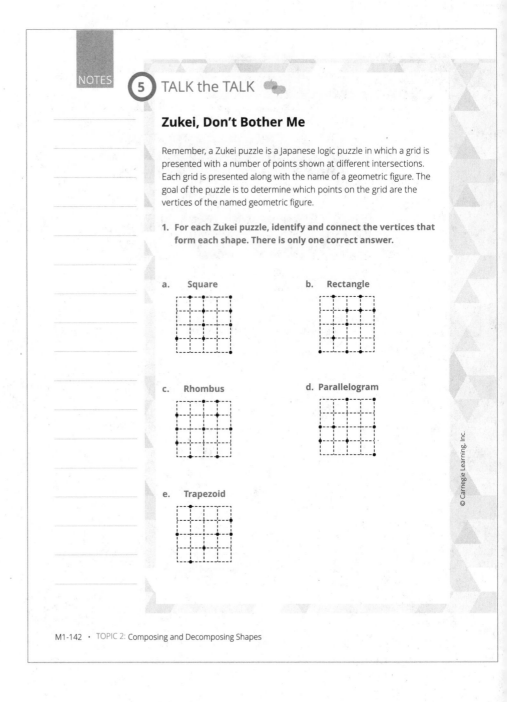

NOTES

5 TALK the TALK

Zukei, Don't Bother Me

Remember, a Zukei puzzle is a Japanese logic puzzle in which a grid is presented with a number of points shown at different intersections. Each grid is presented along with the name of a geometric figure. The goal of the puzzle is to determine which points on the grid are the vertices of the named geometric figure.

1. For each Zukei puzzle, identify and connect the vertices that form each shape. There is only one correct answer.

a. Square

b. Rectangle

c. Rhombus

d. Parallelogram

e. Trapezoid

© Carnegie Learning, Inc.

ASSIGNMENT

Assignment

6 Write

Define each term in your own words. Use the words *diagonal*, *interior angle*, and *midsegment* in your definitions.
1. kite
2. isosceles trapezoid
3. cyclic quadrilateral

7 Remember

The diagonals of a parallelogram bisect each other and the diagonals of a rectangle are congruent. A square, rhombus, and kite have perpendicular diagonals.

The opposite angles of parallelograms are congruent and the opposite angles of cyclic quadrilaterals are supplementary.

8 Practice

1. Determine which quadrilateral each letter in the diagram represents using the list shown.

| Quadrilaterals |

Kites   Squa
Rectangles   Paral
Rhombi   Isosc

2. State as many propertie
each quadrilateral.
   a. Rectangle   b.
   c. Kite   d.
   e. Rhombus   f.

3. Describe how to constru
given diagonal.
   a. Square *WXYZ* given di
   b. Parallelogram *RSTU* t
      diagonal *RT*

9 Stretch

Create a Zukei puzzle for an isosceles trapezoid in which the bases do not lie on the grid lines. Use a minimum of 10 dots. Make sure that your puzzle has only one correct answer.

10 Review

1. Write a conjecture about alternate interior angles. Draw an example to test your conjecture.
2. Draw examples of inscribed angles that intercept the same arc of a circle. What conjecture can you make about the measures of the inscribed angles?

3. Jay walks 3 blocks north and then 4 blocks east to get to the store. If he walks straight back home, how far does Jay walk in all?

4. TV screen sizes are given by their diagonal measure from a top corner to the opposite bottom corner. What is the approximate size of this TV to the nearest inch?

29.4 in.

52.3 in.

5. Use the coordinate plane to approximate each distance. Write each answer as a decimal to the nearest hundredth.
   a. The distance between point *A* and point *C*
   b. The distance between point *D* and point *B*

6. Write
Reflect on your work and clarify your thinking.

7. Remember
Take note of the key concepts from the lesson.

8. Practice
Use the concepts learned in the lesson to solve problems.

9. Stretch
Ready for a challenge?

10. Review
Remember what you've learned by practicing concepts form previous lessons and topics.

Worked Example

When you see a Worked Example:

- Take your time to read through it.
- Question your own understanding.
- Think about the connections between steps.

Ask Yourself:

- What is the main idea?
- How would this work if I changed the numbers?
- Have I used these strategies before?

Worked Example

Consider $\triangle ABC$ and $\triangle ADE$ shown. They are both 45°-45°-90° triangles.

$$\frac{\text{leg length of } \triangle ADE}{\text{hypotenuse length of } \triangle ABC}$$

Triangle ABC is similar to $\triangle ADE$ by the AA Similarity Theorem. Therefore, the lengths of the corresponding sides are proportional.

$$\frac{AE}{AC} = \frac{AD}{AB}$$

You can rewrite the proportion.

side length adjacent to $\angle A$

$$\frac{AE}{AD} = \frac{AC}{AB}$$

length of hypotenuse

So, given the same reference angle measure, the ratio $\dfrac{\text{side length adjacent to reference angle}}{\text{length of hypotenuse}}$ is constant in similar right triangles.

Who's Correct

When you see a Who's Correct icon:

- Take your time to read through the situation.
- Question the strategy or reason given.
- Determine correct or not correct.

Ask Yourself:

- Does the reasoning make sense?
- If the reasoning makes sense, what is the justification?
- If the reasoning does not make sense, what error was made?

5. **Jun says that the sine and cosecant value of every acute angle is less than 1. Todd says that the sine value of every acute angle is less than 1, but the cosecant value is greater than 1. Who is correct? Explain your reasoning.**

Thumbs Up

When you see a Thumbs Up icon:
- Take your time to read through the correct solution.
- Think about the connections between steps.

Ask Yourself:
- Why is this method correct?
- Have I used this method before?

Gabriel

The side length ratios of the opposite side to the hypotenuse or the adjacent side to the hypotenuse is a percent. If the ratio is approximately 0.70, that means the length of the side is about 70% the length of the hypotenuse.

Thumbs Down

When you see a Thumbs Down icon:
- Take your time to read through the incorrect solution.
- Think about what error was made.

Ask Yourself:
- Where is the error?
- Why is it an error?
- How can I correct it?

Alicia
The ratio $\frac{BC}{AB}$ is equal to the ratio $\frac{DC}{AD}$, because the ratio $\frac{\text{side opposite } \angle A}{\text{hypotenuse}}$ is the same for both $\triangle ABC$ and $\triangle ADC$, given the reference angle A, which is 45°.

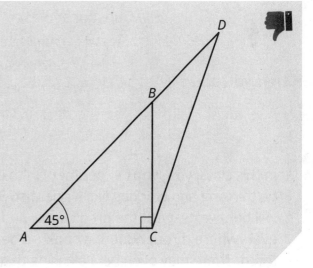

The types of activities within this book require you to make sense of mathematics and to demonstrate your reasoning through problem solving, writing, discussing, and presenting. Effective communication and collaboration are essential skills of a successful learner.

Each activity is denoted with an icon that represents a practice or pair of practices intentionally being developed. To help develop these habits of mind ask yourself the types of questions listed as you work.

With practice, you can develop the habits of mind of a productive mathematical thinker.

▶ Make sense of problems and persevere in solving them.

This practice is evident every day in every lesson. No icon used.

Questions to ask:

- What is this problem asking and what is my plan for answering it?
- What tools do I need to solve this problem?
- Does my answer make sense?

▶ Reason abstractly and quantitatively.
▶ Construct viable arguments and critique the reasoning of others.

Questions to ask:

- What representation can I use to solve this problem?
- How can this problem be represented with symbols and numbers?
- How can I explain my thinking?
- How does my strategy compare to my partner's?

In this class, you won't experiment with beakers full of unearthly liquids, but you'll still be thinking and working like a scientist. So, you will notice patterns, predict how they will behave, test out the predictions, and then unscramble the results. Patterns are everywhere throughout this book, so be **constantly** on the lookout—ready to spot them. There may even be a pleasing pattern buried somewhere in this quotation.

Josh Fisher, Instructional Designer

▶ **Model with mathematics.**
▶ **Use appropriate tools strategically.**

Questions to ask:

- What expression or equation could represent this situation?
- What tools would help me solve this problem?
- What representations best show my thinking?
- How does this answer make sense in the context of the original problem?

▶ **Attend to precision.**

Questions to ask:

- Is my answer accurate?
- Did I use the correct units or labels?
- Is there a more efficient way to solve this problem?
- Is there more sophisticated vocabulary that I could use in my explanation?

▶ **Look for and make use of structure.**
▶ **Look for and express regularity in repeated reasoning.**

Questions to ask:

- What characteristics of this expression or equation are made clear through this representation?
- How can I use what I know to explain why this works?
- Can I develop a more efficient method?
- How could this problem help me to solve another problem?

“It's okay to make mistakes. There is great value in taking risks, making mistakes, and communicating about your mathematical thinking. Only when you reveal your misconceptions, can they be addressed and clarified. You will be amazed at the power you have when you can reason to make sense of the math!”

Janet Sinopoli, Instructional Designer

There are important terms you will encounter throughout this book. It is important that you have an understanding of these words as you get started on your journey through the mathematical concepts. Knowing what is meant by these terms and using these terms will help you think, reason, and communicate your ideas.

ANALYZE

Related Phrases

- Examine
- Evaluate
- Determine
- Observe
- Consider
- Investigate
- What do you notice?
- What do you think?
- Sort and match

Definition

To study or look closely for patterns. Analyzing can involve examining or breaking a concept down into smaller parts to gain a better understanding of it.

Ask Yourself

- Do I see any patterns?
- Have I seen something like this before?
- What happens if the shape, representation, or numbers change?

EXPLAIN YOUR REASONING

Related Phrases

- Show your work
- Explain your calculation
- Justify
- Why or why not?

Definition

To give details or describe how to determine an answer or solution. Explaining your reasoning helps justify conclusions.

Ask Yourself

- How should I organize my thoughts?
- Is my explanation logical?
- Does my reasoning make sense?
- How can I justify my answer to others?

REPRESENT

Definition

To display information in various ways. Representing mathematics can be done using words, tables, graphs, or symbols.

Ask Yourself

- How should I organize my thoughts?
- How do I use this model to show a concept or idea?
- What does this representation tell me?
- Is my representation accurate?

Related Phrases

- Show
- Sketch
- Draw
- Construct
- Create
- Plot
- Graph
- Write an equation
- Complete the table

DESCRIBE

Definition

To represent or give an account of in words. Describing communicates mathematical ideas to others.

Ask Yourself

- How should I organize my thoughts?
- Is my explanation logical?
- Did I consider the context of the situation?
- Does my reasoning make sense?

Related Phrases

- Demonstrate
- Label
- Display
- Compare
- Determine
- Define
- What are the advantages?
- What are the disadvantages?
- What is similar?
- What is different?

PROVE

Definition

To verify the truth of a statement through a sequence of steps and corresponding reasons.

Ask Yourself

- What is the given information?
- What am I trying to prove?
- What additional information follows from each step?
- Can I create an outline of the proof?
- What form of proof can I use?
- Can I work backwards?
- What definitions, postulates, or theorems can I use?

Related Phrases

- Confirm
- Justify
- Convince
- Show
- Demonstrate
- Validate
- Verify

> Imagine a room full of art tools. You and your peers must each use the tools to represent a frog. Some may choose to paint the frog. Others may sculpt or write a poem about it. As a mathematician, you are an artist representing your world with your choice of tools–numbers, equations, graphs, tables, or even words. We can express ourselves in different ways even if we are representing the same idea.

Victoria Fisher, Instructional Designer

Thought Bubbles

Look for these icons as you journey through the textbook. Sometimes they will remind you about things you already learned. Sometimes they will ask you questions to help you think about different strategies. Sometimes they will share fun facts. They are here to help and guide your learning.

Side notes are included to provide helpful insights as you work.

MODULE 1

REASONING WITH SHAPES

The lessons in this module build on your experience analyzing and transforming geometric shapes. In this module, you will make educated guesses about properties and relationships that exist in shapes. You will learn to write formal geometric proofs to verify that these properties and relationships are true in all cases. You will apply rigid motions as geometric functions to plane figures.

Topic 1 Using a Rectangular Coordinate System · · · · · · · · · · · · · **M1-3**

Topic 2 Composing and Decomposing Shapes · · · · · · · · · · · · · **M1-107**

Topic 3 Rigid Motions on a Plane · **M1-201**

Using a Rectangular Coordinate System

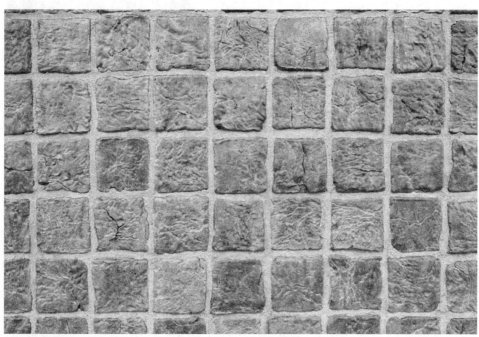

The coordinate plane that you know about is made up of an infinite number of congruent, adjacent squares, like the tiling on a floor or wall.

Lesson 1
The Squariest Square
From Informal to Formal Geometric Thinking M1-7

Lesson 2
Hip to Be Square
Constructing a Coordinate Plane M1-17

Lesson 3
Ts and Train Tracks
Parallel and Perpendicular Lines. M1-33

Lesson 4
Where Has Polly Gone?
Classifying Shapes on the Coordinate Plane. M1-51

Lesson 5
In and Out and All About
Area and Perimeter on the Coordinate Plane. M1-69

Module 1: Reasoning with Shapes

TOPIC 1: USING A RECTANGULAR COORDINATE SYSTEM

Students begin this topic by investigating a geometry puzzle which stimulates the need to measure and then prove that three angles in squares sum to 90°. Students then review the properties of squares and rigid motions and use constructions to build a rectangular coordinate system by creating and transforming squares. Students then study parallel and perpendicular line relationships on the coordinate plane, classify polygons on the coordinate plane, and determine the area and perimeter of shapes on the coordinate plane.

Where have we been?

Students have performed rigid motion transformations of geometric objects in middle school and have explored the properties of triangles, quadrilaterals, and regular polygons. They have studied informal demonstrations of geometric congruence using parallel lines and have a wealth of experience with the coordinate plane from elementary school through middle school.

Where are we going?

In this topic, students are introduced to making conjectures—a theme that will continue into the early parts of the next topic. Students use what they have learned in previous courses to ask formal questions about shapes and lines. These questions will be addressed formally with proofs as students move into later topics in this course.

Using Squares to Show the Slopes of Perpendicular Lines

The diagram shows a diagonal drawn in a 1 unit × 1 unit square. The square is then translated up 1 and right 1. The figure composed of these unshaded squares is then rotated 90° counterclockwise to produce the shaded squares.

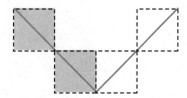

The squares constructed can be those of a coordinate plane. You can use the squares to show that the slopes of perpendicular lines are negative reciprocals of each other.

The Bermuda Triangle

One of the most famous stretches of ocean in the Atlantic is an area between the United States, Puerto Rico, and Bermuda known as the Bermuda Triangle.

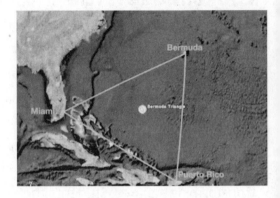

A heavily traveled area by planes and ships, it has become famous because of the many stories about ships and planes lost or destroyed as they moved through the Triangle.

For years, the Bermuda Triangle was suspected of having mysterious, supernatural powers that fatally affected all who traveled through it. Others believed natural phenomena, such as human error and dangerous weather, are to blame for the incidents.

Talking Points

Coordinate geometry can be an important topic to know about for college admissions tests.

Here is an example of a sample question:

In the *xy*-plane, a triangle has vertices at (5, 0), ($\sqrt{2}$, 0), and (2, $\sqrt{10}$). What is the approximate area of the triangle?

You can think of the base as the horizontal line segment. Its length is $5 - \sqrt{2}$, and the height is $\sqrt{10}$. So, the area is

$$\tfrac{1}{2}(\sqrt{10})(5 - \sqrt{2}) \approx 5.67$$

So, the area of the triangle is approximately 5.67 square units.

Key Terms

conjecture
A conjecture is a mathematical statement that appears to be true, but has not been formally proved.

transformation
A transformation is the mapping, or movement, of the points of a figure on a plane according to a common action or operation.

Distance Formula
The Distance Formula states that if (x_1, y_1) and (x_2, y_2) are two points on the coordinate plane, then the distance d between them is given by $d = \sqrt{(x_2 - x_1)^2 + (y_2 - y_1)^2}$.

The Squariest Square

From Informal to Formal Geometric Thinking

Warm Up

Identify and connect the vertices that form a square in each grid.

1.

2.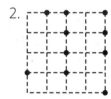

3.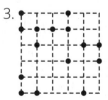

Learning Goals

- Recall properties of geometric figures.
- Understand that the results from measuring tools can be useful in composing a conjecture; however, they are not an acceptable form of mathematical reasoning to validate a conjecture.
- Make a geometric conjecture and use mathematical reasoning to validate it.

Key Terms

- sketch
- draw
- conjecture
- auxiliary line

You have reasoned about lines and shapes in earlier grades and courses. How can you apply formal geometric reasoning to what you know?

The Perfect Square

Can you sketch a perfect square freehand?

1. **Try to sketch a perfect square, like the one shown, without tracing or using tools.**

2. **Explain how you could decide whether one square is closer to "perfect" than another. Use your criteria to judge your and your classmates' best squares.**

3. **List some properties of squares that you know.**

Analyzing a Diagram

In a way, mathematical reasoning is not different from scientific reasoning. In mathematics, you come up with educated guesses and test them to see if they're correct. You can experiment with different patterns and consider arguments about mathematical statements. And, like other scientists, mathematicians gather evidence and become more and more confident about a statement when they obtain more evidence for it.

However, in mathematics, a statement is not true or false until it is proved to be true or false.

Consider the diagram composed of three adjacent squares.

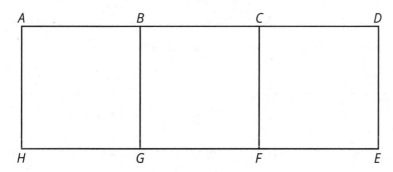

1. **Draw $\overline{AG}$, $\overline{AF}$, $\overline{AE}$. Then label ∠AGH using the letter *a*, label ∠AFG using the letter *b*, and label ∠AEF using the letter *c*.**

2. **Use a protractor to measure ∠*a*, ∠*b*, and ∠*c*. List the angle measures.**

3. **Compare your measurements with your classmates' measurements. What do you notice?**

When you **sketch** a geometric figure, you create the figure without tools. Accuracy is not important. When you **draw** geometric figures, you can use tools such as rulers, protractors, or a coordinate plane to draw exact lengths and areas.

A **conjecture** is a mathematical statement that appears to be true, but has not been formally proved.

In the previous activity, you may have noticed that the sum of the measures of $\angle a$, $\angle b$, and $\angle c$ is close to or equal to 90°. Jayda made a *conjecture* about the sum of the angle measures.

> **Jayda**
> The size of the squares doesn't matter. Given any three adjacent and congruent squares, if the diagonals are drawn in the same way, the sum of the angle measures will always be 90°.

Let's consider a diagram of three differently-sized adjacent and congruent squares. The same lines are drawn and triangles formed.

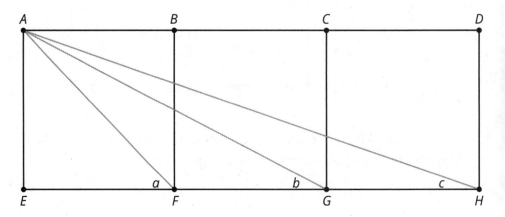

1. **Without measuring, do you think the size of the squares will affect the sum of the measures of $\angle a$, $\angle b$, and $\angle c$? Explain your thinking.**

2. **Use a protractor to test your prediction on these differently-sized squares. Record your results.**

Ask

yourself:

Do your results support Jayda's conjecture?

There are many different ways to verify that the sum of the angle measures could be 90°. Experimenting with different methods and visualizing are important tools that mathematicians use to approach problems in effective ways and gain confidence in their conclusions.

3. **Copy each of the angles** *a*, *b*, **and** *c* **from the diagram onto a different piece of patty paper. How can you manipulate the three angles to show that their sum is 90°?**

Drawing Auxiliary Lines

An **auxiliary line** is a line or line segment added to a diagram to help in solving or proving a concept.

Making arguments about statements in mathematics may seem like a rigid process at times, but it can also involve a lot of creativity. You can, for example, draw extra lines, called *auxiliary lines*, and perform rigid motions like translations, reflections, and rotations when you are reasoning geometrically.

Let's consider a new diagram that is the result of translating the original three squares up and drawing two auxiliary line segments.

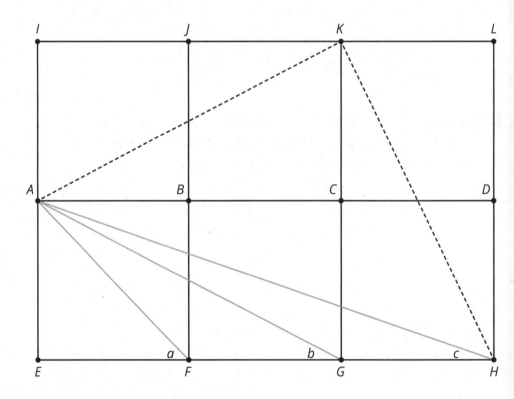

1. **What other angle measures or side lengths can you determine using these added figures? List all the concepts and facts you use.**

TALK the TALK

Proving Yourself

In this course, you will move from making conjectures and creating informal arguments to proving, for good, that certain mathematical statements must be true. You will learn to use properties and definitions to prove or disprove many conjectures.

1. **Write a paragraph describing the differences that you think exist between the informal geometric reasoning you have used in the past and the formal thinking used to prove conjectures. Use examples to illustrate your answer.**

Assignment

Write

Define each term in your own words.

1. sketch
2. draw
3. conjecture
4. auxiliary line

Remember

Mathematicians make conjectures, test predictions, experiment with patterns, and consider arguments and different perspectives.

In mathematics, a statement is not true or false until it is proved to be true or false.

Formal and rigorous mathematical reasoning can involve creative thinking.

Practice

1. A Zukei puzzle is a Japanese logic puzzle in which a grid is presented with a number of points shown at different intersections. Each grid is presented along with the name of a geometric figure. The goal of the puzzle is to determine which points on the grid are the vertices of the named geometric figure. Identify and connect the vertices that form the given shape for each grid.

a. Rhombus

b. Isosceles Triangle

c. Parallelogram

d. Trapezoid

e. Rectangle

f. Isosceles Triangle

g. Square

h. Parallelogram

i. Rectangle

Stretch

Determine what fraction of the square is shaded.
Explain your reasoning.

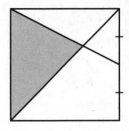

Review

1. Identify the vertical angles.

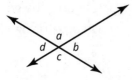

2. Identify the pairs of angles. Describe the measures of the angles in each pair.
   a. Corresponding angles
   b. Alternate interior angles
   c. Alternate exterior angles
   d. Same-side interior angles

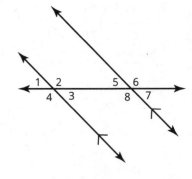

Hip to Be Square

Constructing a Coordinate Plane

Warm Up

Identify whether the transformation shown is a translation, reflection, or rotation. Justify your answer.

1.
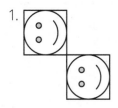

2.

3.
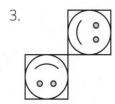

Learning Goals

- Construct a perpendicular line segment and bisector using paper folding and using a compass and straightedge.
- Use construction tools to duplicate a line segment and construct a square.
- Use constructions and rigid motions to create a coordinate plane.
- Identify rigid motions that can be used to create shapes on a coordinate plane.
- Identify the coordinates of vertices of shapes on a coordinate plane.

Key Terms

- construct
- compass
- straightedge
- line
- line segment
- point
- midpoint
- segment bisector
- perpendicular bisector
- diagonal
- transformation
- rigid motion

You have recalled and investigated two-dimensional shapes on a plane. How does the coordinate plane help you to analyze geometric objects?

Getting Back in Shape

You may remember that when you were younger you learned to estimate with counting numbers. Accuracy was not important. Then you learned to count and operate with whole numbers and fractions to determine exact amounts. For example, you could calculate that $(2 \times 5) + (2 \times 3)$ is the same as 2×8, or 16. Later, you learned how to reason accurately without the numbers. You could say that $(a \times b) + (a \times c) = a(b + c)$.

Creating and thinking about geometric objects is similar. In the previous lesson, you sketched a square. When you sketch a geometric figure, you create the figure without tools. Accuracy is not important. When you draw geometric figures, you can use tools such as rulers, protractors, and a coordinate plane to draw exact lengths and areas. Finally, when you *construct* geometric figures, you create exact figures without measurements, using paper folding or a compass and a straightedge—and geometric reasoning!

1. **Draw a right angle. Explain your method.**

A **compass** is a tool used to create arcs and circles.

A **straightedge** is a ruler with no numbers.

In this lesson, you will learn how to **construct** geometric figures. When you construct geometric figures, you create exact figures without measurements, using paper folding or a *compass* and a *straightedge*.

Constructing a Perpendicular Line

You know that a coordinate plane is composed of two intersecting lines—the *x*-axis and *y*-axis.

You can also think of a coordinate plane as being composed of squares. Each square is 1 unit long and 1 unit wide, with the definition of "1 unit" up to the person who constructs the coordinate plane.

In this lesson, you will consider how a coordinate plane is constructed using squares. To construct a square, you will first need to be able to construct perpendicular lines.

Let's start by experimenting with patty paper to construct a line perpendicular to a given line segment.

Worked Example

Draw a line segment on a piece of patty paper.

Fold the line segment so that it lies on top of itself.

Open the patty paper. The crease represents a line perpendicular to the given line segment.

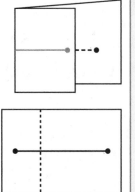

A **line** is described as a straight, continuous arrangement of an infinite number of points. A line has an infinite length, but no width.

A **line segment** is a part of a line between two points on the line, called the endpoints. A distance along a line is the length of a line segment connecting two points on the line.

A **point** is described simply as a location. A point in geometry has no size or shape, but it is often represented using a dot. In a diagram, a point can be labeled using a capital letter.

1. Consider $\overline{AB}$.

   a. Use patty paper to construct 2 different perpendicular lines through $\overline{AB}$.

   b. How can you fold the patty paper so that the perpendicular crease intersects the midpoint of $\overline{AB}$?

A **midpoint** of a line segment is the point that divides the line segment into two congruent segments.

2. Thomas determined the midpoint of a line segment incorrectly. Explain what he did.

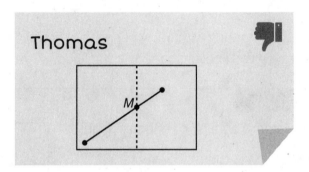

Think about:

How can you be sure that you correctly bisected the line segment?

3. Use patty paper to bisect $\overline{ST}$.

A **segment bisector** is a line, line segment, or ray that divides a line segment into two line segments of equal length. The basic geometric construction used to locate a midpoint of a line segment is called bisecting a line segment.

You can also construct a perpendicular line through a point on a line using a compass and straightedge. To do this construction, you make use of the fact that all the radii of a circle have an equal length.

You can construct a line perpendicular to line ℓ through point B.

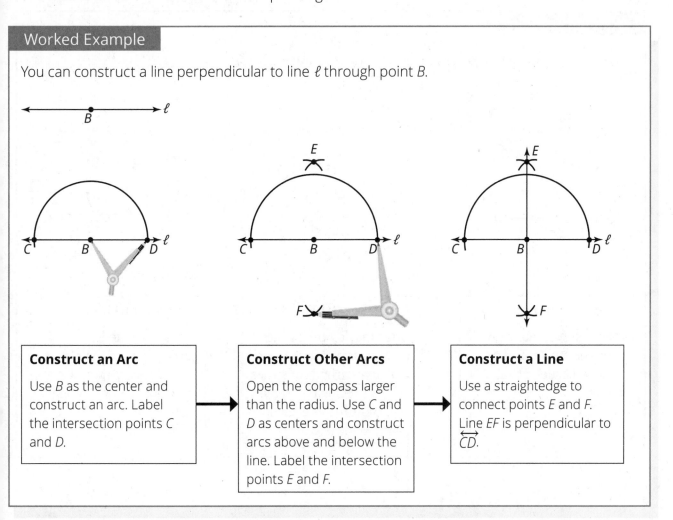

Construct an Arc	Construct Other Arcs	Construct a Line
Use B as the center and construct an arc. Label the intersection points C and D.	Open the compass larger than the radius. Use C and D as centers and construct arcs above and below the line. Label the intersection points E and F.	Use a straightedge to connect points E and F. Line EF is perpendicular to $\overleftrightarrow{CD}$.

4. **Explain why $\overleftrightarrow{EF}$ is a bisector of $\overline{CD}$.**

> A **perpendicular bisector** is a line, line segment, or ray that bisects a line segment and is also perpendicular to the line segment.

5. **Construct a line perpendicular to the given line through point P.**

6. **How are constructing a segment bisector and constructing a perpendicular line through a point on a line different?**

You can also construct a perpendicular line through a point that is not on a line.

Worked Example

You can construct a line perpendicular to line ℓ through point B.

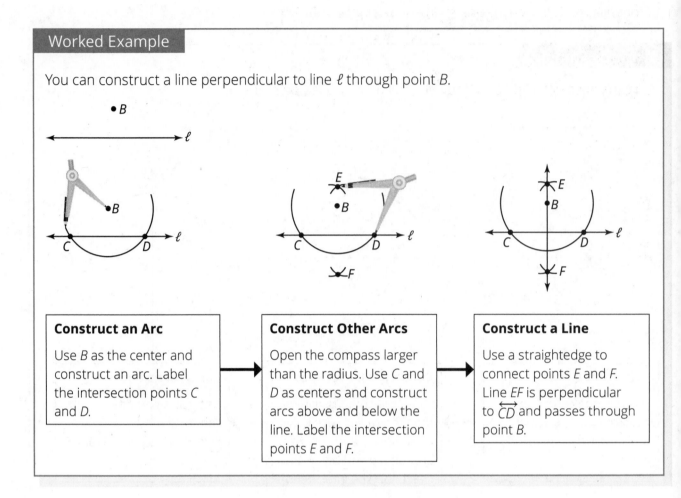

Construct an Arc	**Construct Other Arcs**	**Construct a Line**
Use B as the center and construct an arc. Label the intersection points C and D.	Open the compass larger than the radius. Use C and D as centers and construct arcs above and below the line. Label the intersection points E and F.	Use a straightedge to connect points E and F. Line EF is perpendicular to $\overleftrightarrow{CD}$ and passes through point B.

7. **Construct a line perpendicular to line ℓ through point B.**

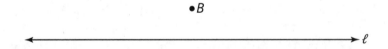

8. Aaron is constructing the perpendicular bisector of $\overline{RS}$. His work is shown.

Aaron says that because the arcs do not intersect, this line segment does not have a midpoint. Kate disagrees and tells him he drew his arcs incorrectly and that he must redraw his arcs to determine the midpoint. Who is correct? Explain your reasoning.

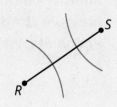

9. Use construction tools to locate the perpendicular bisector of each given line segment. Label each midpoint as *M*.

a.

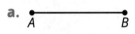

A   B

b. C

D

c. F

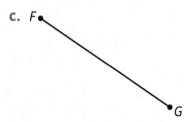

G

10. Choose a point on the perpendicular bisector of one of the line segments in Question 9 and label it *X*. Measure the distances from point *X* to each of the segment's endpoints. Choose another point on the perpendicular bisector and label it *Y*. Measure the distances from point *Y* to each of the segment's endpoints. What do you notice?

11. Make a conjecture about the distance from any point on a perpendicular bisector to the endpoints of the original segment.

Constructing a Square

Along with constructing perpendicular lines, you will need to be able to duplicate line segments in order to construct a square.

There are different ways to use construction tools to duplicate a line segment.

Worked Example

You can duplicate a line segment by constructing an exact copy of the original line segment.

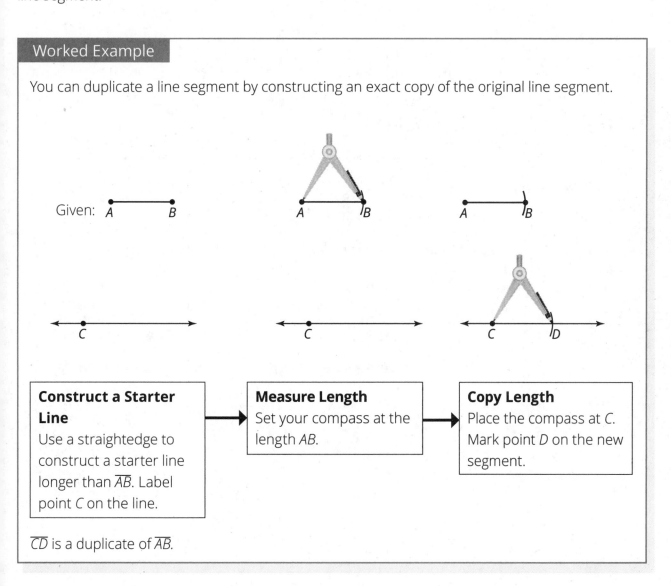

Given: A ———— B

Construct a Starter Line
Use a straightedge to construct a starter line longer than $\overline{AB}$. Label point C on the line.

Measure Length
Set your compass at the length AB.

Copy Length
Place the compass at C. Mark point D on the new segment.

$\overline{CD}$ is a duplicate of $\overline{AB}$.

1. **Construct a line segment that is twice the length of $\overline{AB}$.**

2. Jan and Jackie are duplicating $\overline{AB}$. Their methods are shown.

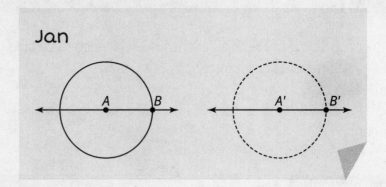

Jan

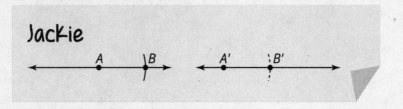

Jackie

Which method is correct? Explain your reasoning.

3. Use a compass and a straightedge to duplicate each line segment.

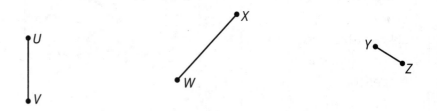

4. Use what you know about duplicating segments and constructing perpendicular lines to construct a square with the same side length as $\overline{JK}$.

5. Use patty paper to verify that the figure you constructed is a square.

6. Draw the *diagonals* of your square and label the angles as shown. What do you notice about the segments and angles? Use patty paper to justify any conjectures.

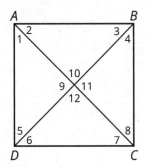

> A **diagonal** is a line segment joining two vertices of a polygon but is not a side of the polygon.

To complete the construction of a coordinate plane, you can perform rigid motions of a constructed square.

Recall that a **transformation** is the mapping, or movement, of the points of a figure on a plane according to a common action or operation. A **rigid motion** is a special type of transformation that preserves the size and shape of the figure.

Felipe used translations to create a coordinate plane.

Remember:

A translation "slides" a figure up, down, left, or right.

A reflection "flips" a figure across a line.

A rotation "spins" a figure about a point.

Felipe
I can translate a square to the right and to the left an infinite number of times. Then, I can translate that entire row of squares up and down an infinite number of times to create a coordinate plane.

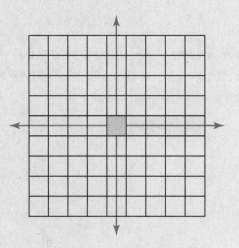

1. **What other sequences of rigid motions of a square can you use to create a coordinate plane? Show your work and explain your reasoning.**

2. The figures shown were each constructed using rigid motions, starting with line segments constructed in one or more squares. Describe a sequence of transformations of a figure that could produce the resulting shape. Then give the coordinates of the vertices of the shape.

a.

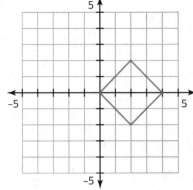

b.

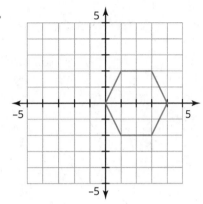

c.

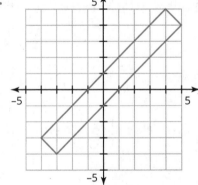

d.

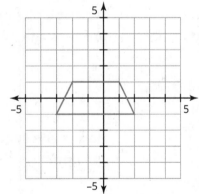

TALK the TALK

Walking on a Thin Line

Consider the line shown on the coordinate plane.

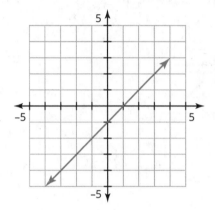

1. Suppose the line was constructed using rigid motions, starting with any line segment constructed in one square. Describe one possible sequence of translations that could produce the line.

2. How is the sequence of translations related to the slope of the line?

3. What is the equation for the line?

Assignment

Write

Describe the similarities and differences of a segment bisector and a perpendicular bisector.

Remember

- A perpendicular bisector is a line, line segment, or ray that bisects a line segment and is also perpendicular to the line segment.
- A translation "slides" a figure up, down, left, or right. A reflection "flips" a figure across a line. A rotation "spins" a figure about a point.

Practice

1. Locate the midpoint of the line segment using construction tools and label it point M. Then explain how you know that point M is the midpoint of $\overline{EF}$.

2. Construct a line perpendicular to each given line and through the given point. Then, explain how you know the constructed line is perpendicular to the given line.

a. 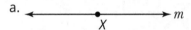   b.

Stretch

Research whether it is possible to trisect a segment using only construction tools. If possible, use construction tools to trisect $\overline{WZ}$ and explain your steps. If not possible, explain why.

Review

1. List three different properties of a square.
2. A right triangle has leg lengths of 6 in. and 8 in. Use the Pythagorean Theorem to determine the length of the hypotenuse. Show your work.

Ts and Train Tracks

Parallel and Perpendicular Lines

Warm Up

Determine the reciprocal of each value.

1. 3

2. −10

3. $\frac{1}{5}$

4. −c

5. $\frac{a}{b}$, $b \neq 0$

Learning Goals

- Construct parallel lines.
- Identify and write the equations of lines perpendicular to given lines.
- Identify and write the equations of parallel lines, including horizontal and vertical lines.

You have constructed line segments, perpendicular lines, squares, and a coordinate plane. How can the coordinate plane be used to justify parallel and perpendicular line relationships?

All Aboard the Clue Train!

You have created lines and shapes by translating, reflecting, and rotating squares on the coordinate plane. Let's explore the slopes of line segments constructed using coordinate plane squares.

Let's consider $\overline{AB}$ on Slope Grid A located at the end of the lesson.

1. **What is the slope of $\overline{AB}$?**

Remember:

The slope of a line indicates both steepness and direction.

2. **Consider how to create a segment parallel to $\overline{AB}$.**

   a. **Trace $\overline{AB}$ onto a piece of patty paper. Then move the segment on the patty paper to create a segment parallel to $\overline{AB}$. Describe your movements.**

   b. **How do you know that these segments are parallel?**

   c. **What is the slope of the segment parallel to $\overline{AB}$?**

3. **Consider how to create a segment perpendicular to $\overline{AB}$.**

   a. **Move the segment on the patty paper to create a segment perpendicular to $\overline{AB}$. Describe your movements.**

   b. **How do you know that these segments are perpendicular?**

   c. **What is the slope of the segment perpendicular to $\overline{AB}$?**

Now let's consider $\overline{CD}$ on Slope Grid B located at the end of the lesson.

4. **What is the slope of $\overline{CD}$?**

5. **Use patty paper to create a segment parallel to $\overline{CD}$.**

   a. **Describe how you know that the segments are parallel.**

   b. **Identify the slope of the segment parallel to $\overline{CD}$.**

6. **Use patty paper to create a segment perpendicular to $\overline{CD}$.**

   a. **Describe how you know that the segments are perpendicular.**

   b. **Identify the slope of the segment perpendicular to $\overline{CD}$.**

7. **Use your investigation to write a conjecture about the slopes of parallel and perpendicular lines.**

ACTIVITY
3.1 Constructing Parallel Lines

In the previous lesson, you constructed perpendicular lines. You can also construct parallel lines.

One strategy used to construct parallel lines is translation. The image of a line that has been translated is either the same line or a parallel line.

If line m is a translation of line ℓ, then the two lines are parallel. Recall that when parallel lines are cut by a transversal, several pairs of congruent angles are formed.

Corresponding angles:
$\angle 8 \cong \angle 1$

Alternate interior angles:
$\angle 1 \cong \angle 6$

Alternate exterior angles:
$\angle 4 \cong \angle 7$

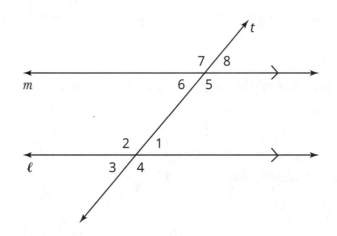

Consider $\overline{AE} \perp$ to $\overleftrightarrow{AD}$ and $\overline{DB} \perp$ to $\overleftrightarrow{AD}$.

1. **Is there enough information to conclude that the two segments are parallel? Explain your reasoning.**

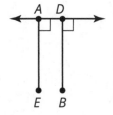

2. Use your reasoning from Question 1 to construct a line parallel
   to line *m* through point *A*. Describe your process.

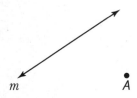

3. Explain why Gage is correct.

Gage

You can duplicate any angle measure, not just right angles,
to construct parallel lines.

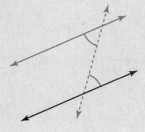

To use Gage's method, you need to know how to use construction tools to duplicate an angle.

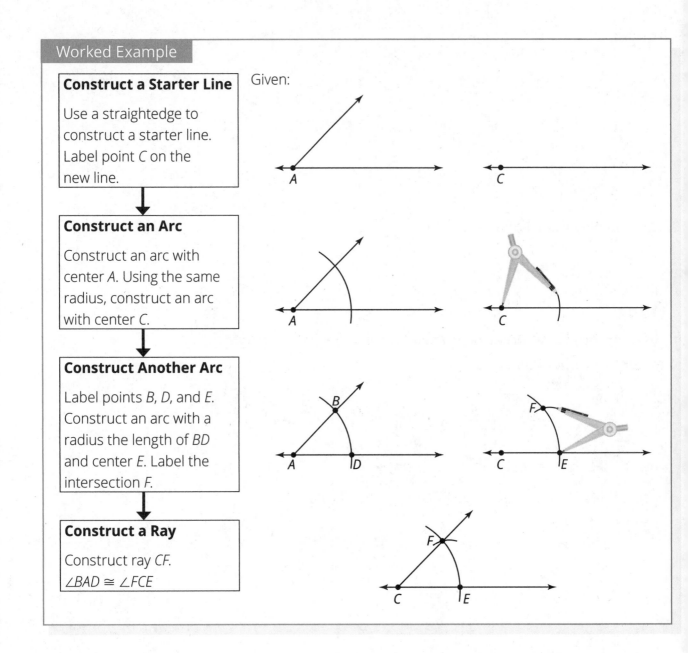

Worked Example

Construct a Starter Line Use a straightedge to construct a starter line. Label point C on the new line.
Construct an Arc Construct an arc with center A. Using the same radius, construct an arc with center C.
Construct Another Arc Label points B, D, and E. Construct an arc with a radius the length of BD and center E. Label the intersection F.
Construct a Ray Construct ray CF. ∠BAD ≅ ∠FCE

Given:

4. **Duplicate angle B. Verify with patty paper.**

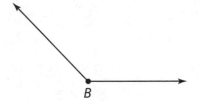

5. Now that you know how to duplicate an angle, use Gage's method to construct a line parallel to line *q*.

6. Consider the line $y = x$ on the coordinate plane shown.

   a. Translate the line $y = x$ to create a parallel line.

   b. Write the equation of your line.

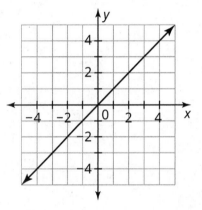

   c. Describe the slopes of parallel lines on the coordinate plane.

ACTIVITY 3.2 Slopes of Perpendicular Lines

Recall that perpendicular lines or lines segments form a right angle at the point of intersection.

Consider the three graphs shown. Each shows a line and its rotation 90° about a point, which is also the point of intersection.

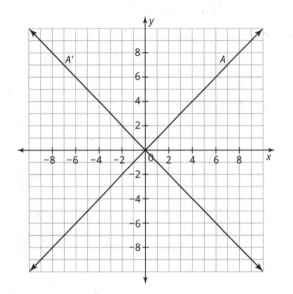

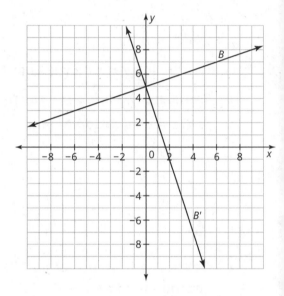

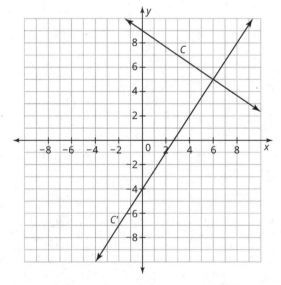

Remember:

The reciprocal of a number $\frac{a}{b}$ is the number $\frac{b}{a}$, where a and b are nonzero numbers. Because the product of a number and its reciprocal is one, reciprocal numbers are also known as multiplicative inverses.

1. **Are the lines in each graph perpendicular? Explain your reasoning.**

2. **Write the equation for each line and its transformation. What do you notice?**

It appears that if two lines are perpendicular, then their slopes are negative reciprocals. Let's investigate.

Worked Example

If two lines are perpendicular, then their slopes are negative reciprocals.

The graph shown can be used to analyze the validity of this statement.

Assumption: $p \perp q$

Let m_1 = slope of line p and let m_2 = slope of line q.

Point R lies on line p.

Conclusion: $m_1 = -\dfrac{1}{m_2}$

Perform a 90° counterclockwise rotation of point R using point O as the center of rotation. Since p and q are perpendicular, the image (point D) will lie on line q due to a 90° rotation.

Since this rotation maps the positive x-axis to the positive y-axis, and the positive y-axis to the negative x-axis, then the coordinates of R (a, b) are transformed into the coordinates of D $(-b, a)$. Graphically, you can follow the movement of lengths a and b under the rotation.

Using the graph, you can identify the slope of line p as $m_1 = \dfrac{b}{a}$, and the slope of line q as $m_2 = \dfrac{a}{-b}$.

Using these slopes, you can demonstrate that $m_1 = -\dfrac{1}{m_2}$.

$$\frac{b}{a} = -\frac{1}{\frac{a}{-b}}$$
$$= -1 \cdot \frac{-b}{a}$$
$$= \frac{b}{a}$$

The slope of line q is the negative reciprocal of the slope of line p.

The product of the slopes of perpendicular lines is −1.

Remember:

The symbol $\perp$ means *is perpendicular to.*

There is often more than one way to prove a theorem. Suppose that point R is rotated 90° clockwise using point O as the center of rotation.

3. Rewrite the assumption and conclusion using the clockwise rotation of point R.

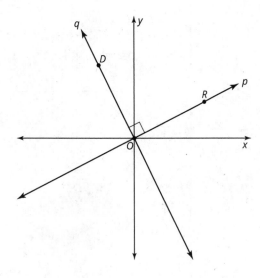

4. Line j and line k are perpendicular. Given each slope of line j, determine the slope of line k.

a. $m = \frac{2}{3}$ b. $m = -\frac{4}{5}$ c. $m = -3$

Consider the graph shown.

1. **Use a straightedge to extend $\overline{GK}$ to create line p, extend $\overline{GH}$ to create line q, extend $\overline{FJ}$ to create line r, and extend $\overline{KL}$ to create line s.**

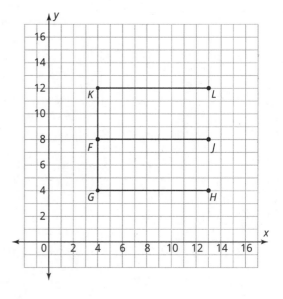

2. **Consider the three horizontal lines you drew for Question 1. For any horizontal line, if x increases by one unit, by how many units does y change?**

3. **Describe the slope of any horizontal line. Explain your reasoning.**

4. **Consider the vertical line you drew in Question 1. Suppose that y increases by one unit. By how many units does x change?**

5. **Describe the slope of any vertical line. Explain your reasoning.**

6. Determine whether each of the given statements is always true, sometimes true, or never true. Explain your reasoning.

   a. All vertical lines are parallel.

   b. All horizontal lines are parallel.

7. Describe the relationship between any vertical line and any horizontal line.

8. Write an equation for a horizontal line and an equation for a vertical line that pass through the point (2, −1).

9. Write an equation for a line that is perpendicular to the line given by $x = 5$ and passes through the point (1, 0).

10. Write an equation for a line that is perpendicular to the line given by $y = -2$ and passes through the point (5, 6).

ACTIVITY 3.4 Writing Equations of Perpendicular Lines

You can write the equation of a perpendicular line using what you know about the slope of that line and any point on that line.

1. Write the equation of the line perpendicular to $y = 2x + 1$ that passes through the point (6, 2).

2. Write the equation of the line perpendicular to $y = -\frac{3}{4}x$ that passes through the point (3, −8).

Remember:

You can use the slope formula to write an equation for any line if you know its slope and one point on that line.

3. Write the equation of the line that passes through the point (6, 2) and is perpendicular to a line that passes through the points (−5, 3) and (−1, −9).

4. Write the equation of a line that passes through the point (−2, 7) and is perpendicular to a line that passes through the points (−6, 1) and (0, 4).

5. A pair of perpendicular lines intersect at the point (5, 9). Write the equation of the line that is perpendicular to the line that also passes through the point (−4, 4).

TALK the TALK

Parallels the Lesson

Previously, you analyzed a worked example that demonstrates, "If two lines are perpendicular, then their slopes are negative reciprocals of each other."

1. **Using similar reasoning, write an explanation that justifies, "If two lines are parallel, then their slopes are equal." Include a sketch.**

    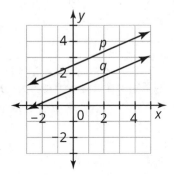

    Assumption: $p \parallel q$

    Let the slope of p be m_1.
    Let the slope of q be m_2.

    Conclusion: $m_1 = m_2$

Slope Grid A

Slope Grid B

Assignment

Write

Explain in your own words why the slope of a vertical line is undefined.

Remember

The slopes of perpendicular lines are negative reciprocals. Any vertical line is perpendicular to any horizontal line.

Practice

Christopher is a developer and plans to build a new development. Use the grid to help Christopher create a map for his development. Each gridline represents one block.

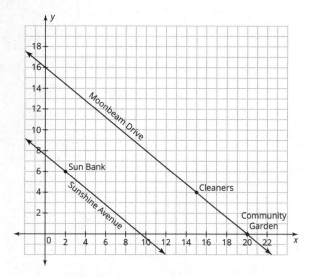

1. There are two main roads that pass through the development, Moonbeam Drive and Sunshine Avenue. Are these two roads parallel to each other? Explain your reasoning.

2. Christopher wants to build a road named Stargazer Boulevard that will be parallel to Moonbeam Drive. On this road, he will build a diner located 7 blocks north of the community garden. Determine the equation of the line that represents Stargazer Boulevard. Show your work. Then draw and label Stargazer Boulevard on the coordinate plane.

3. Christopher wants to build a road named Rocket Drive that connects Sun Bank to Moonbeam Drive. He wants this road to be as short as possible. Determine the equation of the line that represents Rocket Drive. Show your work. Then draw and label Rocket Drive on the coordinate plane.

4. Two office buildings are to be located at the points (8, 4) and (12, 10). Would the shortest road between the two office buildings be a line that is perpendicular to Moonbeam Drive? Explain your reasoning.

5. A straight road named Planet Drive is planned that will connect the diner and the community garden. What is the equation of the line that represents Planet Drive? Show your work. Draw and label Planet Drive on the coordinate plane.

6. Christopher decides that another road to be named Saturn Avenue is needed that will go past the cleaners and be perpendicular to Planet Drive. Determine the equation of the line that represents Saturn Avenue. Show your work. Draw and label Saturn Avenue on the coordinate plane.

Stretch

Triangle *ABC* is located on three lines such that the vertices occur at the points of intersection of pairs of the lines, as shown on the graph. If △*ABC* is rotated 90° counterclockwise around the origin to form △*A′B′C′*, determine the equations of the lines that would contain △*A′B′C′*. Explain your reasoning. Then draw the three lines that contain △*A′BC′* and label △*A′B′C′*.

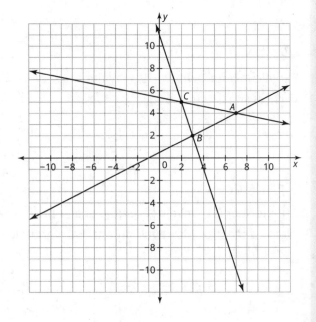

Review

1. Identify each rigid motion as a translation, reflection, or rotation.

a.

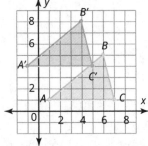

b.

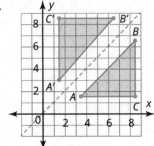

2. Determine the supplement of each angle measure.

   a. 63°   b. 10°   c. 180°

3. Determine the complement of each angle measure.

   a. 10°   b. 75°   c. 45°

4

Where Has Polly Gone?

Classifying Shapes on the Coordinate Plane

Warm Up

Determine the length of each hypotenuse. Round your answer to the nearest tenth, if necessary.

1.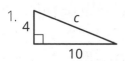

2.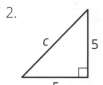

3.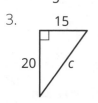

Learning Goals

- Use the Pythagorean Theorem to derive the Distance Formula.
- Apply the Distance Formula on the coordinate plane.
- Classify a triangle given the locations of its vertices on a coordinate plane.
- Determine the coordinates of a fourth vertex, given the coordinates of three vertices of a quadrilateral and a description of the quadrilateral.
- Classify a quadrilateral given the locations of its vertices on a coordinate plane.

Key Terms

- Distance Formula
- Midpoint Formula

You know the slopes of parallel lines are equal and the slopes of perpendicular lines are negative reciprocals. You also know how to determine the length of the hypotenuse of a right triangle. How can you use what you know to classify polygons that lie on a coordinate plane?

You Better Shape Up

Polygons are often classified by properties, such as the lengths of their sides, the relationship between their sides, and the measures of their angles.

The Venn diagram contains three circles each representing a different property. Letters *A* through *H* represent any polygon that has the property described by every circle in which it appears.

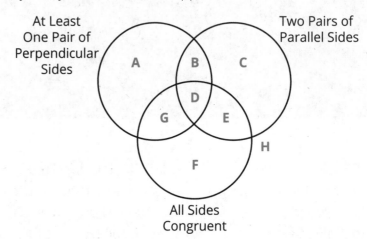

At Least One Pair of Perpendicular Sides

Two Pairs of Parallel Sides

All Sides Congruent

A letter may be used more than once or not at all!

1. **Match each polygon to one of the lettered regions of the Venn diagram. Write the corresponding letter next to each polygon.**

trapezoid	square	isosceles triangle
parallelogram	rhombus	equilateral triangle
rectangle	right triangle	scalene triangle

2. **Is there a region that cannot be matched to one of the polygons? Explain your reasoning.**

Remember:

A trapezoid has at least one pair of parallel sides.

An isosceles triangle has at least two congruent sides.

3. **Use the Venn diagram to compare the properties of each pair of polygons.**

   a. **parallelogram and rhombus**

   b. **rectangle and square**

4. Marla and Flynn analyze the Venn diagram shown.

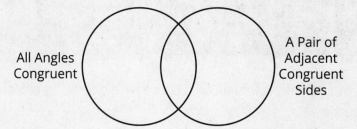

All Angles Congruent

A Pair of Adjacent Congruent Sides

Marla says that the overlapping region describes a rhombus. Flynn says the overlapping region describes a square. Who's correct? Explain your reasoning.

Remember:

Adjacent sides are sides that share a vertex.

5. Determine whether each statement is **always** true, **sometimes** true, or **never** true. Explain your reasoning.

a. A rectangle is a parallelogram.

b. A rhombus is a square.

c. A scalene triangle is a right triangle.

d. A parallelogram is a trapezoid.

e. A right triangle is an equilateral triangle.

Let's analyze quadrilaterals that lie on a coordinate plane and classify them by their properties.

Consider quadrilateral *ABCD* shown.

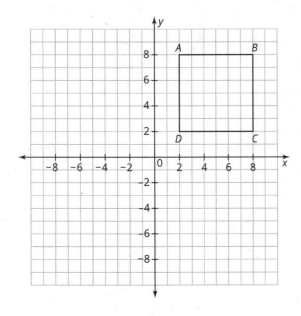

1. **Classify the quadrilateral. Justify your reasoning.**

Now consider quadrilateral *EFGH* shown.

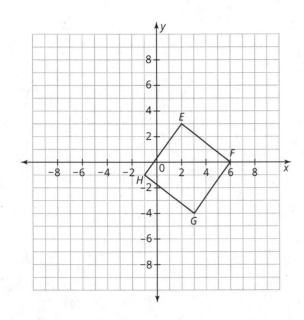

2. **Determine whether quadrilateral *EFGH* can be classified as a parallelogram. Justify your reasoning.**

3. **Determine whether quadrilateral *EFGH* can be classified as a rectangle. Justify your reasoning.**

4. What information do you need to classify quadrilateral *EFGH* as a square?

5. On quadrilateral *EFGH*, draw a right triangle *EFR* such that $\overline{EF}$ is the hypotenuse. Use the Pythagorean Theorem to determine the length of $\overline{EF}$.

You used the Pythagorean Theorem to calculate the distance between two points on the coordinate plane. Your method can be written as the *Distance Formula*. The **Distance Formula** states that if (x_1, y_1) and (x_2, y_2) are two points on the coordinate plane, then the distance d between (x_1, y_1) and (x_2, y_2) is calculated using the formula given.

$$d = \sqrt{(x_2 - x_1)^2 + (y_2 - y_1)^2}$$

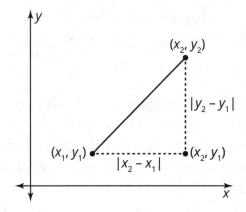

The absolute value symbols are used because the difference represents a distance.

6. When you use the Distance Formula, does it matter which point you identify as (x_1, y_1) and which point you identify as (x_2, y_2)? Explain your reasoning.

7. Can quadrilateral *EFGH* be classified as a square? Justify your reasoning.

8. Use the Distance Formula to calculate the distance between each pair of points. Round your answer to the nearest tenth, if necessary. Show all your work.

a. (1, 2) and (3, 7)

b. (−6, 4) and (2, −8)

c. (−5, 2) and (−6, 10)

9. Calculate the distance between the points (−1, −2) and (−3, −7). Notice the similarity between this problem and Question 8, part (a).

Carlos says that the solution must be the negative of the solution of part (a). Mandy disagrees and says that the solution will be the same as the solution of part (a). Who is correct? Explain your reasoning and state the correct solution.

Classifying Triangles on the Coordinate Plane

Let's analyze triangles that lie on a coordinate plane and classify them by their properties.

Consider △ABC.

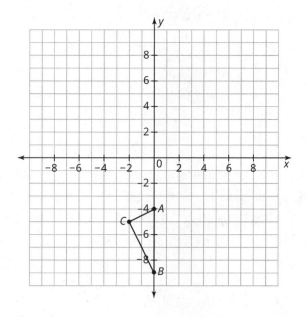

1. **Classify △ABC.**

   a. **Consider the sides of △ABC to describe it as scalene, isosceles, or equilateral. Explain your reasoning.**

   Ask yourself:

   How can you determine the lengths of the sides of this triangle?

   b. **Consider the slope of each side to determine whether △ABC is a right triangle. Justify your conclusion.**

c. Zach used the Pythagorean Theorem to determine whether △*ABC* was a right triangle.

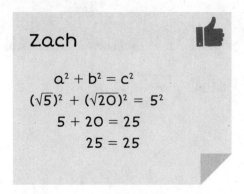

Zach

$$a^2 + b^2 = c^2$$
$$(\sqrt{5})^2 + (\sqrt{20})^2 = 5^2$$
$$5 + 20 = 25$$
$$25 = 25$$

Describe why Zach's reasoning is correct.

You can use the relationship among the sides of a triangle to determine whether the triangle is acute or obtuse. Given *a*, *b*, and *c* are the sides of a triangle with c as the longest side, when $c^2 < a^2 + b^2$, the triangle is acute, and when $c^2 > a^2 + b^2$, the triangle is obtuse.

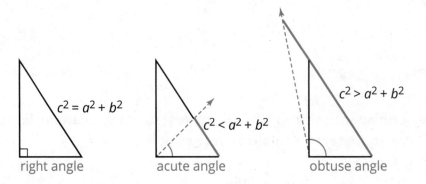

$c^2 = a^2 + b^2$
right angle

$c^2 < a^2 + b^2$
acute angle

$c^2 > a^2 + b^2$
obtuse angle

2. **Determine whether each set of side lengths creates an acute, right, or obtuse triangle.**

a. **42 cm, 36 cm, 15 cm**

b. **18.5 m, 11 m, 15 m**

c. **4 ft, $\sqrt{65}$ ft, 7 ft**

3. Graph △*JKL* using points *J* (−2, 4), *K* (8, 4), and *L* (6, −2).

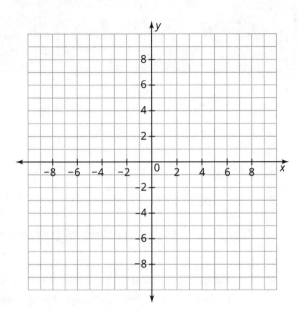

Are you using a straightedge to draw the triangle?

4. Classify △*JKL*.

   a. Consider the sides of △*JKL*. Describe the triangle as scalene, isosceles, or equilateral. Explain your reasoning.

   b. Consider the angles of △*JKL*. Describe the triangle as acute, obtuse, or right. Explain your reasoning.

ACTIVITY

4.3

Determining an Unknown Point of a Quadrilateral

You have classified quadrilaterals by their sides and angles. You can use this information to compose quadrilaterals on a coordinate plane.

Analyze the given points *A*, *B*, and *C*. Suppose you want to plot point *D* such that quadrilateral *ABCD* is a square.

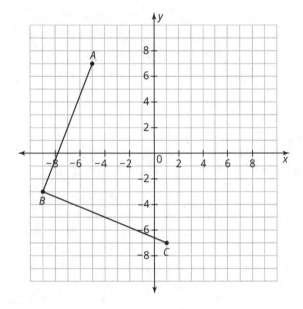

1. **Consider the properties of a square.**

   a. **How does knowing that a square has two pairs of parallel sides help to determine the unknown location?**

   b. **How does knowing that a square has four right angles help to determine the unknown location?**

2. **Determine the location of point *D*. Plot and label point *D* on the coordinate plane.**

3. Use the same locations for points *A*, *B*, and *C* to identify the location of a new point *E*, such that quadrilateral *ABCE* is a trapezoid with only one pair of parallel sides.

a. Identify information that is helpful to locate point *E*. Explain your reasoning.

b. Describe the possible locations of point *E* such that quadrilateral *ABCE* is a trapezoid with only one pair of parallel sides.

ACTIVITY 4.4

Classifying a Quadrilateral on the Coordinate Plane

In this activity, you will classify quadrilaterals by examining the lengths and relationships of their sides.

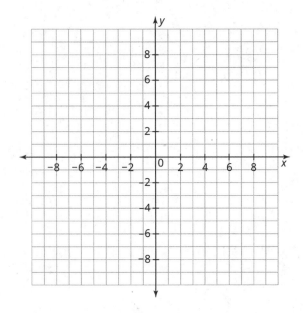

1. Graph quadrilateral *ABCD* using points *A* (−5, 6), *B* (−8, 2), *C* (−5, −2), and *D* (−2, 2).

2. Consider the sides of quadrilateral *ABCD*.

   a. Determine each side length of quadrilateral *ABCD*. Can you classify quadrilateral *ABCD* from its side lengths? If so, identify the type of figure. If not, explain why not.

Think about:

What is the difference between a square and a rhombus?

   b. Determine the slope of each line segment in the quadrilateral. Describe the relationship between the slopes. Can you identify the figure? If so, identify the type of figure. If not, explain why not.

3. Graph quadrilateral *ABCD* using points *A* (8, 8), *B* (3, −7), *C* (10, −6), and *D* (13, 3). Classify this quadrilateral as a trapezoid, a rhombus, a rectangle, a square, or none of these. Explain your reasoning.

Think about:

Which types of figures can you eliminate as you determine information about the figure?

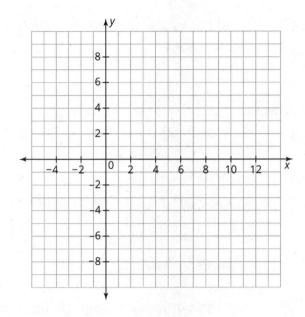

Classifying a Quadrilateral Formed by Midpoints

You have used the Distance Formula to determine the distance between two points. To determine the coordinates of a midpoint, you can use the *Midpoint Formula*.

The **Midpoint Formula** states that if (x_1, y_1) and (x_2, y_2) are two points on the coordinate plane, then the midpoint of the line segment that joins these two points is $\left(\dfrac{x_1 + x_2}{2}, \dfrac{y_1 + y_2}{2}\right)$.

Use the Midpoint Formula to determine the midpoints of each side of the given figures.

Remember:

A midpoint is the point that is exactly halfway between two given points.

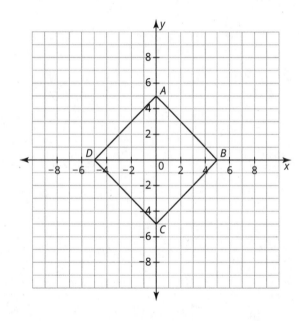

1. **Given square *ABCD*.**

   a. **Determine and label the midpoint of each side of the square.**

   b. **Determine the polygon formed by connecting the consecutive midpoints of each side of a square and justify your conclusion.**

   c. **If the same process was repeated one more time by connecting the consecutive midpoints of each side of the polygon determined in part (a), describe the polygon that would result.**

2. **Sketch any rhombus that is not a square. Label the midpoint of each side of the rhombus.**

   a. **Determine the polygon formed by connecting the consecutive midpoints of each side of a rhombus and justify your conclusion.**

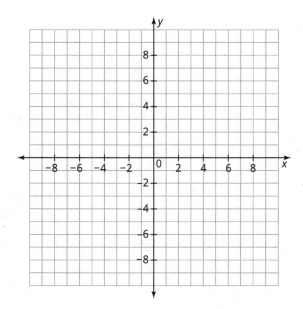

   b. **If the same process was repeated one more time by connecting the consecutive midpoints of each side of the polygon determined in part (a), describe the polygon that would result.**

Talk the Talk

Look, Ma! No Gridlines!

Consider points A (2, 2), B (7, 8), and C (13, 8).

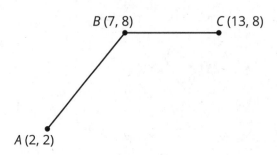

1. **Describe all possible locations for the coordinates of point D such that quadrilateral $ABCD$ is a parallelogram.**

2. **Describe how point D can be located using a translation.**

Assignment

Write

Describe how the Distance Formula and the slope formula can be used to classify triangles and quadrilaterals on the coordinate plane.

Remember

The Distance Formula states that if (x_1, y_1) and (x_2, y_2) are two points on the coordinate plane, then the distance d between the points is given by $d = \sqrt{(x_2 - x_1)^2 + (y_2 - y_1)^2}$.

Practice

1. The grid represents a map of Jose's neighborhood. It shows the locations of his house as well as the houses of four friends.

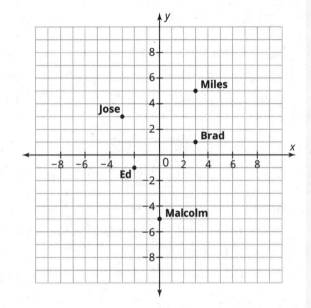

a. Draw a triangle between the houses of Jose, Ed, and Brad. Determine whether this triangle is a scalene, isosceles, or equilateral triangle. Explain your reasoning.

b. Determine whether the triangle is a right triangle. Explain your reasoning. If it is not a right triangle, determine whether it is acute or obtuse.

c. Jose, Miles, and Brad are meeting for band rehearsal. Miles claims that the distance from Jose's house to his house is the same as the distance from Jose's house to Brad's house. Is his claim correct? Explain your answer. What kind of triangle is formed if you connect their houses?

d. A new boy, James, moved into the neighborhood at the location $(-3, -5)$. Plot and label James's house on the grid. Then, determine whether the triangle formed by connecting his house, Jose's house, and Malcolm's house is a right triangle.

2. Susan is an interior floor designer. When designing a new floor, she uses a coordinate grid to represent the room. The client wants a rectangular tile insert to be placed in the floor of the room. The coordinates for 3 of the corners of the insert are $A(-7, -4)$, $B(1, 6)$, and $C(6, 2)$.

a. Plot and label the points on a coordinate plane, then determine the coordinates of the fourth point of the rectangular tile insert. Plot this as point D and connect the points to form the rectangle.

b. To prove the figure you drew is a rectangle, verify that the length of opposite sides are equal.

3. A client of Susan's has asked her to create a new wood floor for his living room. The design will be created by laying wood strips in different directions, as shown on the coordinate grid. Determine whether Quadrilateral ABCD can best be described as a trapezoid, a rhombus, a rectangle, or a square. Explain your reasoning.

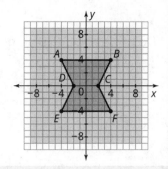

Stretch

The lines that connect points A, B, and C in a coordinate plane form a right triangle. Point A is located at $(-2, 5)$. Point B is located 6 units down from point A and to the left of point A. Point C is located 4 units to the right of point A and down from point A. The angle at point B is a right angle. The slope of the line between point B and point C is $-\frac{1}{3}$. The distance between point A and point B is $\sqrt{40}$. Determine the coordinates of point B and point C.

Review

1. Write the equation of a line that passes through the point $(-8, 2)$ and is parallel to the line $3x - 2y = 12$.

2. Write the equation of a line that passes through the point $(5, -7)$ and is perpendicular to the line $-2x + 6y = -4$.

3. List the properties that are shared by each pair of polygons.
   a. squares and equilateral triangles
   b. rectangles and rhombi

5

In and Out and All About

Area and Perimeter on the Coordinate Plane

Warm Up

Determine the distance between each set of points. Round your answer to the nearest tenth, if necessary.

1. $(2, -3)$ and $(-4, 1)$

2. $(-4.75, -8.5)$ and $(3.25, 5.5)$

3. $\left(\frac{5}{4}, \frac{9}{4}\right)$ and $(0, 10)$

Learning Goals

- Determine the perimeter and area of rectangles and triangles on the coordinate plane.
- Use transformations to discover efficient strategies to determine the perimeter and area of rectangles and triangles.
- Determine the perimeter and the area of composite figures on a coordinate plane.
- Use the Distance Formula to solve real-world problems involving perimeters of parallelograms, trapezoids, and hexagons.
- Decompose polygons—including trapezoids and hexagons—to solve real-world problems involving area.
- Calculate area under a curve to determine distance in an acceleration model.

Key Term

- composite figure

You have used the Distance Formula and the slope formula to classify geometric figures on the coordinate plane. How can you use these same formulas to determine the perimeter and area of polygons on the coordinate plane?

It's Child's Play

A city uses a coordinate grid to map out the locations of two play areas at the park that need to be covered with a rubber surface to prevent injuries. Rectangle *JKLM* represents an area under a swing set and △*NOP* represents an area under a play structure. Each square on the coordinate grid represents one square foot.

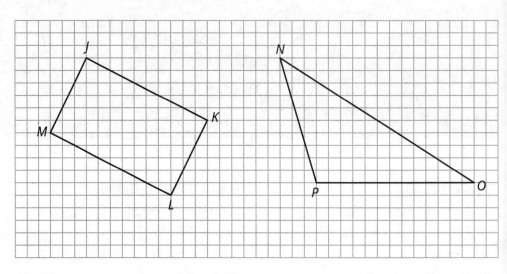

1. **Describe a way you can use the grid to determine the area of rectangle *JKLM* and △*NOP*.**

Perimeter and Area of Figures on the Coordinate Plane

Previously, you classified geometric figures on the coordinate plane by examining the lengths and relationships of their sides. Now, you will determine the perimeter and the area of geometric figures.

1. **Consider rectangle ABCD.**

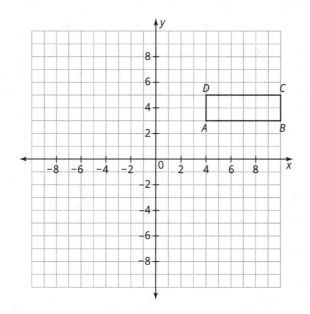

Remember:

The perimeter of a geometric figure is calculated by adding the side lengths.

Remember:

The formula for area of a rectangle is $A = bh$, where A represents the area, b represents the base, and h represents the height.

a. **Determine the perimeter of rectangle ABCD.**

b. **Determine the area of rectangle ABCD.**

2. **Horace says that he determined the area of rectangle *ABCD* by determining the product *CD*(*CB*). Bernice says that Horace is incorrect because he needs to use the base of the rectangle and that the base is $\overline{AB}$, not $\overline{CD}$. Horace responded by saying that $\overline{CD}$ is one of the bases. Who's correct? Explain your reasoning.**

When a rectangle is graphed along gridlines, you can determine the perimeter and area by simply counting units or square units on the coordinate plane. This is true if all coordinates are integers. If they are fractions or decimals, it presents a challenge.

Analyze rectangle *RSTU* on the coordinate plane shown.

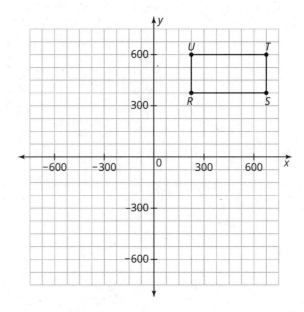

Notice the intervals along the axes.

3. **Calculate the perimeter and area of rectangle *RSTU*.**

4. **How would doubling the height of the rectangle affect the area?**

5. **How would doubling the length of the base of the rectangle affect the area?**

Shantelle used another strategy to determine the perimeter and area of rectangle *RSTU* from the previous activity.

> ## Shantelle
>
> If I translate rectangle *RSTU* to have at least one point of image *R'S'T'U'* on the origin, it is easier to calculate the perimeter and area of rectangle *RSTU* because one of the points will have coordinates (0, 0).

6. How do you know a translation of rectangle *RSTU* will have the same area and perimeter as the pre-image *RSTU*? Explain your reasoning.

7. Explain why Shantelle's rationale is correct.

8. Translate rectangle *RSTU* so that point *R* is located at the origin.

   a. List the coordinates of rectangle *R'S'T'U'*.

   b. Determine the perimeter and area of *R'S'T'U'*. What do you notice?

When the sides of a rectangle do not lie on the gridlines of the coordinate plane, you can use the Distance Formula to determine the lengths of the sides.

9. Consider quadrilateral *LMNO*.

Think about:

Is the quadrilateral a square, a rectangle, or a rhombus?

a. **Determine the perimeter and area of quadrilateral *LMNO*. Round your answer to the nearest hundredth, if necessary.**

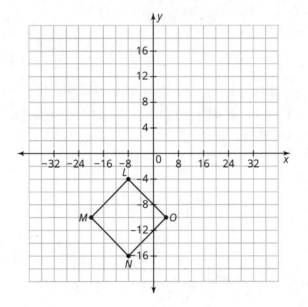

b. **Double the side lengths of quadrilateral *LMNO*. How does this affect the area? What are the new coordinates?**

c. **Describe how you could translate quadrilateral *LMNO* to make the perimeter and area calculations more efficient.**

10. Consider △DEF with vertices D (−5, −9), E (3, −1), and F (3, −9).

a. Determine the perimeter and area of △DEF. Round your answer to the nearest hundredth, if necessary.

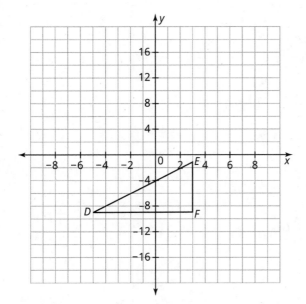

b. Double the height. What are the coordinates of the new triangle? How did this affect the area?

c. Double the length of the base. What are the coordinates of the new triangle? How did this affect the area?

d. Double the length of both the base and the height. How does this affect the area?

11. **Mr. Young gives his class △*DEF* and asks them to determine the area and perimeter. Four of his students decide to first transform the figure and then determine the perimeter and area. Their transformations are shown.**

Michael

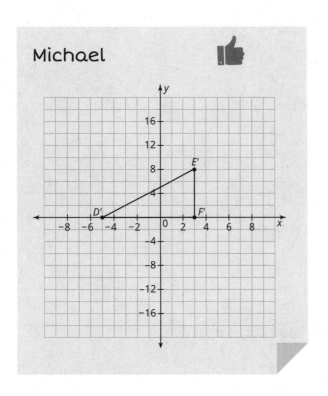

Angelica

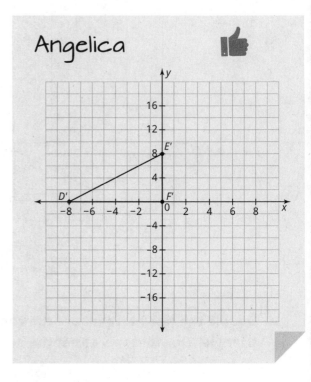

Juan

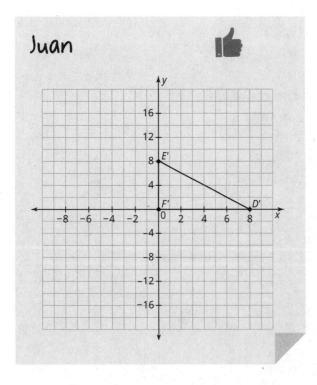

Isabel

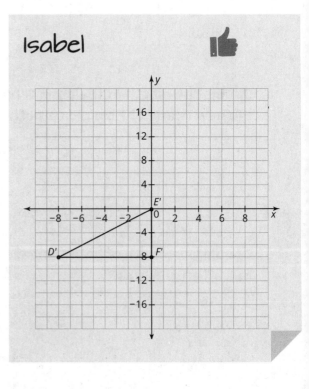

a. Describe the transformation(s) each student made
    to △*DEF*.

b. Whose method do you think is most efficient? Explain
    your reasoning.

c. What do you know about the perimeter and area of all
    the triangles? Explain your reasoning.

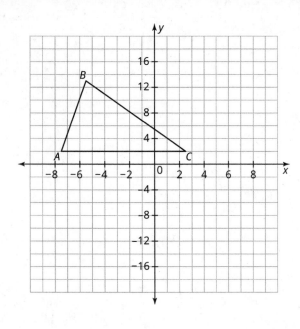

Consider △ABC with vertices A (−7.5, 2), B (−5.5, 13), and C (2.5, 2).

12. **Determine the perimeter of △ABC. Round your answer to the nearest hundredth, if necessary.**

13. **Consider how to determine the area of △ABC.**

    a. **What information is needed about △ABC to determine its area?**

    b. **Arlo says that $\overline{AB}$ can be used as the height. Trisha disagrees and says that $\overline{BC}$ can be used as the height. Randy disagrees with both of them and says that none of the line segments currently on the triangle can be used as the height. Who is correct? Explain your reasoning.**

    c. **Draw and label $\overline{BD}$ to represent the height of △ABC. Then, determine the height of △ABC.**

    d. **Determine the area of △ABC.**

14. Consider a more efficient way to determine the area and
    perimeter of △ABC.

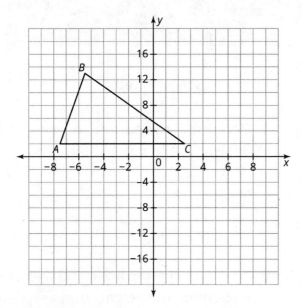

a. Transform △ABC on the coordinate plane. Label the image
   A'B'C'. Describe the transformation(s) completed and explain
   your reasoning.

b. Determine the perimeter and area of △A'B'C'. Round your
   answer to the nearest hundredth, if necessary.

c. Compare these calculations to your previous calculations.
   How did the translation change your calculations?

ACTIVITY 5.2 Calculating Heights of Triangles

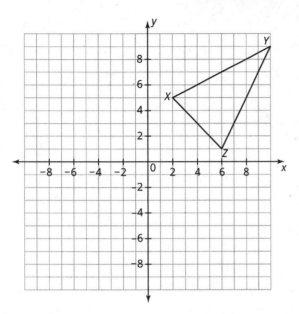

Consider △XYZ with vertices X (2, 5), Y (10, 9), and Z (6, 1).

1. **Determine the perimeter of △XYZ. Round your answer to the nearest hundredth, if necessary.**

2. **To determine the area, you will need to determine the height. How will determining the height of this triangle be different from determining the height of the triangles in previous activities?**

3. **Jonas wanted to transform the triangle to make the calculations easier. How can you determine that Jonas did not transform the triangle correctly?**

Remember:

The altitude, or height, of a triangle is the perpendicular distance from a vertex to the line containing the opposite side.

Jonas
I can rotate the triangle so the base is on a gridline to determine its height.
The triangle has a height of 8 units.

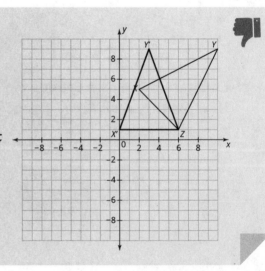

Let's use $\overline{XY}$ as the base of $\triangle XYZ$. You can draw $\overline{ZW}$ to represent the height. Remember that the height is perpendicular to the base. To determine the length of the height, you need to locate point W, which is located at the intersection of $\overline{XY}$ and $\overline{ZW}$.

Worked Example

Calculate the slope of the base, $\overline{XY}$.

$$m = \frac{y_2 - y_1}{x_2 - x_1} = \frac{9 - 5}{10 - 2} = \frac{4}{8} = \frac{1}{2}$$

Determine the slope of the height, $\overline{ZW}$.

$$m = -2$$

You can write equations for $\overleftrightarrow{XY}$ and $\overleftrightarrow{ZW}$ and solve the system to determine where the two lines intersect.

Determine the equations of the lines containing the base and the height.

Base $\overleftrightarrow{XY}$
$X\,(2, 5),\ m = \frac{1}{2}$
$y - y_1 = m(x - x_1)$
$y - 5 = \frac{1}{2}(x - 2)$
$y = \frac{1}{2}x + 4$

Height $\overleftrightarrow{ZW}$
$Z\,(6, 1),\ m = -2$
$y - y_1 = m(x - x_1)$
$y - 1 = -2(x - 6)$
$y = -2x + 13$

Solve the system of equations to determine the coordinates of the point of intersection.

$\frac{1}{2}x + 4 = -2x + 13$
$\frac{5}{2}x = 9$
$x = \frac{18}{5}$

$y = -2x + 13$
$y = -2\left(\frac{18}{5}\right) + 13$
$y = \frac{29}{5}$

4. **Identify the coordinates of the point of intersection. Plot this point on the coordinate plane and label it point W. Draw $\overline{ZW}$ to represent the height.**

5. **Determine the area of $\triangle XYZ$.**

   a. **Determine the height of the triangle.**

   b. **Determine the area of the triangle.**

You know that any side of a triangle can be thought of as the base of the triangle.

6. **Predict whether using a different side as the base will result in a different area of the triangle. Explain your reasoning.**

Let's consider your prediction.

7. **Triangle *XYZ* is graphed on the coordinate plane. This time consider side $\overline{XZ}$ as the base.**

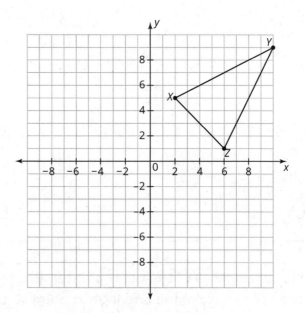

a. **Let point *V* represent the intersection point of the height, $\overline{YV}$, and the base. Determine the coordinates of point *V*.**

b. Determine the height of △**XYZ**.

c. Determine the area of △**XYZ**.

8. Triangle *XYZ* is graphed on the coordinate plane. Determine the area of △*XYZ* using side $\overline{YZ}$ as the base.

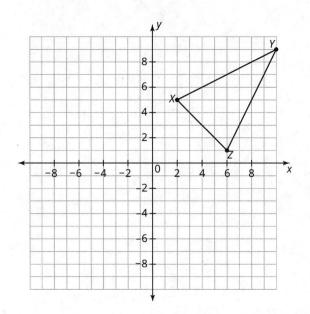

9. Compare the three areas you determined for △*XYZ*. Was your prediction in Question 6 correct?

Perimeter and Area of a Composite Figure

The method you used to determine the perimeter of a rectangle or triangle can be used with any polygon. You can use the Distance Formula to calculate the distance between any set of vertices and then add the lengths of all the sides.

You can determine the area of a *composite figure* by dividing the figure into a combination of rectangles and triangles. A **composite figure** is a figure that is formed by combining different shapes.

Carter has an irregular backyard because it backs onto the foothill of a mountain and is very rocky. The composite figure graphed on the coordinate plane represents the flat area of Carter's backyard. Each interval of the coordinate plane represents two yards.

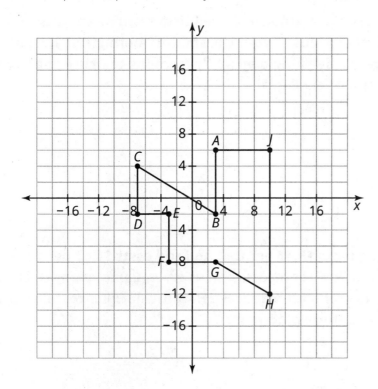

1. Carter will install fencing all around the flat area of his backyard. Determine the amount of fencing he needs to the nearest whole yard.

2. Carter wants to lay grass sod in the flat area of his backyard. Determine the total area of sod he needs.

3. Compare the method you used to determine the area of sod Carter needs to your classmates' methods. If you had a different way of dividing up the composite figure, did your answers differ? Explain why or why not.

4. Fencing costs $5.45 per foot and sod costs $0.62 per square foot. To allow for measurement error, Carter plans to buy an extra 10% of both materials. How much will it cost Carter to purchase these materials?

A pattern for a quilt patch is drawn on a coordinate plane, where each
interval represents one inch. Parallelogram *ABCD* represents the patch.

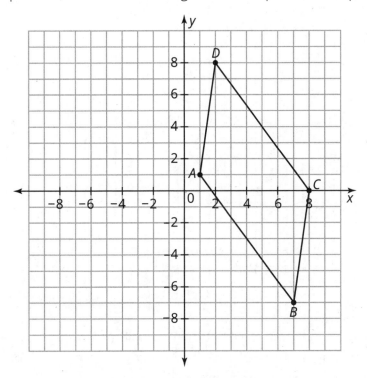

1. **Bryce is in charge of buying the ribbon that will be sewn
   around the outside of each patch. How many inches of ribbon
   are needed for each patch?**

Aida's bedroom is on the top floor of her house. In her room, the roof slants downward, creating two congruent trapezoid-shaped walls. One of the walls in her room is represented on the coordinate plane by quadrilateral *ABCD*. Each interval on the coordinate plane represents one foot.

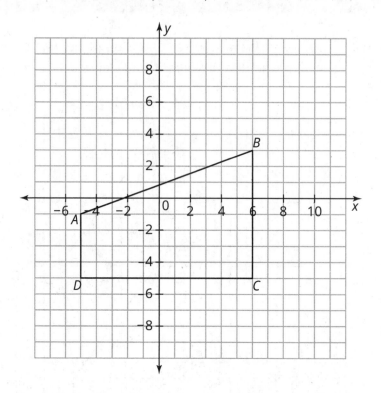

Aida and Marco are going to paint the two walls and want to place a strip of painter's tape along each edge of the walls so the paint does not touch any other wall, the ceiling, or the floor.

2. **What is the length of painter's tape (to the nearest whole foot) that Aida and Marco need to cover the edges of both walls?**

Ask

yourself:

How can you use a transformation of trapezoid *ABCD* on the coordinate plane as part of your strategy?

3. Marco says he can draw a diagonal to divide trapezoid *ABCD* into a right and an isosceles triangle to determine the area of the trapezoid. Aida says she can draw a horizontal line segment to divide trapezoid *ABCD* into a rectangle and a right triangle. Who's correct? Explain your reasoning.

4. One gallon of paint covers approximately 400 square feet. Aida estimates she has about one fourth of a gallon of paint remaining of the color she wants to use. Does she have enough paint for both walls? Explain your reasoning.

Emma and Kevin are designing a gazebo for the local park. The polygon shown on the coordinate plane represents the base of the gazebo. Each interval on the coordinate plane represents two feet.

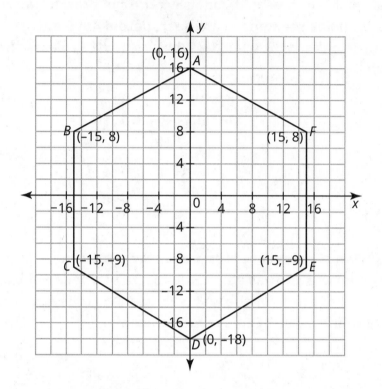

5. **The base of the gazebo needs to be built with lengths of lumber around the outside to support the floorboards. What is the length of lumber needed for the outside of the base?**

6. **How many square feet of floorboards are needed for the base of the gazebo? Describe how you determined your answer and show your work.**

The graph shows the constant speed of a car on the highway over the course of 2.5 hours.

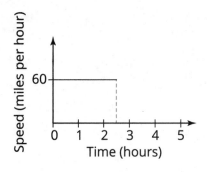

7. **Describe how you could calculate the distance the car traveled in 2.5 hours using what you know about area.**

8. **How far did the car travel in 2.5 hours?**

The graph you used is called a velocity-time graph. In a velocity-time graph, the area under the line or curve gives the distance.

The graph shown describes the speed and the time of a passenger jet's ascend.

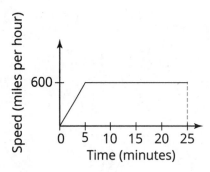

9. **How can you use the graph to determine the distance the jet has traveled in 25 minutes?**

10. Determine the distance the jet has traveled:

   a. in 25 minutes.

   b. in the first 5 minutes.

11. Consider the ascent of a passenger jet.

   a. Draw a velocity-time graph to model the ascent of a passenger jet using the information given.
      • The jet took 7 minutes to reach a top speed of 600 miles per hour.
      • The jet continued to travel at a constant speed of 600 miles per hour.
      • The jet left the airport 4 hours ago.

   b. How many miles has the jet traveled?

TALK the TALK

Vive les Maths!

Eva is using a map to estimate the area of France. She thinks the country looks like a hexagon and draws the polygon shown to approximate its shape.

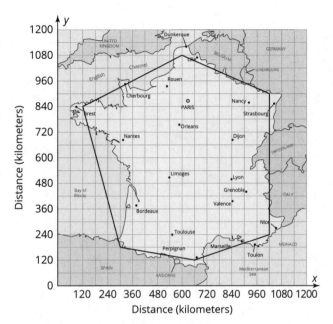

1. Determine which statements are true. Justify your answers.
   - The coastline of France is greater than 5000 km.

   - The coastline of France is less than 5000 km.

   - The coastline of France is approximately 5000 km.

   - The area of France is greater than 1,000,000 sq km.

   - The area of France is less than 1,000,000 sq km.

   - The area of France is approximately 1,000,000 sq km.

2. If the population of France is approximately 104 people per square kilometer, how many people live in France?

Assignment

Write

Describe how you can determine the area of a composite figure.

Remember

Rigid transformations can make calculating the perimeter and area of figures on the coordinate plane more efficient.

Any side of a triangle can be considered its base, and the height of the triangle is the perpendicular distance from the base to the opposite vertex.

Practice

1. Olivia translates rectangle *WXYZ* vertically up 1 unit and horizontally to the right 4 units to produce the image *W'X'Y'Z'*. Thom translates the rectangle vertically up 6 units and horizontally to the right 5 units to produce the image *W"X"Y"Z"*.

   a. Would you prefer to use Olivia's translation or Thom's translation to determine the perimeter and area of the rectangle? Explain your reasoning.

   b. Calculate the perimeter and area of the rectangle. Show your work.

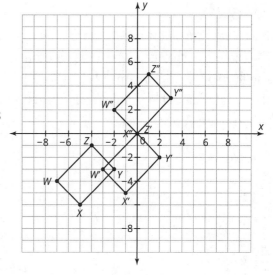

2. Composite figure *ABCDEFG* is given.

   a. Determine the perimeter of figure *ABCDEFG*.

   b. Determine the area of figure *ABCDEFG*.

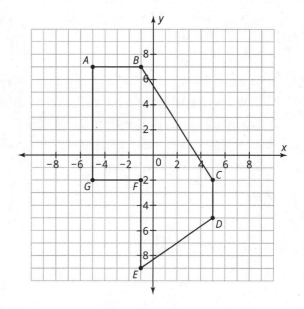

3. Cisco claims that $\overline{GH}$ is the height of $\triangle EFG$, and Beth claims that $\overline{GJ}$ is the height of $\triangle EFG$.

a. Who is correct? Justify your response.

b. Calculate the area of $\triangle EFG$. Show your work.

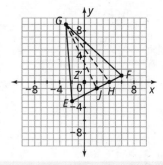

Stretch

Parallelograms *JKLM* and *JKPR* are given. Without calculating each area, determine whether or not the area of parallelogram *JKPR* is twice that of the area of parallelogram *JKLM*. Explain how you determined your answer.

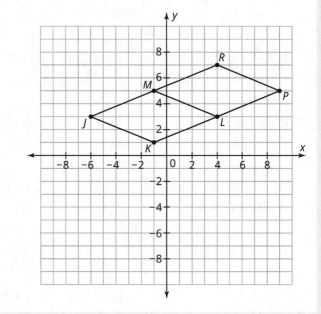

Review

1. The quadrilateral *ABCD* has the vertices *A* (−5, 4), *B* (0, 6), *C* (1, 3), and *D* (−4, 1). Determine whether it can be classified as a parallelogram. Justify your reasoning.

2. Triangle *DEF* has the vertices *D* (−2, 3), *E* (2, −1), and *F* (−5, −4). Determine whether it is scalene, isosceles, or equilateral. Explain your reasoning.

3. Solve for *b* in the equation $\frac{a - b}{12} = 11 - 6a$.

Using a Rectangular Coordinate System Summary

KEY TERMS

- sketch
- draw
- conjecture
- auxiliary line
- construct
- compass
- straightedge
- point

- line
- line segment
- midpoint
- segment bisector
- perpendicular bisector
- diagonal
- transformation

- rigid motion
- translation
- reflection
- rotation
- Distance Formula
- Midpoint Formula
- composite figure

LESSON 1

The Squariest Square

When you **sketch** a geometric figure, you create the figure without tools. Accuracy is not important. When you **draw** geometric figures, you can use tools such as rulers and protractors and the coordinate plane to draw exact lengths and areas.

A **conjecture** is a mathematical statement that appears to be true, but has not been formally proven. You can move from making conjectures and informal arguments to proving that certain mathematical statements must be true. You can use properties and definitions to prove or disprove many conjectures.

An **auxiliary line** is a line or line segment added to a diagram to help in solving or proving a concept. For example, the dashed line drawn parallel to $\overline{AB}$ through point C is an auxiliary line that can be used to reason geometrically about the sum of the measures of the interior angles of a triangle.

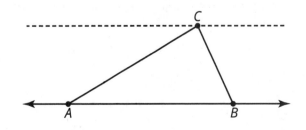

When you **construct** geometric figures, you create exact figures without measurements, using only a **compass** and a **straightedge**. A compass is a tool used to create arcs and circles. A straightedge is a ruler with no numbers.

A **point** is described simply as a location. A point in geometry has no size or shape, but it is often represented using a dot. In a diagram, a point can be labeled using a capital letter. A **line** is described as a straight, continuous arrangement of an infinite number of points. A line has an infinite length, but no width. Arrowheads are used to indicate that a line extends infinitely in opposite directions. In a diagram, a line can be labeled with a lowercase letter positioned next to the arrowhead. A **line segment** is a part of a line between two points on the line, called the endpoints. A distance along a line is the length of a line segment connecting two points on the line. A line segment $\overline{AB}$ has the distance AB.

The **midpoint** of a segment is the point that divides the segment into 2 congruent segments. A **segment bisector** is a line, line segment, or ray that divides a line segment into two line segments of equal length. The basic geometric construction used to locate a midpoint of a line segment is called bisecting a line segment.

You can use patty paper to bisect a line segment.

Draw a line on the paper.

Fold the paper so the endpoints of the line segment lie on top of each other.

Open the paper. The crease represents the segment bisector, and the midpoint is located where the crease intersects the line segment.

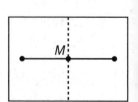

To construct a segment bisector using only a compass and straightedge, you make use of the fact that all the radii of a circle have an equal length.

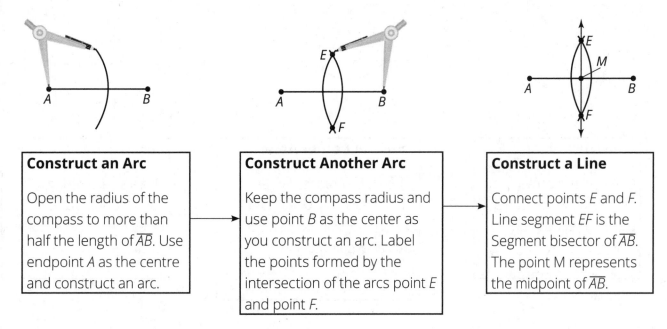

Construct an Arc	**Construct Another Arc**	**Construct a Line**
Open the radius of the compass to more than half the length of $\overline{AB}$. Use endpoint *A* as the centre and construct an arc.	Keep the compass radius and use point *B* as the center as you construct an arc. Label the points formed by the intersection of the arcs point *E* and point *F*.	Connect points *E* and *F*. Line segment *EF* is the Segment bisector of $\overline{AB}$. The point M represents the midpoint of $\overline{AB}$.

Line *EF* bisects $\overline{AB}$. Point *M* is the midpoint of $\overline{AB}$.

A perpendicular bisector is a line, line segment, or ray that bisects a line segment and is also perpendicular to the line segment.

You can use a compass and straightedge to create a perpendicular bisector.

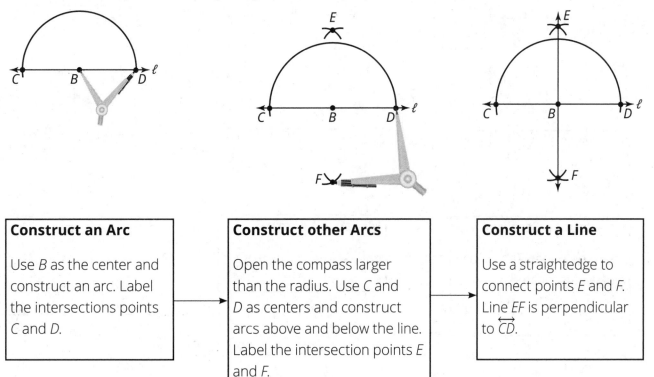

Construct an Arc	**Construct other Arcs**	**Construct a Line**
Use *B* as the center and construct an arc. Label the intersections points *C* and *D*.	Open the compass larger than the radius. Use *C* and *D* as centers and construct arcs above and below the line. Label the intersection points *E* and *F*.	Use a straightedge to connect points *E* and *F*. Line *EF* is perpendicular to $\overleftrightarrow{CD}$.

You can also construct a perpendicular line through a point not on a line.

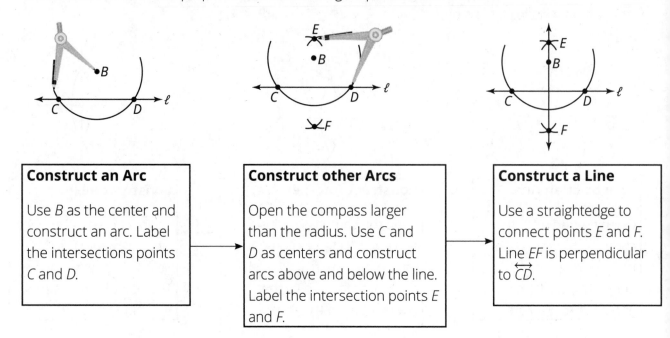

Construct an Arc	Construct other Arcs	Construct a Line
Use B as the center and construct an arc. Label the intersections points C and D.	Open the compass larger than the radius. Use C and D as centers and construct arcs above and below the line. Label the intersection points E and F.	Use a straightedge to connect points E and F. Line EF is perpendicular to $\overleftrightarrow{CD}$.

You can duplicate a line segment by constructing an exact copy of the original line segment.

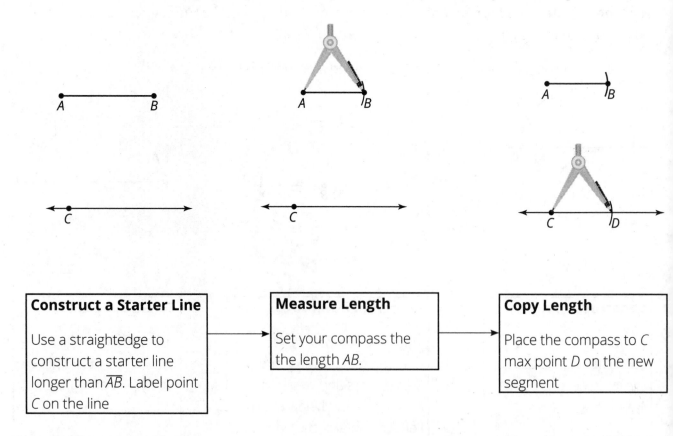

Construct a Starter Line	Measure Length	Copy Length
Use a straightedge to construct a starter line longer than $\overline{AB}$. Label point C on the line	Set your compass the the length AB.	Place the compass to C max point D on the new segment

Line segment *CD* is a duplicate of $\overline{AB}$.

A **diagonal** is a line segment joining two vertices of a polygon but is not a side of the polygon.

A **transformation** is the mapping, or movement, of the points of a figure on a plane according to a common action or operation. A **rigid motion** is a special type of transformation that preserves the size and shape of the figure. Three types of rigid motion transformations are translations, reflections, and rotations. A **translation** "slides" a figure up, down, left, or right. A **reflection** "flips" a figure across a line. A **rotation** "spins" a figure about a point.

LESSON

3

Ts and Train Tracks

You can construct parallel lines.

For example, to construct a line parallel to line *m* through point *A*, you can construct a line *s* perpendicular to line *m*. Then, construct a line perpendicular to *m* through point *A*. If two lines are perpendicular to the same line, then they are parallel to each other.

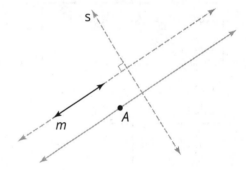

You can also construct parallel lines by duplicating an angle formed by a transversal and a line. You can duplicate an angle using constructions.

Construct a Starter Line

Use a straightedge to construct a starter line. Label point *C* on the new line.

Construct an Arc

Construct an arc with center *A*. Using the same radius, construct an arc with center *C*.

Construct Another Arc

Label points *B*, *D*, and *E*. Construct and arc with radius *BD* and center *E*. Label the intersection *F*.

Construct a Ray

Construct ray *CF*.
∠*BAD* ≅ ∠*FCE*.

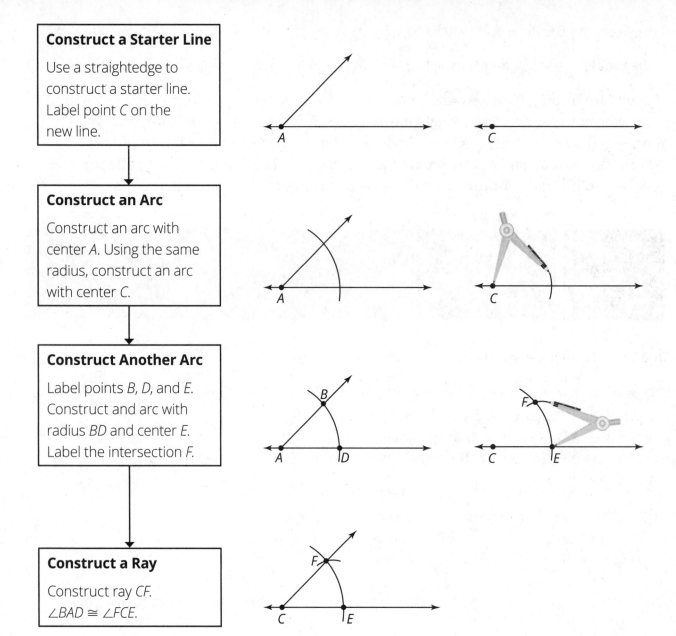

Perpendicular lines or line segments form a right angle at the point of intersection. You can think of perpendicular lines as a line and its rotation 90° about a point, which is also the point of intersection.

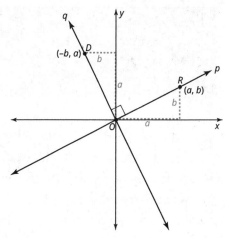

The product of the slopes of perpendicular lines is −1.

For example, consider the graph.

The slope of line q is the negative reciprocal of the slope of line p because $\frac{b}{a} \cdot \frac{a}{-b} = -1$.

The slope of any horizontal line is 0 since no matter the change for x, there is 0 change for y. The slope of any vertical line is undefined since no matter the change for y, there is 0 change for x.

All horizontal lines are parallel to each other since their slopes are equal and all vertical lines are parallel since their slopes are equal. A horizontal and a vertical line are always perpendicular to each other.

For example, to write an equation for a line that passes through the point $(-4, -2)$ and is perpendicular to the line $y = 3$, first determine that the line given by $y = 3$ is a horizontal line. Therefore, a line that is perpendicular to $y = 3$ is a vertical line. A vertical line that passes through the point $(-4, -2)$ has the equation $x = -4$.

You can use what you know about the slopes of perpendicular lines and slope-intercept form to write the equation of a perpendicular line.

For example, consider the line $y = 4x - 1$. Write the equation of the line that passes through the point $(-4, 2)$ and is perpendicular to $y = 4x - 1$.

The slope of $y = 4x - 1$ is 4. The slope of the line perpendicular to $y = 4x - 1$ must have a slope of $-\frac{1}{4}$, since $4 \cdot -\frac{1}{4} = -1$.

Using the given point and slope-intercept form, you can set up an equation to solve for b, the y-intercept.

$$2 = -\frac{1}{4}(-4) + b$$
$$2 = 1 + b$$
$$b = 1$$

Therefore, the equation of the line that passes through the point $(-4, 2)$ and is perpendicular to $y = 4x - 1$ is $y = -\frac{1}{4}x + 1$.

Since a line and its translation are parallel to each other, the slopes of parallel lines are equal.

You can use the Pythagorean Theorem to calculate the distance between two points on the coordinate plane. This method can be written as the Distance Formula. The **Distance Formula** states that if (x_1, y_1) and (x_2, y_2) are two points on the coordinate plane, then the distance d between (x_1, y_1) and (x_2, y_2) is given by $d = \sqrt{(x_2 - x_1)^2 + (y_2 - y_1)^2}$.

Note that absolute value symbols are used because length is always positive.

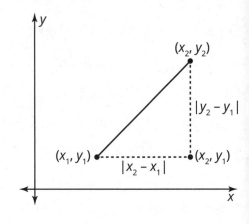

You can apply the Distance Formula to determine the lengths of the sides of polygons on the coordinate plane.

For example, classify $\triangle ABC$ as scalene, isosceles, or equilateral by determining AC, CB, and AB.
Since points A and B have the same x-value, determine the length of AB by determining the absolute value of the difference in the y-values.

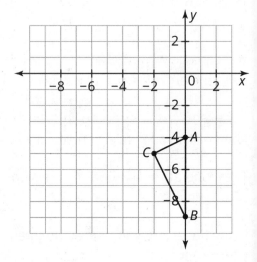

$$AB = |-4 - (-9)|$$
$$AB = 5$$

Then, use the Distance Formula to determine AC and CB.

$$d = \sqrt{(2)^2 + (1)^2} \qquad d = \sqrt{(4)^2 + (2)^2}$$
$$d = \sqrt{5} \qquad\qquad d = \sqrt{20}$$
$$AC = \sqrt{5} \qquad\qquad CB = \sqrt{20}$$

Since all sides of the triangle are different lengths, the triangle is scalene.

The slopes of adjacent sides of a polygon can also be used to determine if the sides form a right angle since the slopes of perpendicular lines are negative reciprocals of each other. For example, in $\triangle ABC$, $\overline{AC}$ has a slope of $\frac{1}{2}$ and $\overline{BC}$ has a slope of -2. Since $\frac{1}{2}$ and -2 are negative reciprocals, the line segments form a right angle and $\triangle ABC$ can be classified as a right scalene triangle.

Given three points of a quadrilateral, the fourth point can be determined using the Distance Formula and the characteristics of the specific quadrilateral.

For example, given points A, B, and C, point D can be placed at $(5, 3)$ to create a square or at $(3, -2)$ to create a trapezoid.

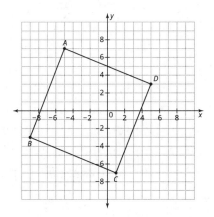 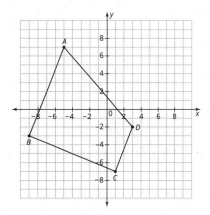

To determine the coordinates of the midpoint of a segment on the coordinate plane, you can use the Midpoint Formula. The **Midpoint Formula** states that if (x_1, y_1) and (x_2, y_2) are two points on the coordinate plane, then the midpoint of the line segment that joins these two points is $\left(\frac{x_1 + x_2}{2}, \frac{y_1 + y_2}{2} \right)$.

LESSON 5

In and Out and All About

The Distance Formula can be used to determine the perimeter and area of rectangles and triangles on the coordinate plane. The perimeter of a geometric figure is calculated by adding the side lengths. The formula for the area of a rectangle is $A = bh$, and the formula for the area of triangle is $A = \frac{1}{2} bh$, where A represents area, b represents the base, and h represents height.

To determine the area of a triangle, first determine the height of the triangle. The altitude, or height, of a triangle is the perpendicular distance from a vertex to the line containing the opposite side, represented by a line segment.

For example, again consider △ABC with vertices A (−7.5, 2), B (−5.5, 13), and C (2.5, 2). The height of the triangle can be created using a line segment from vertex B to base $\overline{AC}$.

The height is 13 − 2 = 11 units.

The length of the base, $\overline{AC}$, is |−7.5 − 2.5| = 10 units.

$A = \frac{1}{2}(11)(10) = 55$

The area of the triangle is 55 square units.

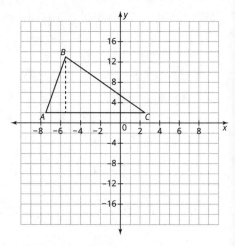

When the base of a triangle is not horizontal, the points that can be used to create a height perpendicular to the base must be identified algebraically by determining the equation of the line containing the base and the equation of the line perpendicular to the base that passes through the opposite vertex, and then solving the system of equations.

You can translate shapes on the coordinate plane to make the process of determining the perimeter and area more efficient. Translations are rigid motions that preserve the size and shape of a figure. The pre-image and the image are congruent because in a translation, all vertices must be rigidly moved from one location to another location.

You can determine the area of a **composite figure** by dividing the figure into a combination of rectangles and triangles. A composite figure is a figure that is formed by combining different shapes.

For example, suppose Aida has a bedroom that is on the top floor of her house. The roof slants downward, creating two congruent trapezoid shaped walls. One of the walls in her room is represented on the coordinate plane by quadrilateral ABCD. Each interval on the coordinate plane represents one foot.

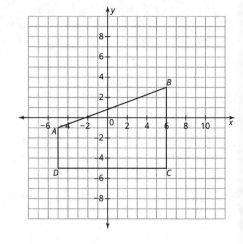

You can determine the area of quadrilateral ABCD by breaking it into a triangle and a rectangle and determining the area of each.

The area of the triangle with vertices at (−5, −1), (6, 3), and (6, −1), is 22 square feet. The area of the rectangle with vertices at (−5, −1), (6, −1), (6, −5), and (−5, −5) is 44 square feet.

The area of the wall is 22 square feet + 44 square feet = 66 square feet.

Composing and Decomposing Shapes

A chord is a line segment joining any two points on a circle. All diameters are chords, but not all chords are diameters.

Lesson 1
Running Circles Around Geometry
Using Circles to Make Conjectures M1-111

Lesson 2
The Quad Squad
Conjectures About Quadrilaterals. M1-127

Lesson 3
Into the Ring
Constructing an Inscribed Regular Polygon M1-145

Lesson 4
Tri- Tri- Tri- and Separate Them
Conjectures About Triangles M1-161

Lesson 5
What's the Point?
Points of Concurrency. M1-175

Module 1: Reasoning with Shapes

TOPIC 2: COMPOSING AND DECOMPOSING SHAPES

This topic begins with students using circles to conjecture about line and angle relationships. Students also use circles to conjecture about quadrilaterals. They then explore the properties of isosceles triangles and make conjectures about triangles. As students begin to formalize their conjectures and consider the truth of statements and their converses, they consider a conjecture about the base angles of isosceles triangles and test whether the converse is true. To conclude the topic, students investigate points of concurrency by constructing the circumcenter, incenter, centroid, and orthocenter.

Where have we been?

Throughout elementary and middle school, students have informally investigated many of the relationships explored in this topic. In grade 8, they used informal arguments to establish facts about angle pairs created when parallel lines are cut by a transversal. Students have an intuitive understanding about the properties of many of the shapes considered in this topic.

Where are we going?

In future topics, students will formally prove many of the conjectures they write in this topic. Through exploration, construction, and conjecture, students can develop an intuitive understanding of whether they believe a relationship to be actually true. Once they believe that it's true, they will be better equipped to prove that it is true in all cases.

Constructing Diagrams to Make Conjectures

In geometry, you construct diagrams to help you reason about abstract relationships involving shapes and distances. You can make conjectures about these relationships using the diagrams.

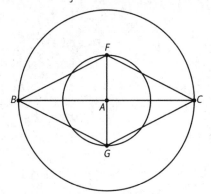

A parallelogram can be constructed using two concentric circles as shown. Because this is the case, you can make conjectures about the diagonals of any parallelogram.

It All Comes Back Around to Circles

Amusement parks are popular destinations. Many people like rides that go fast, like roller coasters. Others prefer more relaxing rides. One of the most popular rides is the Ferris wheel.

The invention of the Ferris wheel is credited to George Washington Gale Ferris, Jr., who debuted his new ride at the World's Columbian Exposition in Chicago, Illinois, in 1893. It was 264 feet tall, had a capacity of 2160 people, took 10 minutes to complete a revolution, and cost 50 cents to ride.

The well-known London Eye in England shown here is the tallest Ferris wheel in the Western Hemisphere.

Talking Points

Geometry with circles can be important to know about for college admissions tests.

Here is an example of a sample question:

$\overline{BC}$ is a diameter of Circle O and $\triangle ABC$ is inscribed in the circle. If $AB = AO$, what is the degree measure of $\angle ABO$?

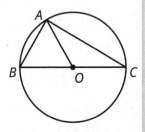

To solve this problem, you should notice that $\overline{AO}$ is a radius of the circle. All radii of a circle are congruent, so $AB = AO = OB$, and $\triangle ABO$ is an equilateral triangle.

An equilateral triangle has three congruent angle measures which must sum to 180°, so the measure of $\angle ABO$ must be 60°.

Key Terms

inscribed angle
An inscribed angle is an angle whose vertex is on a circle and whose sides contain chords of the circle.

cyclic quadrilateral
A cyclic quadrilateral is a quadrilateral whose vertices all lie on a single circle.

circumcenter
The circumcenter is the point of concurrency of the three perpendicular bisectors of a triangle.

incenter
The incenter is the point of concurrency of the three angle bisectors of a triangle.

orthocenter
The orthocenter is the point of concurrency of the three altitudes of a triangle.

Running Circles Around Geometry

Using Circles to Make Conjectures

Warm Up

Write a description of each geometric object and provide an example.

1. point

2. line

3. line segment

4. circle

Learning Goals

- Construct circles, parallel lines, and perpendicular bisectors.
- Identify line segments, lines, and angles associated with the interior and exterior of circles.
- Make conjectures about vertical angles, alternate interior angles, corresponding angles, and points on the perpendicular bisector of a line segment in order to write theorems.
- Make conjectures about inscribed angles on a diameter and the angles formed where tangent lines intersect radii of a circle.

Key Terms

- central angle
- major arc
- minor arc
- secant
- chord
- inscribed angle
- intercepted arc
- tangent
- circumscribed angle
- theorem
- postulate

You know a lot about geometry and can reason with geometric objects. How can you use what you know about circles to make conjectures about line and angle relationships?

Freehand Circle Drawing Championship

Teacher Alexander Overwijk, as a little joke, told his math classes for over a decade that he was a "World Freehand Circle Drawing Champion" because he could draw perfect circles on the board.

But the championship didn't really exist, until a video of Overwijk's circle-drawing ability went viral, launching the first World Freehand Circle Drawing Championship in 2007.

Can you draw a perfect circle freehand?

1. **Try to draw a perfect circle, like the one shown, without tracing or using tools.**

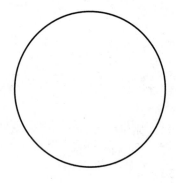

2. **Explain how you could decide whether one circle is closer to "perfect" than another. Use your criteria to judge your and your classmates' best circles.**

3. **What is the measure of an angle that forms a perfect circle? What is the arc measure of that angle?**

Circle Parts and Bisectors

Let's investigate what you know about circles and their parts.

1. **Use a compass to construct a circle in the space provided. Label the center point, *O*.**

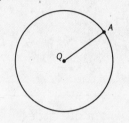

A radius is a line segment from the center of a circle to a point on the circle.

2. **Use the definitions to complete the construction and answer each question.**

   a. **Construct a diameter of the circle. Label the endpoints *D* and *M*. Point *O* is the midpoint of the diameter.**

   b. **How many central angles and arcs are produced by drawing a diameter and what are their measures? Explain how you know.**

A diameter of a circle is a line segment passing through the center of the circle with endpoints on the circle.

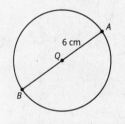

   c. **What name is given to each half of the circle created by the diameter?**

A **central angle** is an angle with its vertex at the center of a circle, like ∠*AQC*. An arc is a part of a circle, like $\overset{\frown}{AC}$. The measure of $\overset{\frown}{AC}$ is the measure of the central angle formed by the endpoints.

3. **Construct a perpendicular bisector of the circle's diameter. Label the points of intersection of the perpendicular bisector and the circle as points *P* and *B*.**

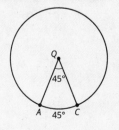

Two points on a circle determine a major arc and a minor arc. The arc with the greater measure, $\overgroup{ACB}$, is the **major arc**. The other arc, $\overgroup{AB}$, is the **minor arc**.

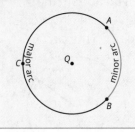

A **secant** of a circle is a line that intersects the circle at two points. In this circle, $\overleftrightarrow{CD}$ is a secant.

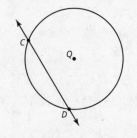

A **chord** is a segment whose endpoints are points on a circle. In this circle, $\overline{CD}$ is a chord.

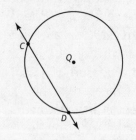

4. Use the definitions to identify the circle parts and answer each question.

   a. Identify all the drawn radii of the circle created by the diameter and its perpendicular bisector.

   b. What central angles and arcs are produced by the diameter and its perpendicular bisector and what are their measures? Explain how you know.

5. Draw a line through two of your labeled points on the circle to form a secant and a chord that is not a diameter.

   a. Use a protractor to measure the angles of the triangle and a ruler to measure the side lengths.

   b. Classify the triangle you have created.

6. Compare your circle diagrams with your classmates' diagrams.

   a. Did everyone create the same triangle? The same type of triangle?

   b. Are all circles similar? Congruent?

Think about:

Are all circles similar?

7. What conjecture can you make about this type of triangle?

**ACTIVITY
1.2** Angle and Arc Relationships

Let's use your geometric knowledge to make a few more conjectures. Consider the circle and triangle Josh constructed.

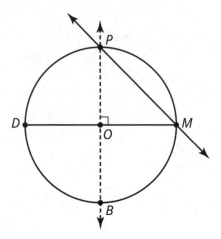

Angles *POM* and *DOB* are vertical angles. Angles *BOM* and *POD* are vertical angles.

1. **Faith and Tre each made a conjecture about the measures of vertical angles. Consider their conjectures and determine who's correct. Explain why the other conjecture is incorrect.**

   ### Faith
   All vertical angles
   are congruent
   and measure 90°.

   ### Tre
   All vertical angles are
   congruent.

2. Consider the central angles ∠*MOP* and ∠*POD* and their arcs
$\overarc{MP}$ and $\overarc{PD}$.

   a. What do you know about the sum m∠*MOP* + m∠*POD*?

   b. What can you conjecture about the sum m$\overarc{MP}$ + m$\overarc{PD}$?

3. Construct $\overleftrightarrow{EL}$ through the center of the circle parallel to $\overleftrightarrow{PM}$,
so that ∠*EOP* and ∠*LOM* are both acute angles. Then make
conjectures about each angle pair.

   a. ∠*PMO* and ∠*EOD*

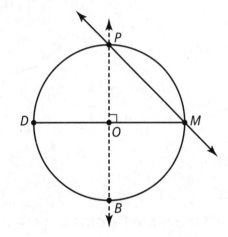

   b. ∠*MPO* and ∠*POE*

   c. Make a conjecture about another angle pair that you know
      something about.

ACTIVITY
1.3

Inscribed Angles, Arcs, and Tangents

Let's investigate some relationships among inscribed angles and arc measures to make some more conjectures.

1. **Consider Dawn's completed diagram. Identify two inscribed angles in the diagram.**

An **inscribed angle** is an angle whose vertex is on a circle and whose sides contain chords of the circle.

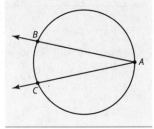

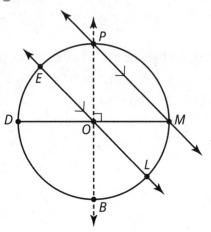

The vertex of ∠*PMD* is on the circle. The two rays of the angle intersect the circle at points *P* and *D*. This makes $\overset{\frown}{PD}$ an *intercepted arc* of ∠*PMD*. An **intercepted arc** is a part of a circle that lies in the interior of an angle with endpoints that are the intersection of the sides of the angle and the circle.

2. **Central angle *POD* also intercepts $\overset{\frown}{PD}$. Compare the measures of ∠*POD* and ∠*PMD*. What do you notice?**

3. Vicki conjectured that the measure of an inscribed angle is equal to the measure of a central angle when both angles intercept the same arc.

   Do you agree or disagree with Vicki's conjecture? Draw examples to justify your answer.

4. Consider the measures of inscribed angles that intercept the same arc. What conjecture can you make about this relationship? Use examples to explain your reasoning.

5. **Ameet measured each of the inscribed angles that intercept a semicircle. He conjectured that the measure of any inscribed angle that intercepts a semicircle arc is equal to 90°.**

   Do you agree or disagree with Ameet's conjecture? Draw examples to justify your answer.

A **tangent** to a circle is a line that intersects a circle in exactly one point, called the point of tangency.

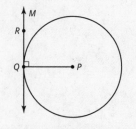

Tad drew two *tangent* lines to the circle, one through point *L* and one through point *G* to form a *circumscribed angle*, ∠*GQL*.

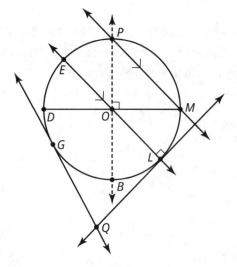

A **circumscribed angle** has its two sides tangent to the circle.

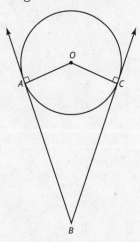

6. **What conjecture can you make about the measures of angles formed by tangent lines and the radii of a circle? Draw examples to explain your reasoning.**

TALK the TALK

Draw Whatcha Know

You have explored and measured different relationships to make and analyze several conjectures throughout this lesson. In mathematics, you often have to prove a solution is correct. In geometry, *theorems* are used to verify statements. A **theorem** is a statement that can be proven true using definitions, *postulates*, or other theorems. A **postulate** is a mathematical statement that is not proven but is considered true.

The table shows the conjectures that were made in this lesson. You will prove these as theorems in upcoming lessons.

1. **Based on your explorations in this lesson, draw an example of each conjecture.**

a. **All circles are similar.**	
b. **Vertical angles are congruent.**	

c. When the measures of two angles *x* and *y* are added, the sum is the measure of another angle, *z*.	
d. When the measures of two arcs *x* and *y* are added, the sum is the measure of another arc, *z*.	
e. When two parallel lines are crossed by a transversal, alternate interior angles are congruent.	

f. When two parallel lines are crossed by a transversal, corresponding angles are congruent.	
g. When an inscribed angle intercepts the same arc as a central angle, the inscribed angle has half the measure of the central angle.	
h. Two inscribed angles that intercept the same arc have the same measure.	

i. When an inscribed angle intercepts a semicircle arc, the inscribed angle measures 90°.	
j. The angle formed by a tangent line and a radius of a circle is 90°.	

Assignment

Write

Match each term with the best description.

1. secant
2. major arc
3. minor arc
4. conjecture
5. inscribed angle
6. intercepted arc
7. tangent
8. circumscribed angle
9. theorem
10. postulate

a. a presumption that something is true or false
b. a line that intersects a circle at exactly one point
c. an angle that has two sides tangent to a circle
d. an angle with a vertex that is on a circle and sides that contain chords of the circle
e. the arc with the greater measure
f. a mathematical statement that cannot be proven but is considered true
g. a statement that can be proven
h. a line that passes through two points on a circle
i. the arc of a circle with endpoints that are intersected by two rays of an angle
j. the arc with the lesser measure

Remember

Circles can be helpful in constructing geometric figures in order to make conjectures about line and angle relationships.

When you conjecture, you use what you know through experience and reasoning to presume that something is true. The proven statement of a conjecture is called a theorem.

Practice

1. Write a conjecture about each geometric object described. Draw examples to test your conjecture.

   a. Vertical angles
   b. Points on the perpendicular bisector of a line segment
   c. Inscribed angles that intercept the same arc of a circle
   d. Tangent

2. Draw examples of inscribed angles that intercept the diameter of the circle. What conjecture can you make about the measure of the inscribed angle?

Stretch

Consider the circle with a center at point *P*. Construct the perpendicular bisectors of chord *MN* and chord *ST*. Then make a conjecture about the perpendicular bisectors of chords in a circle.

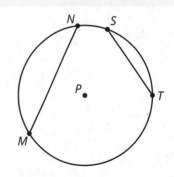

Review

Determine the area of each composite figure. Each grid square measures 1 unit by 1 unit.

1.

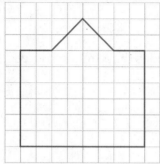

2.

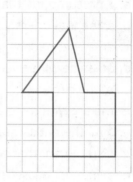

3.

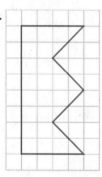

4.

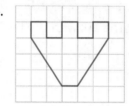

5. Determine each unknown measure in the figure.
   Explain your reasoning.

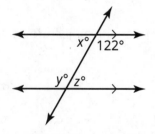

The Quad Squad

Conjectures About Quadrilaterals

2

Warm Up

Classify each figure using as many names as possible.

1.

2.

3.

4.

Learning Goals

- Use diagonals to draw quadrilaterals.
- Make conjectures about the diagonals of special quadrilaterals.
- Make conjectures about the angle relationships of special quadrilaterals.
- Categorize quadrilaterals based upon their properties.
- Make conjectures about the midsegments of quadrilaterals.
- Understand that the vertices of cyclic quadrilaterals lie on the same circle.

Key Terms

- coincident
- interior angle of a polygon
- kite
- isosceles trapezoid
- midsegment
- cyclic quadrilateral

You have classified quadrilaterals by their side measurements and side relationships. What conjectures can you make about different properties of quadrilaterals?

Cattywampus

A quadrilateral may be convex or concave. The quadrilaterals you are most familiar with—trapezoids, parallelograms, rectangles, rhombi, and squares—are convex. For a polygon to be convex it contains all of the line segments connecting any pair of points. It is concave if and only if at least one of its interior angles is greater than 180°.

Think about:

Why can a concave quadrilateral have only one angle greater than 180°?

Consider the two quadrilaterals shown. A quadrilateral has exactly two diagonals.

Convex	Concave

1. **Draw the diagonals in the two quadrilaterals shown. What do you notice?**

2. **Make a conjecture about the diagonals of a convex quadrilateral and about the diagonals of a concave quadrilateral.**

The diagonals of any convex quadrilateral create two pairs of vertical angles and four linear pairs of angles.

3. **Label the vertices of the convex quadrilateral as well as the point of intersection of the diagonals. Identify each pair of vertical angles and each linear pair of angles.**

ACTIVITY 2.1 Quadrilaterals Formed Using Concentric Circles

Let's explore the diagonals of different convex quadrilaterals. Consider a pair of concentric circles with center *A*. Diameter $\overline{BC}$ is shown.

Use a new piece of patty paper for each quadrilateral. For precision, it is important to use a straightedge when tracing or drawing line segments.

1. **Draw quadrilateral *BDCE* by following these steps.**
   - Construct the perpendicular bisector to $\overline{BC}$ through point *A* of the concentric circles.
   - Use patty paper to trace $\overline{BC}$.
   - Without moving the patty paper, draw diameter $\overline{DE}$ of the inner circle in such a way that it is not perpendicular or *coincident* to $\overline{BC}$.
   - Connect the endpoints of the diameters to draw quadrilateral *BDCE*.

   > Two line segments are **coincident** if they lie exactly on top of each other.

   a. **What do you know about $\overline{BC}$ and $\overline{DE}$?**

   b. **Use a ruler to measure the lengths of each side of the quadrilateral. What do you notice?**

   c. **Use a protractor to determine the measure of each interior angle of the quadrilateral. What do you notice?**

   > An **interior angle of a polygon** is an angle inside the polygon between two adjacent sides.

   d. **What do you know about $\overline{BE}$ and $\overline{DC}$?**

   e. **What names can be used to describe quadrilateral *BDCE*? Explain your reasoning. Write the name of the quadrilateral on the patty paper.**

   > Keep this quadrilateral to compare with other quadrilaterals that you will create in this lesson.

2. Draw quadrilateral *BFCG* by following these steps.

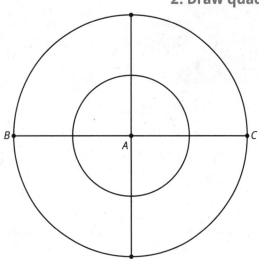

- Use patty paper to trace $\overline{BC}$.
- Without moving the patty paper, draw diameter $\overline{FG}$ of the inner circle perpendicular to $\overline{BC}$.
- Connect the endpoints of the diameters to draw quadrilateral *BFCG*.

a. **What do you know about $\overline{BC}$ and $\overline{FG}$?**

b. **Use a ruler to measure the lengths of each side of the quadrilateral. What do you notice?**

c. **Use a protractor to determine the measure of each interior angle of the quadrilateral. What do you notice?**

d. **What names can be used to describe quadrilateral *BFCG*? Explain your reasoning. Write the name of the quadrilateral on the patty paper.**

3. **Consider Elijah's statement. What error did Elijah make?**

Elijah
In the quadrilateral BFCG that I drew, ∠BFC and ∠CGB are circumscribed angles.

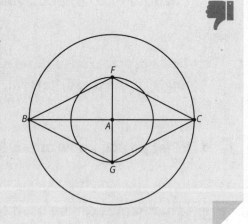

4. **Draw quadrilateral *BHCJ* by following these steps.**

- Use patty paper to trace $\overline{BC}$.
- Without moving the patty paper, draw point *H* where the perpendicular bisector intersects the inner circle and point *J* where it intersects the outer circle, such that $\overline{HJ}$ contains point *A*.
- Connect the points to draw $\overline{HJ}$.
- Connect the endpoints of the line segments to create quadrilateral *BHCJ*.

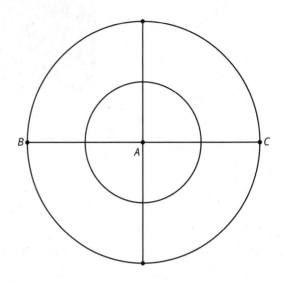

a. **What do you know about $\overline{BC}$ and $\overline{HJ}$?**

b. **Use a ruler to measure the lengths of each side of the quadrilateral. What do you notice?**

c. **Use a protractor to determine the measure of each interior angle of the quadrilateral. What do you notice?**

The quadrilateral you drew is a *kite*. A **kite** is a quadrilateral with two pairs of equal adjacent sides. If the diagonals of a quadrilateral are perpendicular, non-congruent, and only one bisects the other, it can only be classified as a kite.

5. **Write the name of the quadrilateral on the patty paper.**

In the previous activity, you drew quadrilaterals using a pair of concentric circles. Now let's draw quadrilaterals using only one circle. Circle *P* with diameter $\overline{QR}$ is shown.

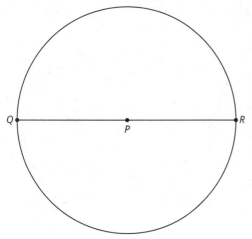

Use a new piece of patty paper for each quadrilateral. For precision, it is important to use a straightedge when tracing or drawing line segments.

1. **Draw quadrilateral *QSRT* by following these steps.**
   - Construct the perpendicular bisector to $\overline{QR}$ through point *P*.
   - Use patty paper to trace $\overline{QR}$.
   - Without moving the patty paper, draw diameter $\overline{ST}$ of circle *P* in such a way that it is not perpendicular or coincident to $\overline{QR}$.
   - Connect the endpoints of the diameters to draw quadrilateral *QSRT*.

   a. **What do you know about $\overline{QR}$ and $\overline{ST}$?**

   b. **Use a ruler to measure the lengths of each side of the quadrilateral. What do you notice?**

   c. **Use a protractor to determine the measure of each interior angle of the quadrilateral. Which conjecture that you made in the previous lesson does this measurement support?**

   d. **What names can be used to describe quadrilateral *QSRT*? Explain your reasoning. Write the most specific name for the quadrilateral on the patty paper.**

2. **Draw quadrilateral *QVRW* by following these steps.**

- Use patty paper to trace $\overline{QR}$.
- Without moving the patty paper, draw diameter $\overline{VW}$ of circle P perpendicular to $\overline{QR}$.
- Connect the endpoints of the diameters to draw quadrilateral *QVRW*.

a. What do you know about $\overline{QR}$ and $\overline{VW}$?

b. Use a ruler to measure the lengths of each side of the quadrilateral. What do you notice?

c. Use a protractor to determine the measure of each interior angle of the quadrilateral. Does this measurement support the same conjecture from Question 1? Explain your reasoning.

d. What names can be used to describe quadrilateral *QVRW*? Explain your reasoning. Write the most specific name for the quadrilateral on the patty paper.

A trapezoid is a quadrilateral with at least one pair of parallel sides, known as the bases. If the other pair of sides are not parallel, they are known as the legs. A special type of trapezoid is an *isosceles trapezoid*. An **isosceles trapezoid** is a trapezoid with congruent legs.

3. Consider the isosceles trapezoid shown.

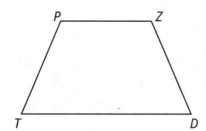

   a. **Use a piece of patty paper to trace the trapezoid and draw diagonals $\overline{TZ}$ and $\overline{PD}$.**

   b. **Use a ruler to measure $\overline{TZ}$ and $\overline{PD}$. What do you notice?**

   c. **Do $\overline{TZ}$ and $\overline{PD}$ bisect each other? Explain how you determined your answer.**

   d. **Use a protractor to determine the measure of each interior angle of the quadrilateral. What do you notice?**

Save the quadrilaterals you drew on your pieces of patty paper. You'll need them later.

Making Conjectures About Quadrilaterals

In the previous two activities, you used the properties of the diagonals to discover each member of the quadrilateral family. You investigated the relationships between the diagonals of quadrilaterals.

1. **Make a conjecture about the diagonals of the described quadrilaterals. Explain your reasoning using examples.**

    a. **parallelograms**

    b. **rectangles**

    c. **quadrilaterals with pairs of adjacent congruent sides**

You also investigated the relationships between the interior angles of quadrilaterals.

2. **Make a conjecture about the interior angles of the described quadrilaterals. Explain your reasoning using examples.**

   a. **parallelograms**

   b. **rectangles**

   c. **kites**

3. **Nichole observed the relationship between the interior angles of the isosceles trapezoid. She conjectured that trapezoids have two pairs of congruent angles that are adjacent to each other.**

   Do you think Nichole's conjecture is correct? Draw examples to justify your answer.

Use the quadrilaterals you drew on your pieces of patty paper and the observations you made to complete the table.

4. **Identify the properties that are always true for the given quadrilateral by placing an X in the appropriate box.**

	Property	Parallelogram	Rectangle	Rhombus	Square	Isosceles Trapezoid	Kite
Side Relationships	a. Opposite sides are parallel.						
	b. Only one pair of opposite sides is parallel.						
	c. Opposite sides are congruent.						
	d. Only one pair of opposite sides is congruent						
	e. All sides are congruent.						
	f. 2 pairs of consecutive sides are congruent.						
Angle Relationships	g. Opposite angles are congruent.						
	h. At least one pair of opposite angles is congruent.						
	i. All angles are right angles.						
Diagonal Relationships	j. Diagonals bisect each other.						
	k. Diagonals are perpendicular.						
	l. Diagonals are congruent.						

5. **Determine whether each statement is true or false. If it is false, explain why.**

   a. A square is also a rectangle.

   b. A rectangle is also a square.

   c. A parallelogram is also a trapezoid.

   d. The diagonals of a trapezoid are congruent.

   e. A kite is also a parallelogram.

   f. The diagonals of a rhombus bisect each other.

Knowing certain properties of each quadrilateral makes it possible to construct the quadrilateral given only a single diagonal.

6. **Describe how you could construct each named quadrilateral with the given diagonal.**

   a. Parallelogram *WXYZ* given diagonal $\overline{WY}$

   b. Rhombus *RHOM* given diagonal $\overline{RO}$

   c. Kite *KITE* given diagonal $\overline{KT}$

Consider quadrilateral *QUAD*.

1. **Construct the midpoint of each side of quadrilateral *QUAD*.**

2. **How many possible midsegments are there for any quadrilateral?**

> A **midsegment** of a polygon is any line segment that connects two midpoints of the sides of the polygon.

3. **Draw the midsegments that connect the midpoints of adjacent sides. What shape does it appear you drew using the midsegments of quadrilateral *QUAD*?**

Revisit the quadrilaterals you drew on patty paper in this lesson.

4. **Draw the midsegments connecting midpoints of adjacent sides for each of the quadrilaterals you drew on patty paper. Make a conjecture about the figure created by connecting adjacent midpoints of a quadrilateral.**

5. **Does your conjecture hold true for concave quadrilaterals? Use a drawing to justify your answer.**

Let's explore one of the midsegments of a trapezoid.

6. **Use the given parallel line segments and a straightedge to complete this question.**

   a. **Draw any trapezoid with only one pair of parallel sides. Label the vertices.**

   b. **Construct the midsegment of your trapezoid that connects the non-parallel sides. Label the endpoints.**

   c. **Use your ruler to determine the length of each base and the length of the midsegment.**

   d. **Determine the average of the lengths of the bases. What do you notice?**

   e. **Compare your answer to part (d) with those of your classmates. Make a conjecture about the midsegment of a trapezoid that connects non-parallel sides.**

Cyclic Quadrilaterals

Some of the quadrilaterals you drew in this lesson are *cyclic quadrilaterals*. A **cyclic quadrilateral** is a quadrilateral whose vertices all lie on a single circle.

1. **Identify any cyclic quadrilaterals you drew on your pieces of patty paper.**

2. **What is the sum of the measures of the opposite angles in the cyclic quadrilaterals you identified?**

Consider quadrilateral *MATH* inscribed in circle *O*.

3. **Use a protractor to determine the measure of each interior angle of quadrilateral *MATH*. Write the measurements in the diagram.**

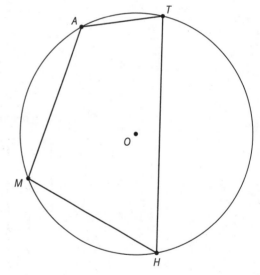

4. **Determine each sum.**

   a. **m∠M + m∠T**   b. **m∠A + m∠H**

5. **Make a conjecture about the measures of opposite angles of a cyclic quadrilateral.**

6. **Is an isosceles trapezoid a cyclic quadrilateral? Explain your reasoning.**

TALK the TALK

Zukei, Don't Bother Me

Remember, a Zukei puzzle is a Japanese logic puzzle in which a grid is presented with a number of points shown at different intersections. Each grid is presented along with the name of a geometric figure. The goal of the puzzle is to determine which points on the grid are the vertices of the named geometric figure.

1. **For each Zukei puzzle, identify and connect the vertices that form each shape. There is only one correct answer.**

a. **Square**

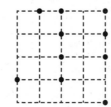

b. **Rectangle**

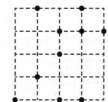

c. **Rhombus**

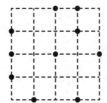

d. **Parallelogram**

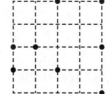

e. **Trapezoid**

Assignment

Write

Define each term in your own words. Use the words *diagonal, interior angle,* and *midsegment* in your definitions.

1. kite
2. isosceles trapezoid
3. cyclic quadrilateral

Remember

The diagonals of a parallelogram bisect each other and the diagonals of a rectangle are congruent. A square, rhombus, and kite have perpendicular diagonals.

The opposite angles of parallelograms are congruent and the opposite angles of cyclic quadrilaterals are supplementary.

Practice

1. Determine which quadrilateral each letter in the diagram represents using the list shown.

    Kites   Squares
    Rectangles   Parallelograms
    Rhombi   Isosceles Trapezoids

2. State as many properties as you can about each quadrilateral.

    a. Rectangle   b. Isosceles trapezoid
    c. Kite   d. Parallelogram
    e. Rhombus   f. Square

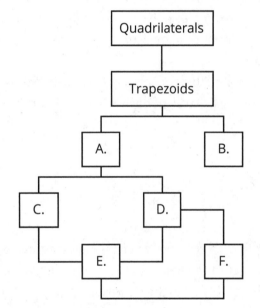

3. Describe how to construct each quadrilateral using the given diagonal.

    a. Square *WXYZ* given diagonal *WY*
    b. Parallelogram *RSTU* that is non-rectangular given diagonal *RT*

Stretch

Create a Zukei puzzle for an isosceles trapezoid in which the bases do not lie on the grid lines. Use a minimum of 10 dots. Make sure that your puzzle has only one correct answer.

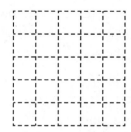

Review

1. Write a conjecture about alternate interior angles. Draw an example to test your conjecture.

2. Draw examples of inscribed angles that intercept the same arc of a circle. What conjecture can you make about the measures of the inscribed angles?

3. Jay walks 3 blocks north and then 4 blocks east to get to the store. If he walks straight back home, how far does Jay walk in all?

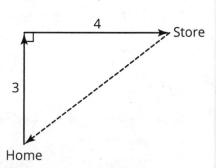

4. TV screen sizes are given by their diagonal measure from a top corner to the opposite bottom corner. What is the approximate size of this TV to the nearest inch?

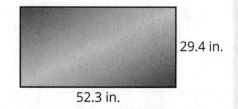

52.3 in.

5. Use the coordinate plane to approximate each distance. Write each answer as a decimal to the nearest hundredth.
   a. The distance between point A and point C
   b. The distance between point D and point B

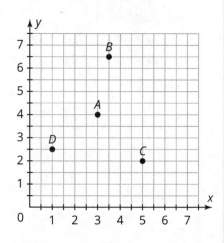

Into the Ring

Constructing an Inscribed Regular Polygon

Warm Up

Use patty paper to identify a geometric figure that is congruent to each figure in the diagram. Describe the transformation(s) you used.

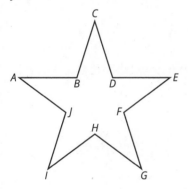

1. $\overline{AB}$

2. $\angle FGH$

3. $\angle AJI$

Learning Goals

- Use construction tools to duplicate an angle.
- Construct a regular hexagon inscribed in a circle using a variety of strategies.
- Construct a square inscribed in a circle using patty paper and using a compass and straightedge.
- Use construction tools to bisect an angle.
- Construct an equilateral triangle using a compass and straightedge.
- Construct an equilateral triangle inscribed in a circle.

Key Terms

- inscribed polygon
- angle bisector

You have used construction tools to construct figures in a plane. How can you construct a regular polygon inscribed in a circle?

Duped

You can use your construction skills to duplicate a line segment inside a circle.

1. **Consider circle A.**

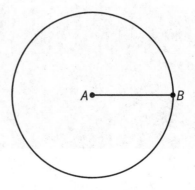

a. **Construct $\overline{BC}$ congruent to $\overline{AB}$ in circle A so that point C lies on circle A.**

b. **Connect points A and C. What do you know about the length of $\overline{AC}$?**

c. **What type of triangle is △ABC? Explain your reasoning.**

d. **What do you know about the angle measures of △ABC?**

Not only can you copy a line segment using construction, remember that you can also copy an angle.

1. **Duplicate angle *B*. Verify with patty paper.**

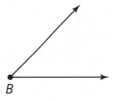

B

2. **Construct an angle that is twice the measure of ∠*A*. Then explain how you performed the construction.**

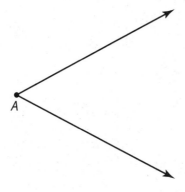

A

3. How is duplicating an angle similar to duplicating a line segment? How is it different?

4. In the Getting Started, you constructed an equilateral triangle *ABC*. Duplicate the 60° angle shown to construct 5 additional equilateral triangles that share the center of the circle as a vertex. What do you notice about the polygon you have constructed?

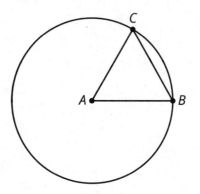

Constructing an Inscribed Hexagon

In the Getting Started, you created an equilateral triangle by duplicating the length of the radius to create a chord. You can use what you know about copying a line segment to construct a regular hexagon inscribed in a circle using a compass and straightedge.

> An **inscribed polygon** is a polygon drawn inside another polygon or circle in which all the vertices of the interior polygon lie on the outer figure.

1. Use circle *A* to complete your construction.

a. **Copy the radius of circle *A*.**

b. **Create 6 chords around the circumference of circle *A* so that they are congruent to the radius and their endpoints are equidistant from each other.**

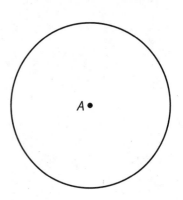

c. **Connect consecutive endpoints of the chords.**

The figure you constructed is a regular hexagon inscribed in a circle.

2. How can you copy an angle to verify that the inscribed hexagon is a regular hexagon?

Remember:

A regular polygon is a polygon with all sides congruent and all angles congruent.

3. What do you know about the measures of the interior angles of a regular hexagon?

In a previous activity, you constructed a square given a side length. Let's now consider how to inscribe a square inside a circle. One way to create a square is to use transformations.

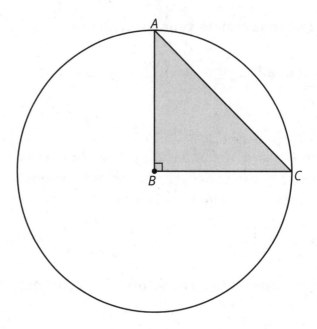

1. Circle *B* contains a right triangle, △*ABC*, with points *A* and *C* on the circle and point *B* at the center. Describe each element using a term associated with a circle.

   a. ∠*B*

   b. $\overline{BC}$ and $\overline{BA}$

   c. $\overline{AC}$

2. Use patty paper to rotate the right triangle to create square *ACDE*. How do you know all 4 vertices lie on the circle?

3. Verify that you created a square inscribed in circle *B*. To do this, you need to show that all side lengths of the square are equal and each interior angle measures 90°.

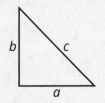
a. Show that all side lengths are equal. Suppose *BC* = *x*. Determine each side length of the square. Label each length.

b. Verify that each interior angle measure of the square is 90°.

4. Consider $\overline{AD}$ and $\overline{CE}$.

a. Describe each line segment in terms of the circle and in terms of the square.

b. Describe the relationship between $\overline{AD}$ and $\overline{CE}$.

Think
about:

Is an inscribed
square a cyclic
quadrilateral?

5. Use diagonals to construct a square inscribed in circle *O*.
Describe your process.

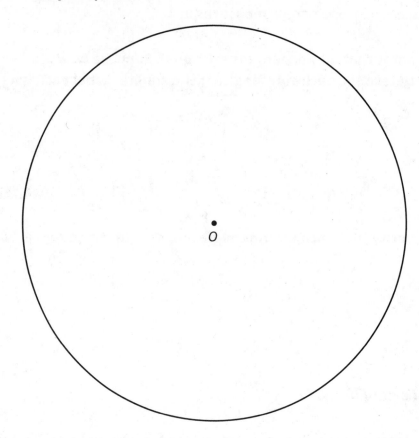

ACTIVITY
3.4
Bisecting an Angle

Just as line segments can be bisected, angles can be bisected too. If a ray is drawn through the vertex of an angle and divides the angle into two angles of equal measure, or two congruent angles, this ray is called an **angle bisector**. The construction used to create an angle bisector is called bisecting an angle.

One way to bisect an angle is using patty paper.

Worked Example

Draw an angle on the patty paper.

Fold the patty paper so that the rays lie on top of each other. The fold should pass through the vertex of the angle.

Open the patty paper. The crease represents the angle bisector.

> Lines and line segments can also bisect an angle.

1. **Angela states that as long as the crease goes through the vertex, it is an angle bisector. Is she correct? Why or why not?**

You can also bisect an angle using a compass and a straightedge.

Worked Example

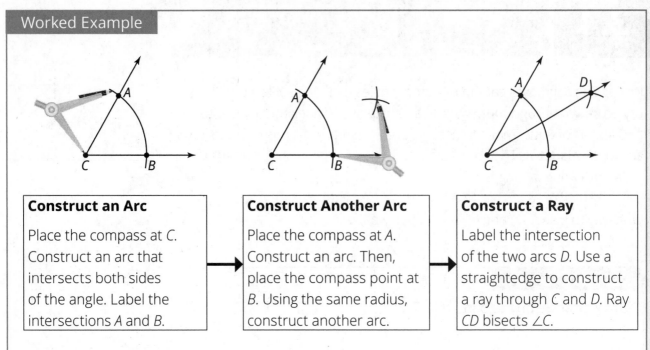

Construct an Arc

Place the compass at *C*. Construct an arc that intersects both sides of the angle. Label the intersections *A* and *B*.

Construct Another Arc

Place the compass at *A*. Construct an arc. Then, place the compass point at *B*. Using the same radius, construct another arc.

Construct a Ray

Label the intersection of the two arcs *D*. Use a straightedge to construct a ray through *C* and *D*. Ray *CD* bisects ∠*C*.

2. **Construct the bisector of ∠A. Use patty paper to verify your construction.**

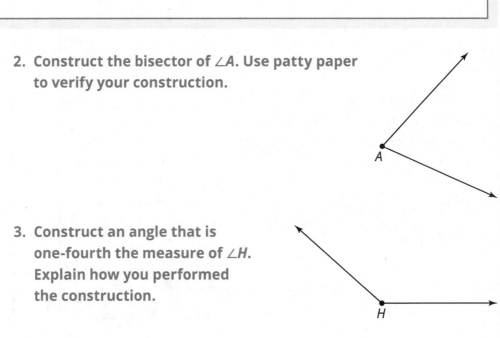

3. **Construct an angle that is one-fourth the measure of ∠H. Explain how you performed the construction.**

4. **Describe how to construct an angle that is one-eighth the measure of ∠H from Question 3.**

ACTIVITY 3.5

Constructing and Inscribing an Equilateral Triangle

In this activity, you will construct an equilateral triangle. To perform the construction, you will use only a compass and straightedge and rely on the basic geometric constructions you have learned, such as duplicating a line segment.

1. Sophie claims that she can construct an equilateral triangle by constructing and then duplicating a line segment three times and having the endpoints of all three line segments intersect. Roberto thinks that Sophie's method will not result in an equilateral triangle.

   Is Sophie correct? Explain why Sophie's reasoning or Roberto's reasoning is incorrect.

2. Construct an equilateral triangle using the given side length. Then, describe the steps you performed for the construction.

Remember:

An equilateral triangle has three congruent sides and three congruent angles.

An inscribed equilateral triangle is an equilateral triangle inside a circle with all of its vertices touching the circle.

Think about:

How can you use the process for constructing an inscribed regular hexagon to inscribe an equilateral triangle?

3. **Show two different ways to construct an inscribed equilateral triangle using each circle given. Explain your process for each construction.**

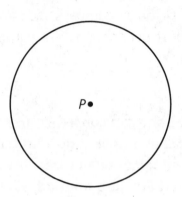

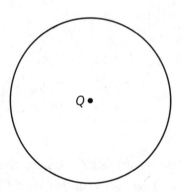

TALK the TALK

Playing the Angles

Within a circle, an interesting relationship exists between the measure of a central angle and the measure of any inscribed angle that intercepts the same arc of the circle.

1. **Consider Circle O.**

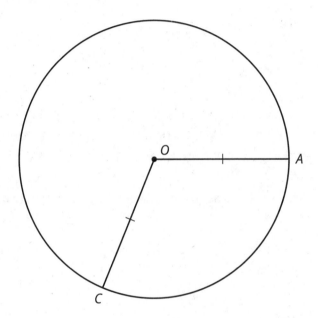

What do an inscribed angle and an inscribed polygon have in common?

   a. **Draw two different inscribed angles that intercept the same arc as the one intercepted by ∠COA.**

   b. **Use patty paper to analyze your diagram. Make a conjecture regarding a relationship you notice.**

2. **Use the constructions you have learned to construct an angle with a measure of 75° using only a compass and straightedge. Summarize your process.**

You have constructed a regular quadrilateral (square), a regular hexagon, and a regular triangle (equilateral triangle) inscribed in a circle. What other regular polygons can you inscribe in a circle?

3. **Inscribe a regular octagon in the circle provided, if possible.**

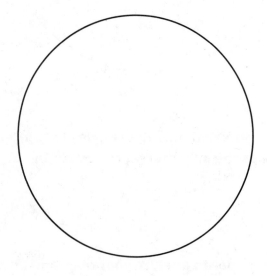

Assignment

Write

Explain how to bisect an angle using patty paper and using a compass and straightedge.

Remember

• An angle bisector is a line, line segment, or ray that is drawn through the vertex of an angle and divides the angle into two congruent angles.
• All regular polygons can be inscribed in a circle. Some regular polygons, such as an equilateral triangle, square, hexagon and octagon, can be inscribed in a circle using a compass and straightedge.

Practice

1. Duplicate each angle using construction tools.

   a.
   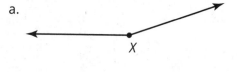

   b.
   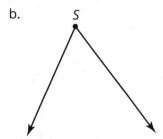

2. Inscribe a hexagon inside a circle. Explain your process.
3. Construct a square inscribed in a circle. Then, explain how you know the figure is a square, and how you know it is inscribed.
4. Construct the angle bisector of each given angle.

   a.
   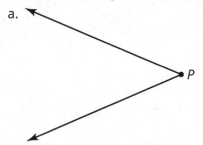

   b.
   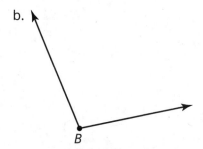

5. Construct a 15° angle using only a compass and straightedge. Summarize your steps.
6. Inscribe an equilateral triangle inside a circle. Explain your process.

Stretch

Determine two different constructions you could use to construct an angle with a measure of 45° using only a compass and straightedge. Summarize the processes and show both constructions.

Review

1. Identify the quadrilaterals that match each description.

   a. opposite sides are parallel

   b. at least one pair of opposite angles is congruent

2. Write an equation for a line that is perpendicular to the given line.

   a. $y = 4x - 1$

   b. $y = x + 2$

3. Write an equation for a line that is parallel to the given line.

   a. $x = 3$

   b. $y = -\frac{1}{2}x - \frac{5}{2}$

Tri- Tri- Tri- and Separate Them

Conjectures About Triangles

Warm Up

The points represent possible vertices of a polygon. Identify and connect the vertices that form each given figure.

1. right triangle

2. isosceles triangle

3. isosceles right triangle

Learning Goals

- Construct circles, parallel lines, and perpendicular bisectors.
- Write a conjecture as a statement and write the converse of the conjecture.
- Identify and draw exterior angles of triangles and midsegments of triangles.
- Make conjectures about the sum of the interior angles of a triangle, exterior angles of a triangle, triangle side length inequalities, and midsegments of a triangle.

Key Terms

- conditional statement
- converse
- hypothesis
- conclusion
- biconditional statement
- base angles
- exterior angle
- remote interior angles

You have made conjectures about line and angle relationships and about quadrilaterals using circles. What conjectures can you make about triangles using circles?

Not an Illusion

In the previous lesson, you created quadrilaterals and made conjectures about them. When you divide a quadrilateral along any one of its diagonals, you create two triangles.

Think

about:

How can you use your conjectures from the previous lesson about the properties of quadrilaterals to describe the triangles formed?

1. **Identify each quadrilateral. Then, classify the triangles formed by dividing the quadrilateral using each diagonal. Explain your reasoning.**

a.

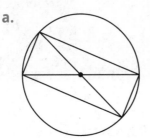

b.

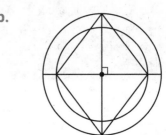

c.

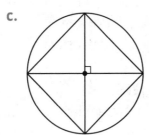

d.

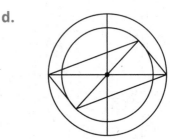

ACTIVITY 4.1

Base Angles, Angle Pairs, and Converses

Previously, you made conjectures like this:

> "If two parallel lines are cut by a transversal, then the corresponding angles are congruent."

You can also make conjectures about the *converse* of statements. The **converse** of an if-then statement is the statement that results from interchanging the **hypothesis** (the "if" part) and the **conclusion** (the "then" part) of the original statement.

An "If...then..." statement is also referred to as a **conditional statement**.

Worked Example

To form the converse of a conditional statement, interchange the hypothesis and conclusion.

Conditional Statement: If a point lies on the perpendicular bisector of a line segment, then the point is equidistant from the endpoints of the line segment.

Converse Statement: If a point is equidistant from the endpoints of a line segment, then the point lies on the perpendicular bisector of the line segment.

---

1. **Write the converse of the conjecture stated above about parallel lines and corresponding angles.**

2. **Do you think both the original statement and the converse are true? Why or why not?**

Do you think that
all conditional
statements and
their converses
are biconditional
statements?

When a conditional statement and its converse are both true, this is called a *biconditional statement*. A **biconditional statement** is a statement written in the form "if and only if p, then q." It is a combination of both a conditional statement and the converse of that conditional statement.

3. **Consider the conditional statement: If Estelle goes out in the rain without an umbrella, she will get wet.**

   Write the converse and determine whether this is a biconditional statement.

4. **David observed that the angles opposite the congruent sides of an isosceles triangle are congruent. He conjectured that if two sides of a triangle are congruent, then the angles opposite the congruent sides are always congruent.**

   Do you think this conjecture is correct? Create isosceles triangles and use a protractor to measure angles to test David's conjecture.

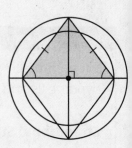

The congruent sides
of an isosceles triangle
are called the legs. The
other side is called the
base and the angles
between the base and
the congruent sides are
called **base angles**.

5. **Write the converse of David's conjecture. Do you think the converse is true? How could you test the converse conjecture?**

Testing a conjecture and proving it to be a theorem are not the same thing. Remember, a theorem has been proved true in all cases. A proof requires reasoning using definitions and theorems, whereas testing involves making observations, noting counterexamples, and using measuring tools.

Triangle Sum, 30°-60°-90°, and Exterior Angles

Let's construct a new diagram, investigate the relationships, and make a few more conjectures about triangles.

1. **Construct circle *R* and circle *S*, each with radius *RS*. Label the two points of intersection as point *T* and point *V*.**

    R   *S*

2. **Draw line segments to form △*RST*. Explain why the triangle you created is an equilateral triangle. What does this tell you about the relationship between point *T* and the endpoints of $\overline{RS}$?**

In the previous activity, the worked example states that if a point is on a perpendicular bisector of a line segment, then it is equidistant from the endpoints of the line segment.

3. **Consider the converse statement.**

   a. **Construct the perpendicular bisector of $\overline{RS}$. Label the point where the perpendicular bisector intersects the line segment as point *Q*.**

   b. **Determine whether the converse is true. If this conjecture is true, what can you say about points *T* and *V*?**

4. Consider △QST. Justify each measurement.

   a. Determine each angle measure.

   b. If QS = x, determine the measures of TS and TQ.

5. Damon drew line AR parallel to $\overline{ST}$ and drew line RS. He marked two pairs of congruent angles:

   - ∠ARB ≅ ∠TSR
   - ∠ART ≅ ∠RTS

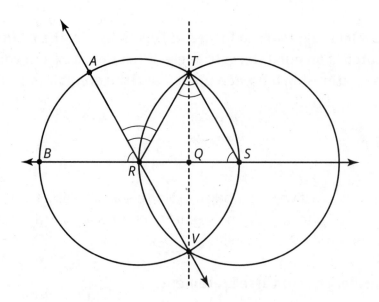

a. What conjectures did Damon use to mark the congruent angle pairs?

Think about:

What conjectures did you use to describe the angle and arc additions?

b. Consider the central angles $\angle TRS$, $\angle TRA$, and $\angle ARB$ and their intercepted arcs: $\overset{\frown}{ST}$, $\overset{\frown}{TA}$, and $\overset{\frown}{AB}$. What is the sum of the measures of these central angles? What is the sum of the measures of the corresponding intercepted arcs?

c. Using Damon's diagram, what can you conjecture about the sum of the measures of the interior angles of a triangle? Explain your reasoning.

An **exterior angle** of a polygon is an angle that forms a linear pair with an interior angle of the polygon. The **remote interior angles** of a triangle are the two angles that are not adjacent to the specified exterior angle.

A portion of Damon's diagram is shown. Consider △RST. Angle *TRB* is an *exterior angle* and ∠*RST* and ∠*STR* are *remote interior angles* of △*RST*.

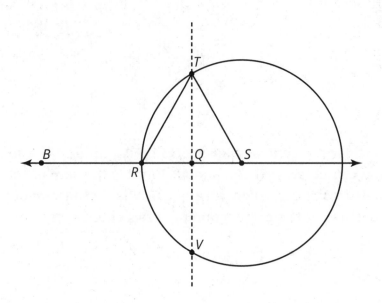

6. **What conjecture can you make about the measures of the exterior angle, ∠TRB, and the two remote interior angles, ∠RTS and ∠TSR?**

7. **Each interior angle of a triangle has two corresponding exterior angles. Identify each exterior angle and use a protractor to test your conjecture from Question 6. What do you notice?**

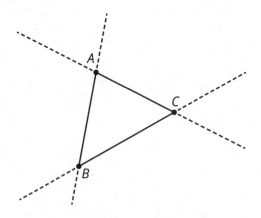

Consider the diagram shown.

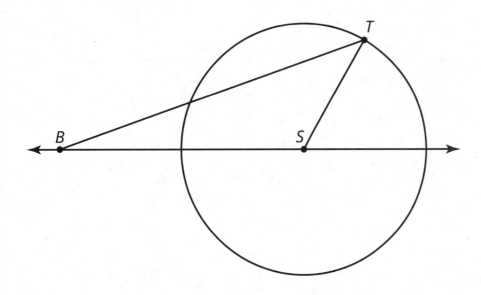

1. **Measure the side lengths of △TBS.**

2. **Move point *T* to different locations on the circle to create three triangles with side lengths *ST* and *SB*.**

Previously, when you studied triangles, you may have learned a conjecture that the sum of the lengths of two sides of a triangle is always greater than the length of the third side.

3. **How can you use the diagram and the triangles you drew to demonstrate that this conjecture is true? Explain your reasoning.**

4. Consider the diagram that shows point *T* at two different
   locations on the circle that create triangles with side lengths
   ST and *SB*.

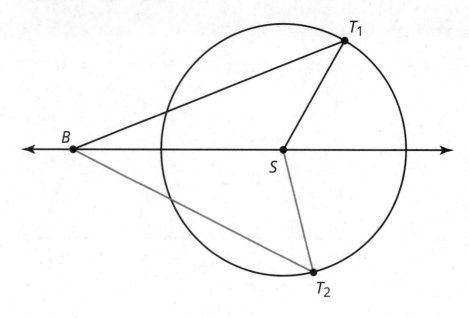

a. For each triangle, determine and label the midpoint of $\overline{ST}$ as
   point *X* and label the midpoint of $\overline{BT}$ as point *Y*. Connect the
   midpoints to form a midsegment.

b. Measure and compare the midsegments with $\overline{SB}$ and the
   length of *SB*. Measure and compare the angles formed by
   the midsegments and the angles formed at the base of each
   triangle. What do you notice? What conjecture can you make
   about the midsegment of each triangle?

TALK the TALK

You Will Only Come to This Conclusion

You have investigated different relationships to make and analyze several conjectures about triangles throughout this lesson. You will prove these as theorems in upcoming lessons.

1. **Describe the difference between a conjecture and a theorem.**

2. **Based on your observations, draw an example of each conjecture made in this lesson.**

a. The base angles of an isosceles triangle are congruent.	
b. A point that lies on a perpendicular bisector of a line segment is equidistant from the endpoints of the line segment.	

c. The measure of the exterior angle of a triangle is equal to the sum of the measures of the two remote interior angles.	
d. The sum of the measures of the interior angles of a triangle is 180°.	
e. The length of the third side of a triangle cannot be equal to or greater than the sum of the measures of the other two sides.	
f. The midsegment of a triangle is one-half the measure and parallel to the third side.	

Assignment

Write

If a conditional statement is true, can you assume the converse is also true?
Use examples to justify your reasoning.

Remember

The converse of a conditional statement and is formed by interchanging the hypothesis and conclusion of the conditional statement. When a conditional statement and its converse are both true, this is called a biconditional statement.

Practice

1. Write a conjecture about the geometric objects in each part. Then write the converse of the conjecture. Draw examples to test each conjecture.
    a. base angles of an isosceles triangle and their opposite sides
    b. the interior angles of a triangle
    c. corresponding angles and alternate interior angles
    d. the side lengths of a triangle

2. Draw examples of triangle midsegments. What conjecture can you make about the midsegment of a triangle?

Stretch

1. Consider the circle with center *P*. Chords *QR* and *ST* are congruent. Draw △*QPR* and △*SPT*.
    a. Is △*QPR* congruent to △*SPT*? Explain your reasoning.
    b. Draw the altitude of each triangle. How do the two altitudes compare? Explain your reasoning.
    c. Write a conjecture about the distance of congruent chords from the center of the circle. Then write the converse of the conjecture.

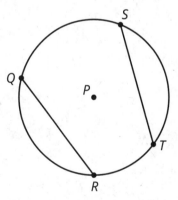

Review

1. State as many properties as you can about a kite.

2. State as many properties as you can about a rectangle.

3. Determine the median of the data in each set.

    a. {2, 3, 1, 0, 5, 5, 10}

    b. {7, 7, 8.5, 9, 9.1, 9.5}

    c. {1, 2, 3, 4, 5, 6, 7, 8, 9, 10}

5

What's the Point?

Points of Concurrency

Warm Up

1. Describe how you can construct a perpendicular bisector.

2. Describe how you can construct an angle bisector.

Learning Goals

- Construct the circumcenter, incenter, centroid, and orthocenter.
- Use points of concurrency to construct the inscribed and circumscribed circles of a triangle.
- Understand that the three medians of a triangle meet at a point.

Key Terms

- concurrent
- point of concurrency
- circumcenter
- circumscribed circle
- incenter
- median
- centroid
- altitude
- orthocenter

You have constructed the perpendicular bisector of a line segment and the angle bisector of an angle. What happens when you make these constructions on all sides or all angles of a triangle?

It Comes Back Around

You have used circles to explore relationships involving triangles. Let's investigate what happens when you connect any three points on a circle to create different types of triangles.

1. **Construct a circle and label the center. Then, draw any three points on the circle. Draw chords between the points to create a triangle.**

2. **What is the relationship between the center of the circle and each vertex of your triangle?**

3. **Compare your triangle with your classmates' triangles. What do you notice?**

4. **Draw three lines, each of which passes through the center of the circle and through a vertex of your triangle.**

The lines you drew are *concurrent* lines. **Concurrent** lines, rays, and line segments are three or more lines, rays, or line segments intersecting at a single point.

> The **point of concurrency** is the point at which concurrent lines, rays, or line segments intersect.

5. **Are there other sets of three lines that pass through the center of the circle? Explain your reasoning.**

Tiago and Lezlee have been given the task of building an information kiosk for the zoo. They want the kiosk to be easily accessible from each of the various exhibits. Three of the exhibits at the zoo are shown.

Elephantastic
●

● Primate Paradise

● Giraffrica

1. **Tiago suggests building the kiosk so that it is equidistant from Giraffrica and Primate Paradise.**

   a. **Lezlee says that for the kiosk to be equidistant from Primate Paradise and Giraffrica, it must go at the midpoint of the line segment between the two exhibits. Is Lezlee correct? Explain your reasoning.**

   b. **Use a construction to show all possible locations of the kiosk so that it is equidistant from Giraffrica and Primate Paradise. Explain your reasoning.**

2. Lezlee suggests building the kiosk so that it is equidistant from Elephantastic and Primate Paradise. Use a construction to show all possible locations of the kiosk so that it is equidistant from these two exhibits. Explain your reasoning.

3. Tiago then wonders where the kiosk could be built so that it is equidistant from Elephantastic and Giraffrica. Use a construction to show all possible locations of the kiosk so that it is equidistant from these two exhibits. Explain your reasoning.

4. Describe how to determine a location that is the same distance from all three exhibits. Is there more than one possible location that is equidistant from all three exhibits? Explain your reasoning.

5. Verify that the location you described in Question 4 is equidistant from each exhibit.

You constructed a point of concurrency using the perpendicular bisectors of a triangle.

6. **Construct the three perpendicular bisectors of each triangle.**

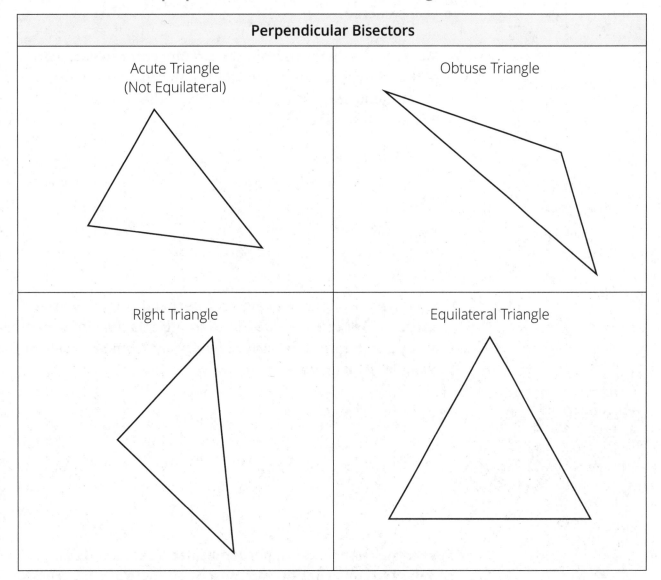

Perpendicular Bisectors

Acute Triangle
(Not Equilateral)

Obtuse Triangle

Right Triangle

Equilateral Triangle

7. **Make a conjecture about the location of the intersection of the three perpendicular bisectors of any triangle. Is the intersection located inside, outside, or on the triangle?**

The **circumcenter** is the point of concurrency of the three perpendicular bisectors of a triangle.

8. **Consider the four triangles and the perpendicular bisectors you constructed.**

    a. **Measure the distance from the circumcenter to each vertex of the triangle. Is the circumcenter always, sometimes, or never equidistant from each vertex of the triangle? Explain your reasoning.**

    b. **Measure the distance along each perpendicular from the circumcenter to each side of the triangle. Is the circumcenter always, sometimes, or never equidistant from each side of the triangle? Explain your reasoning.**

A **circumscribed circle** is a circle that passes through all the vertices of a polygon.

Circle Q is circumscribed around $\triangle ABC$.

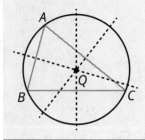

9. **Revisit the triangles with perpendicular bisectors. Use a compass to construct the circumscribed circle of each triangle.**

10. **What does the circumcenter tell you about the relationship between circles and triangles? Explain your reasoning.**

Two major highways leading out of Northville and Eastville meet in Midville.

A developer wants to build a shopping center that is equidistant from each highway.

1. **Use a construction to show all possible locations of the shopping center so that it is equidistant from each highway. Explain your reasoning.**

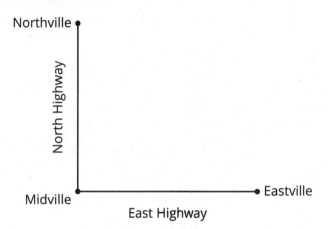

The Northeast Highway will be built to connect Northville and Eastville. The developer decides to build the shopping center equidistant from the three highways.

2. **Use constructions to determine whether there is a single point that is equidistant from the three highways. Explain your reasoning.**

3. **Construct the three angle bisectors of each triangle.**

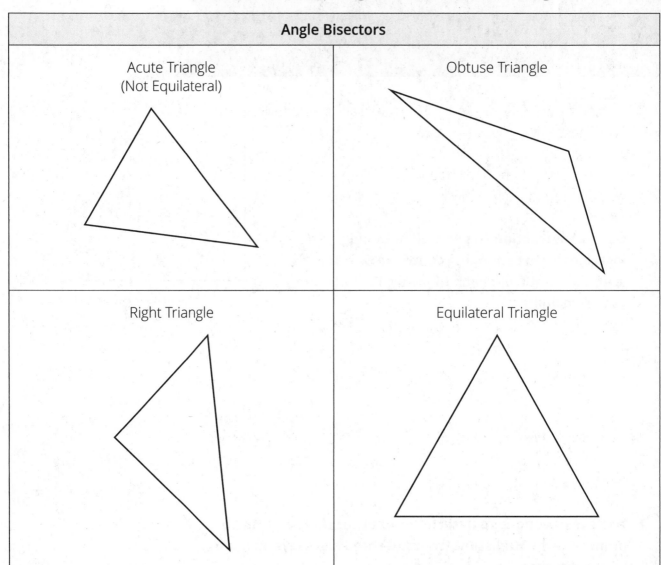

4. **Make a conjecture about the location of the intersection of the three angle bisectors of any triangle. Is the intersection located inside, outside, or on the triangle?**

The **incenter** is the point of concurrency of the three angle bisectors of a triangle.

5. **Consider the four triangles and the angle bisectors you constructed.**

   a. **Measure the distance from the incenter to each vertex of the triangle. Is the incenter always, sometimes, or never equidistant from each vertex of the triangle? Explain your reasoning.**

   b. **Measure the perpendicular distance from the incenter to each side of the triangle. Is the incenter always, sometimes, or never equidistant from each side of the triangle? Explain your reasoning.**

6. **Revisit the triangles with angle bisectors. Use a compass to construct the inscribed circle of each triangle.**

Remember:

An inscribed circle is a circle drawn inside a polygon such that it is tangent to each side.

Circle Q is inscribed in △ABC.

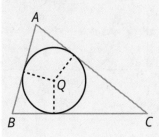

7. **What does the incenter tell you about the relationship between circles and triangles? Explain your reasoning.**

A **median** of a triangle is a line segment that connects a vertex to the midpoint of the opposite side.

1. **Construct the three medians of each triangle.**

Medians	
Acute Triangle (Not Equilateral)	Obtuse Triangle
Right Triangle	Equilateral Triangle

2. Make a conjecture about the location of the intersection of the three medians of any triangle. Is the intersection located inside, outside, or on the triangle?

The **centroid** is the point of concurrency of the three medians of a triangle. It is also known as the center of gravity.

3. Consider the four triangles and the medians you constructed.

   a. Measure the distance from the centroid to each vertex of the triangle. Is the centroid always, sometimes, or never equidistant from each vertex of the triangle? Explain your reasoning.

   b. Measure the perpendicular distance from the centroid to each side of the triangle. Is the centroid always, sometimes, or never equidistant from each side of the triangle? Explain your reasoning.

The centroid divides each median into two line segments.

4. Compare the distance from the centroid to the vertex and the distance from the centroid to the midpoint of the opposite side in each of the triangles in the graphic organizer. What is the ratio?

ACTIVITY

5.4

Investigating the Orthocenter

An **altitude** of a triangle is a line segment that is perpendicular to a side of the triangle and has one endpoint at the opposite vertex.

1. Construct the three altitudes of each triangle.

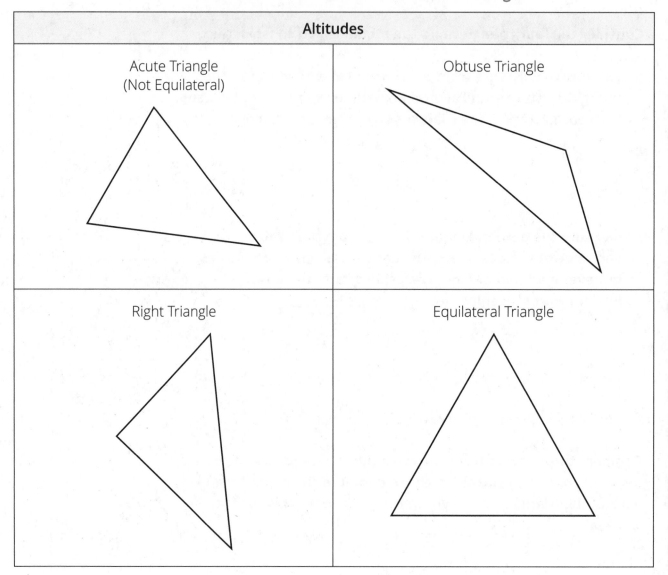

Altitudes

Acute Triangle
(Not Equilateral)

Obtuse Triangle

Right Triangle

Equilateral Triangle

2. Make a conjecture about the location of the intersection of the three altitudes of any triangle. Is the intersection located inside, outside, or on the triangle?

The **orthocenter** is the point of concurrency of the three altitudes of a triangle.

3. Consider the four triangles and the altitudes you constructed.

   a. Measure the distance from the orthocenter to each vertex of the triangle. Is the orthocenter always, sometimes, or never equidistant from each vertex of the triangle? Explain your reasoning.

   b. Measure the perpendicular distance from the orthocenter to each side of the triangle. Is the orthocenter always, sometimes, or never equidistant from each side of the triangle? Explain your reasoning.

TALK the TALK

I Concur

Look back at the points of concurrency you determined for the different triangles in this lesson.

1. **Complete the table to describe the location of each point of concurrency for acute, obtuse, and right triangles.**

Point of Concurrency	Acute Triangle	Obtuse Triangle	Right Triangle
Circumcenter			
Incenter			
Centroid			
Orthocenter			

2. **Examine the circumcenter, incenter, centroid, and orthocenter for each equilateral triangle. What do you notice?**

3. **What is the minimum number of lines you need to construct to identify the circumcenter, incenter, centroid, and orthocenter of a triangle? Explain your reasoning.**

4. Determine which point of concurrency is most appropriate in each situation.

   a. A flea market is situated on a triangular piece of land. Each entrance is located at one of the three vertices of triangle. Joanie wants to set up her merchandise at a location that is equidistant from all three entrances.

   b. An artist is building a mobile with several metal triangles of various sizes. The triangles are connected to each other using steel rods and the rods are welded onto each triangle at a point which would allow the triangle to balance horizontally.

   c. Jim's backyard is a triangular plot of land. He is using fencing to build a circular dog pen. He wants the dog pen to be as large as possible and needs to determine the location of the center of the circular dog pen.

5. **Complete the table to describe the construction required to determine each point of concurrency.**

Point of Concurrency	Located where the three _____ intersect.
Circumcenter	
Incenter	
Centroid	
Orthocenter	

Assignment

Write

Describe the similarities and differences between each pair of terms.

1. concurrent and point of concurrency
2. incenter and orthocenter
3. centroid and circumcenter
4. altitude and median

Remember

For every triangle:

- The circumcenter is the point of concurrency of the perpendicular bisectors of each side.
- The incenter is the point of concurrency of the angle bisectors.
- The centroid is the point of concurrency of the medians.
- The orthocenter is the point of concurrency of the altitudes.

Practice

1. Use a compass and straightedge to perform each construction.

a. Construct the incenter of △DEF.

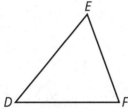

b. Construct the circumcenter of △ABC.

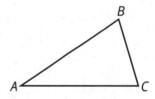

c. Construct the circumcenter of △DEF.

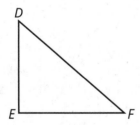

d. Construct the circumcenter of △GHI.

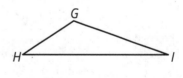

e. Construct the centroid of △ABC.

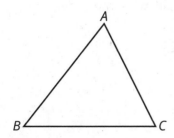

f. Construct the orthocenter of △JKL.

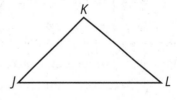

2. Write the term that best completes each statement.

    a. The incenter of a triangle is the point of concurrency of the _____ of a triangle.

    b. The circumcenter of a triangle is the point of concurrency of the _____ of a triangle.

    c. The centroid of a triangle is the point of concurrency of the _____ of a triangle.

    d. The orthocenter of a triangle is the point of concurrency of the _____ of a triangle.

Stretch

1. The Euler Line is a line that represents the relationship between the centroid, circumcenter and orthocenter of any triangle.

    a. Construct an isosceles triangle and determine all four points of concurrency. How do the points relate to the Euler Line?

    b. What happens if the triangle is equilateral?

2. Determine the coordinates of the centroid of the triangle on the coordinate grid.

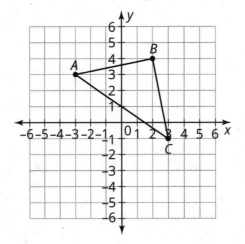

Review

1. Write a conjecture about points on the perpendicular bisector of a line segment. Then, write the converse of the conjecture.

2. Write a conjecture about the sides of an equilateral triangle. Then, write the converse of the conjecture.

3. Determine whether each statement is biconditional.

    a. If a figure is a square, then it is a rectangle.

    b. If two angles are congruent, then they have the same measure.

Composing and Decomposing Shapes Summary

KEY TERMS

- central angle
- chord
- secant
- major arc
- minor arc
- inscribed angle
- intercepted arc
- tangent
- circumscribed angle
- theorem
- postulate
- coincident
- interior angle of a polygon
- kite
- isosceles trapezoid
- midsegment
- cyclic quadrilateral
- inscribed polygon
- angle bisector
- conditional statement
- converse
- hypothesis
- conclusion
- biconditional statement
- base angles
- exterior angle
- remote interior angles
- concurrent
- point of concurrency
- circumcenter
- circumscribed circle
- incenter
- median
- centroid
- altitude
- orthocenter

A circle is the set of all points in a plane equidistant from a given point, the center of the circle. A diameter ($\overline{DB}$) of a circle is a line segment passing through the center (point A) of the circle with endpoints on the circle. The radius ($\overline{AC}$, $\overline{AD}$, $\overline{AB}$) is the distance from the center of a circle to a point on the circle. A **central angle** is an angle with its vertex at the center of a circle, like $\angle DAC$. A **chord** ($\overline{EF}$) is a segment whose endpoints are points on a circle. A chord is formed by the intersection of the circle and a **secant** line, like $\overleftrightarrow{EF}$.

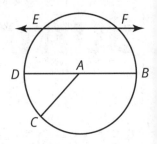

Two points on a circle determine a major arc and a minor arc. The arc with the greater measure is the **major arc**, like $\overarc{DBC}$ The other arc is the **minor arc**, like $\overarc{DC}$.

An **inscribed angle** is an angle whose vertex is on a circle and whose sides contain chords of the circle. In this circle, $\angle CAB$ is the inscribed angle. We can also say that $\overarc{CB}$ is an **intercepted arc** because the rays of the angle cross the circle at points C and B. The measure of the intercepted arc is twice that of the inscribed angle.

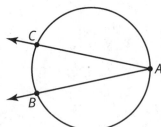

For example, if m$\angle CAB = 35°$, then m$\overarc{CB} = 70°$.

A **tangent** to a circle is a line that intersects the circle in exactly one point, called the point of tangency.

For example, the tangent line $\overleftrightarrow{QR}$ forms a right angle with the radius $\overline{PQ}$ where the two intersect at the point of tangency, point Q.

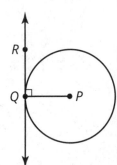

A **circumscribed angle** has its two sides tangent to the circle with a vertex that is outside of the circle.

For example, $\angle XYZ$ is a circumscribed angle.

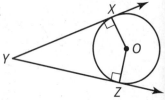

In mathematics, you often have to prove a solution is correct. In geometry, theorems are used to verify statements. A **theorem** is a statement that can be proven true using definitions, postulates, or other theorems. A **postulate** is a mathematical statement that is not proved but is considered true.

The Quad Squad

A quadrilateral may be convex or concave. The quadrilaterals you are most familiar with—trapezoids, parallelograms, rectangles, rhombi, and squares—are convex. A concave quadrilateral has one angle that is greater than 180°.

A quadrilateral has exactly two diagonals. The diagonals of any convex quadrilateral create two pairs of vertical angles and four linear pairs of angles. You can use the diameters of circles to draw the diagonals of different quadrilaterals as long as the two segments are not coincident. Two line segments are **coincident** if they lie exactly on top of each other.

An **interior angle of a polygon** is an angle inside the polygon between two adjacent sides. The interior angles of special quadrilaterals have different relationships.

For example, the four interior angles of a rectangle are congruent while only opposite interior angles of a parallelogram are congruent.

A **kite** is a quadrilateral with two pairs of equal adjacent sides. If the diagonals of a quadrilateral are perpendicular, non-congruent, and only one bisects the other, it can only be classified as a kite.

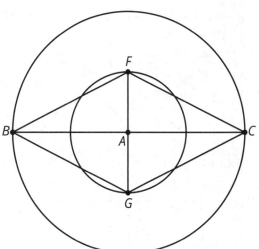

For example, consider the quadrilateral formed using two concentric circles. The inner circle and outer circle have two diameters that bisect each other. Connecting points B, F, C, and G will form a kite that is also a rhombus.

A trapezoid is a quadrilateral with at least one pair of parallel sides, known as the bases. If the other pair of sides are not parallel, they are known as the legs. A special type of trapezoid is an isosceles trapezoid. An **isosceles trapezoid** is a trapezoid with congruent legs.

Property	Parallelogram	Rectangle	Rhombus	Square	Isosceles Trapezoid	Kite
Opposite sides are parallel.	X	X	X	X		
Only one pair of opposite sides is parallel.					X	
Opposite sides are congruent	X	X	X	X		
Only one pair of opposite sides is congruent					X	
Opposite angles are congruent.	X	X	X	X		
At least one pair of opposite angles is congruent.						X
Diagonals bisect each other.	X	X	X	X		
Diagonals are perpendicular.			X	X		X
Diagonals are congruent.		X		X		
All angles are right angles.		X		X		
All sides are congruent.			X	X		
2 pairs of consecutive sides are congruent.			X	X		X

A **midsegment** of a polygon is any line segment that connects two midpoints of the sides of the polygon. The midsegment of a trapezoid that connects the midpoints of the two non-parallel sides of the trapezoid is parallel to each base. The length of this midsegment is equal to half the sum of the lengths of its bases

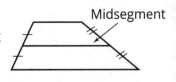
Midsegment

A **cyclic quadrilateral** is a quadrilateral whose vertices all lie on a single circle. The opposite angles of a cyclic quadrilateral are supplementary. The sum of either pair of opposite angles is 180°.

You can use what you know about copying a line segment to construct an inscribed polygon, such as a regular hexagon. An **inscribed polygon** is a polygon drawn inside another polygon or circle in which all of the vertices of the interior polygon lie on the outer figure. Each line segment that forms the hexagon is the same length as the radius of the circle. Use a compass to measure the radius. Then without changing the width of the compass, place the point on any point on the circle and construct an arc that intersects the circle. The point of intersection will be the endpoint of the line segment. Repeat the process on each new endpoint until the inscribed polygon has six sides.

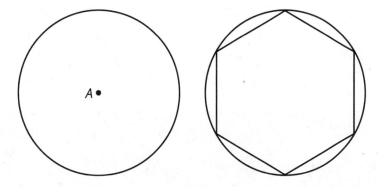

To construct a square, you can use a transformation of an inscribed polygon.

For example, circle B contains a right triangle, $\triangle ABC$, with points A and C on the circle and point B at the center. To create a square, rotate $\triangle ABC$ to create an inscribed square with all 4 vertices touching the circle.

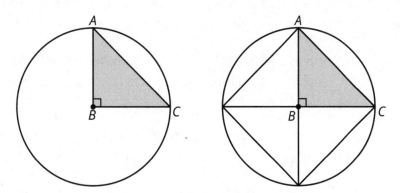

Just as line segments can be bisected, angles can be bisected too. If a ray is drawn through the vertex of an angle and divides the angle into two angles of equal measure, or two congruent angles, this ray is called an **angle bisector**. The construction used to create an angle bisector is called bisecting an angle. You can bisect an angle using patty paper or constructions.

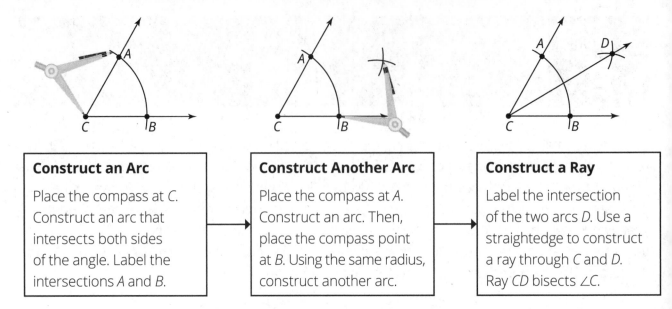

Construct an Arc	**Construct Another Arc**	**Construct a Ray**
Place the compass at *C*. Construct an arc that intersects both sides of the angle. Label the intersections *A* and *B*.	Place the compass at *A*. Construct an arc. Then, place the compass point at *B*. Using the same radius, construct another arc.	Label the intersection of the two arcs *D*. Use a straightedge to construct a ray through *C* and *D*. Ray *CD* bisects ∠*C*.

Since an equilateral triangle is composed of three equal line segments and three equal angles, you can also use patty paper or a compass and a straightedge to construct an equilateral triangle on its own or inscribed in a circle.

LESSON
4

Tri- Tri- Tri- and Separate Them

When you divide a quadrilateral along any one of its diagonals, you create two triangles.

An "If ...then..." statement is also referred to as a **conditional statement**. The **converse** of an if-then statement is the statement that results from interchanging the **hypothesis** (the "if" part) and the **conclusion** (the "then" part) of the original statement.

For example, consider the conditional statement: "If a polygon has three sides, then the polygon is a triangle." The hypothesis is, "A polygon has three sides." The conclusion is, "The polygon is a triangle." The converse is: "If a polygon is a triangle, then the polygon has three sides."

When a conditional statement and its converse are both true, this is called a biconditional statement. A **biconditional statement** is a statement written in the form "if and only if *p*, then *q*."

For example, consider the previous conditional statement and its converse. Both statements are true. The biconditional statement is: "If and only if a polygon three sides, then the polygon is a triangle."

An isosceles triangle has a vertex angle that is formed by the two congruent sides. The congruent sides of an isosceles triangle are called the legs. The other side is called the base and the angles between the base and the congruent sides are called **base angles**.

An equilateral triangle is a triangle in which all three sides are equal in length. All three angle measures of an equilateral triangle are also congruent.

The sum of the measures of the interior angles of a triangle is 180°.

An **exterior angle** of a polygon is an angle that forms a linear pair with an interior angle of the polygon.

For example, ∠TRB is an exterior angle of △RST.

The **remote interior angles** of a triangle are the two angles that are not adjacent to the specified exterior angle.

For example, ∠RST and ∠STR are remote interior angles of △RST.

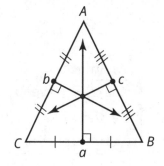

The measure of the exterior angle of a triangle is equal to the sum of the measures of the two remote interior angles.

The sum of the lengths of two sides of a triangle is always greater than the length of the third side.

The midsegment of a triangle is one-half the measure and parallel to the third side.

Concurrent lines, rays, and line segments are three or more lines, rays, or line segments that intersect at a single point. The **point of concurrency** is the point at which concurrent lines, rays, or segments intersect.

The **circumcenter** is the point of concurrency of the three perpendicular bisectors of a triangle. It is equidistant from the vertices.

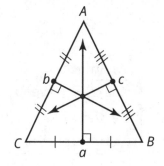

A **circumscribed circle** is a circle that passes through all the vertices of a polygon.

For example, circle Q is circumscribed around △ABC.

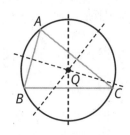

The **incenter** is the point of concurrency of the three angle bisectors of a triangle. It is equidistant from the sides.

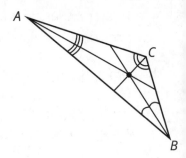

A **median** of a triangle is a line segment that connects a vertex to the midpoint of the opposite side. The **centroid** is the point of concurrency of the three medians of a triangle. The centroid of a triangle divides each median into two parts so that the distance from the centroid to the vertex is twice the distance from the centroid to the midpoint of the opposite side.

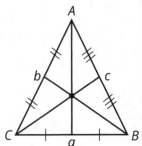

An **altitude** of a triangle is a line segment that is perpendicular to a side of the triangle and has one endpoint at the opposite vertex. The **orthocenter** is the point of concurrency of the three altitudes of a triangle.

Points of concurrency are a valuable tool in constructing geometric figures. When circumscribing a triangle you can use the circumcenter to identify the center of the circle. The circumcenter is equidistant from each of the vertices, and when the circle passes through each of them, the perpendicular bisectors will become the radii. You can also use the incenter of a triangle to inscribe a circle.

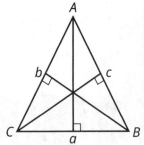

Points of concurrency can lie on the interior of a triangle, the exterior of a triangle, or on the triangle.

	Acute Triangle	Obtuse Triangle	Right Triangle
Incenter	Interior	Interior	Interior
Circumcenter	Interior	Exterior	On Hypotenuse
Centroid	Interior	Interior	Interior
Orthocenter	Interior	Exterior	At Vertex of Right Angle

The incenter, circumcenter, centroid, and orthocenter for an equilateral triangle are the same point.

TOPIC 3
Rigid Motions on a Plane

A whirligig is all about rotation, though some of the more elaborate ones may illustrate translations and reflections as well. Whirligigs go by many names: pinwheels, spinners, buzzers, gee-haws, whirlyjigs, whirlybirds, or whirlies.

Lesson 1
Put Your Input In, Take Your Output Out
Geometric Components of Rigid Motions M1-205

Lesson 2
Bow Thai
Translations as Functions M1-217

Lesson 3
Staring Back at Me
Reflections as Functions M1-229

Lesson 4
Turn Yourself Around
Rotations as Functions M1-243

Lesson 5
OKEECHOBEE
Reflectional and Rotational Symmetry M1-257

Module 1: Reasoning with Shapes

TOPIC 3: RIGID MOTIONS ON A PLANE

This topic begins by reminding students of what they know about functions via a function machine. Instead of having a numeric or algebraic input and output, a geometric function machine has a geometric figure as the input and output. Students investigate simple geometric transformation machines, describing how each input shape is "carried" by geometric objects in the transformation machine to result in the output shape. Students then consider each of the rigid motions as functions and identify geometric figures with line symmetry and rotational symmetry.

Where have we been?

Students know that two figures are congruent if and only if there exists a sequence of one or more rigid motions that carries one of the figures onto the other. They have described the effect of rigid motion on two-dimensional figures using coordinates. This topic builds on this knowledge, removing the coordinate plane and requiring students to rely on geometric reasoning.

Where are we going?

In this topic, students begin the formal study of congruence and lay the groundwork for their study of similarity and trigonometry. Here they explain how the criteria for triangle congruence (SSS, SAS, and ASA) follow from the definition of congruence in terms of rigid motion. They will use the triangle congruence theorems in future topics to prove a wide range of geometric theorems.

Rigid Motions as Functions

A translation is a function, T, which takes as its input, b, the location of a point along a line and outputs $T_{AB}(b)$, the new location of the point after it has undergone a translation, or a slide, on the plane a distance of AB in the direction from point A to point B.

$$T_{AB}(P) = P'$$

$$T_{AC}(P) = P''$$

Reflections and rotations are also rigid motions which can be expressed as functions which map a set of points to another set of points.

¡Que Viva la Matemática!

Most textbooks are translated from English into at least one other language, usually Spanish. And in some school districts, general memos and letters to parents may be translated into many different languages!

Of course, translating a language means something completely different from the word *translating* in geometry. The same can be said for *reflection*. A reflection pool is a place where one can reflect on one's thoughts, while also admiring reflections in the pool of still water.

Talking Points

Rotational and reflectional symmetry will often be addressed on standardized tests. Here is a sample question:

The figure shows two perpendicular lines, s and r, intersecting at point P in the interior of a trapezoid. Line r is parallel to the bases and bisects both legs of the trapezoid. Line s bisects both bases of the trapezoid.

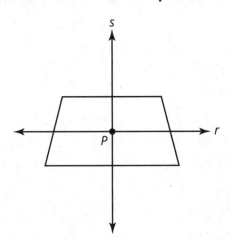

Which transformation will always carry the figure onto itself?

The figure has reflectional symmetry. A reflection across line s will carry the figure onto itself. The figure does not have rotational symmetry.

Key Terms

isometry
An isometry is a rigid motion transformation that preserves size and shape.

concentric circles
Concentric circles are circles with a common center point.

rotational symmetry
A plane figure can also have rotational symmetry if you can rotate the figure more than 0° but less than 360° and the resulting figure is the same as the original figure in the original position.

Put Your Input In, Take Your Output Out

Geometric Components of Rigid Motions

Warm Up

1. Identify the vertices that form a rectangle. Explain why the figure is a rectangle.

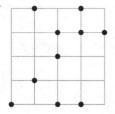

2. Identify four vertices that form a trapezoid. Explain why the figure is a trapezoid.

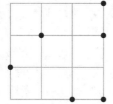

Learning Goals

- Know precise definitions of line segment, angle, and distance along a line.
- Translate lines to produce parallel lines.

Key Terms

- collinear points
- angle
- ray
- rotation angle

You know a lot about rigid motions, such as translations, reflections, and rotations. How do you use straight lines and angles to represent rigid motion transformations?

Transformation Machine

You have learned about function machines, which take a value as input and output another value. In this topic, you will learn to think about geometric rigid motions as functions. These functions can be represented with function machines as well, or transformation machines.

1. **Each transformation machine on the left shows a different rigid motion. For each transformation machine on the right, draw an input shape on patty paper. Then apply the transformation and draw the output shape.**

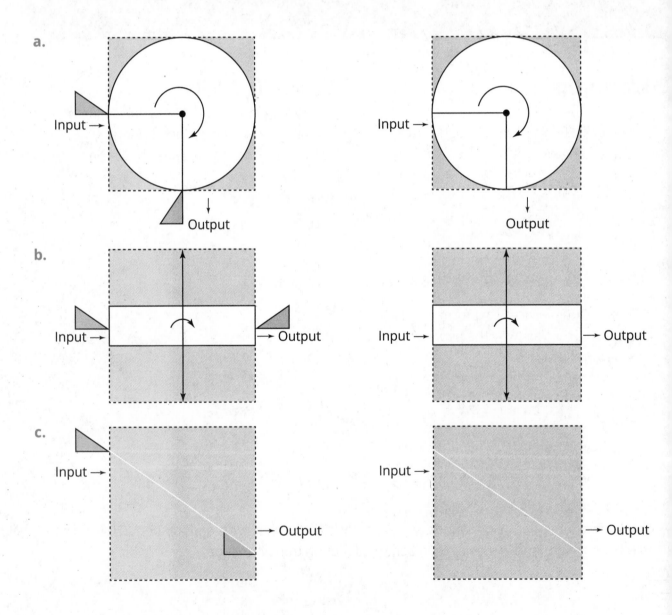

a.

b.

c.

2. Identify the rigid motion represented by each
   transformation machine.

3. Describe each transformation function. Explain how each input
   shape is "carried" by geometric objects in the transformation
   machine to result in the output shape.

Points and lines are essential building blocks of geometry. They are called undefined terms.

Recall that a point in geometry has no size or shape, but it is often represented using a dot. In a diagram, a point can be labeled using a capital letter. A line is described as a straight, continuous arrangement of an infinite number of points. A line has an infinite length, but no width. Arrowheads are used to indicate that a line extends infinitely in opposite directions. In a diagram, a line can be labeled with a lowercase letter positioned next to the arrowhead.

Points that lie along the same line are called **collinear points**. Recall that a line segment is a part of a line between two points on the line, called the endpoints. A distance along a line is the length of a line segment connecting two points on the line. A line segment *AB* has the distance *AB*.

1. **Consider the translation machine from the Getting Started.**

   a. **Suppose that the input to the machine is a line as shown. Describe the output of the translation machine.**

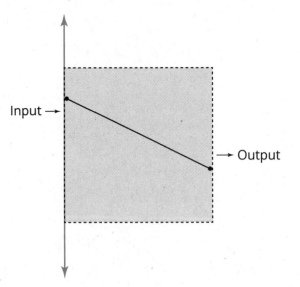

b. **Suppose that the translation machine is a set of parallel line segments as shown. How does this change the output of the machine when the input is a line?**

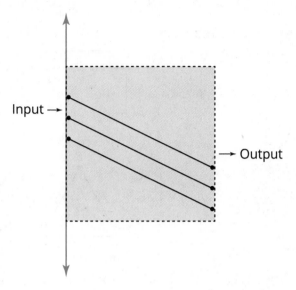

2. **Identify the line segments and distances that were used in the translation machines in the previous activity.**

3. **Are the line segments in the translation machine in Question 1, part (b), congruent? Use patty paper to justify your answers, and explain your reasoning.**

Congruent line segments are line segments that have the same length. They represent equal distances.

An **angle** is a set of points consisting of a vertex point and two rays extending from the vertex point. A **ray** is a portion of a line that begins with a single point and extends infinitely in one direction.

A **rotation angle** is a directed angle based on a circle. Positive rotation angles turn counterclockwise, and negative rotation angles turn clockwise.

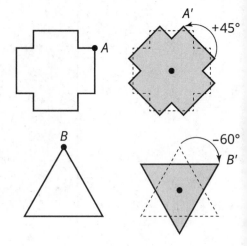

4. **Identify the rotation angle that was used in the rotation machine in the Getting Started.**

TALK the TALK

Shake It All About

The diagram on the next page shows a transformation machine. The transformation machine is designed to provide a path for each of the input shapes, a triangle and a square, to move from the start line through the machine and map back onto itself. The transformation is comprised of line segments, figures with and without center points, and two target shapes. To use the transformation machine you must first trace the target shape onto patty paper.

The transformation machine has these rules:

- The elements in the transformation machine provide ways to move your input shape. Your input shape must be connected to any of the lines or figures in the transformation machine by at least one vertex in order for it to be translated, rotated, or reflected.
- Any dashed or solid line allows you to translate your input shape.
- Any figure with a solid center point allows you to rotate your input shape around that center. The figure carries your input shape around the rotation.
- Any figure with a dashed line allows you to reflect your input shape across that line. The figure carries your input shape across the reflection.

Use the larger diagram of the transformation machine located at the end of the lesson.

1. **Copy one of the target shapes onto patty paper. Place the input shape on the start line in an orientation of your choosing. Then determine a sequence of translations, reflections, and rotations that maps the input shape onto the corresponding target shape.**

Think about:

You can use this diagram to help you predict the effects of your transformations before you test them on the larger diagram at the end of the lesson.

Remember:

A pre-image is a figure prior to a transformation. The image is the figure after the transformation.

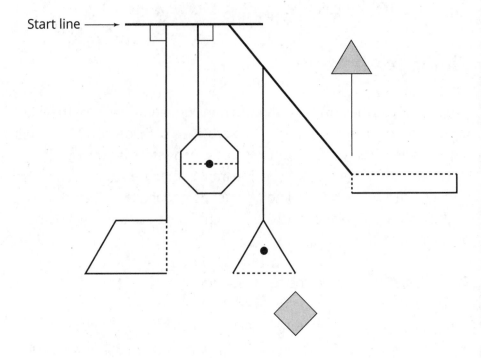

Start line →

2. **Describe the sequence of transformations you used to transform each pre-image to each image. Label points on the transformation machine so that you can precisely describe your transformations.**

3. **Consider the transformations performed on each pre-image to map it onto the image. Are the images congruent to the pre-images? Explain why or why not.**

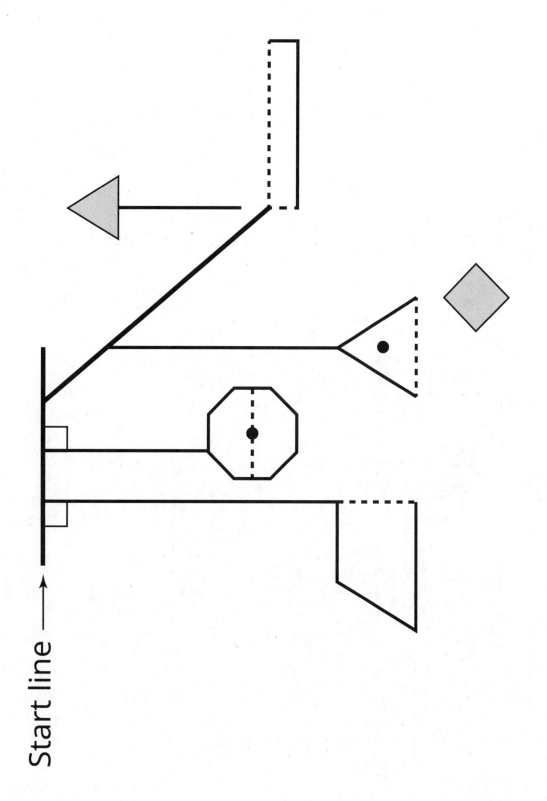

Start line →

Write

Complete each sentence with a term from the box.

line segment	point	collinear points	line	ray	angle	rotation angle

1. A(n) _____ is a location in space.

2. A(n) _____ is a straight continuous arrangement of an infinite number of points.

3. Points that are all located on the same line are _____.

4. A(n) _____ is a portion of a line that includes two points and all of the collinear points between the two points.

5. A(n) _____ is a portion of a line that begins with a single point and extends infinitely in one direction.

6. A(n) _____ is a directed angle.

7. A(n) _____ is a set of points consisting of a vertex point and two rays extending from the vertex point.

Remember

Translations can be described using lines and line segments. Reflections can be described using lines. Rotations can be described using rotation angles.

Pre-images transformed by rigid motions such as translations, reflections, and rotations are congruent to their images.

Practice

Create a transformation machine to perform each sequence of transformations. Describe the geometric objects you used to create each machine. Draw an example of a transformation performed by the transformation machine.

1. translate a figure to the left then translate the figure up

2. translate a figure down then reflect the figure across a horizontal line

3. rotate a figure clockwise 180° then translate the figure to the right

4. reflect a figure across a vertical line then rotate the figure clockwise 90°

5. translate a figure up then reflect the figure across a vertical line

6. rotate a figure clockwise 90° then reflect the figure across a horizontal line

7. translate a figure to the right then reflect the figure across a horizontal line

8. reflect a figure across a horizontal line then translate the figure down

9. translate a figure to the left, rotate the figure counterclockwise 90°, then reflect the figure across a vertical line

10. rotate a figure clockwise 90°, translate the figure down, and then reflect the figure across a horizontal line

Stretch

Determine three different transformation machines that could be used to get the figure at position A to position B. Describe the geometric objects you used to create each machine. Draw an example of a transformation performed by the transformation machine.

Review

1. Construct each figure described.

    a. Duplicate $\overline{AB}$.

    b. Duplicate $\angle D$.

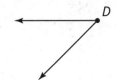

2. Construct the angle bisector of each given angle.

    a.

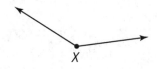

    b.

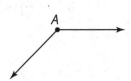

3. Determine whether the two lines are parallel, perpendicular, or neither. Explain your reasoning.

    a. $2x - 3y = 15$ and $y = -\frac{3}{2}x - 10$

    b. $-\frac{6}{5}x + 4y = \frac{1}{5}$ and $-3(x - \frac{10}{3}y) = 17$

Bow Thai

Translations as Functions

Warm Up

Each coordinate plane shows the graph of $f(x)$. Sketch the graph of $g(x)$.

1. $g(x) = f(x) - 2$

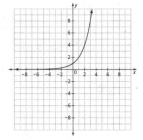

2. $g(x) = f(x - 3)$

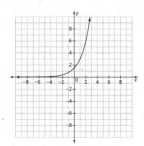

Learning Goals

- Represent translations on the plane.
- Describe translations as functions that take points on the plane as inputs and produce translated points as outputs.
- Compare transformations that preserve distance and angles, called isometries, to transformations which are not isometries.

Key Terms

- translation
- isometry

You have learned how to represent the horizontal or vertical translation of a function. How can you write geometric translations of figures on the plane as functions?

Universal Translator

Recall that you used translations in the transformation machine in Lesson 1: *Put Your Input In, Take Your Output Out.* You translated figures along straight lines or line segments.

1. **Lines *m*, *n*, and *t* are parallel lines. Draw a translation of each vertex of the triangle along the line the point is located on. Translate each point to the right along the line a distance equal to *AB*. Connect the points to form a triangle.**

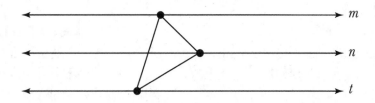

> Points *M*, *N*, and *T* are necessary to name each ray.

2. **Rays *XM*, *XN*, and *XT* share a vertex point. Draw a translation of each vertex of the triangle along the ray the point is located on. Translate each point to the right along the ray a distance equal to *AB*. Connect the points to form a triangle.**

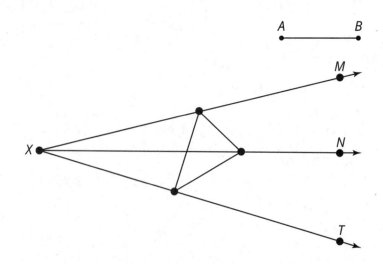

3. Rays *XM* and *XN* share a vertex point, and line *t* is parallel to $\overrightarrow{XN}$. Draw a translation of each vertex of the triangle along the ray or line the point is located on. Translate each point to the right along the ray or line a distance equal to *AB*. Connect the points to form a triangle.

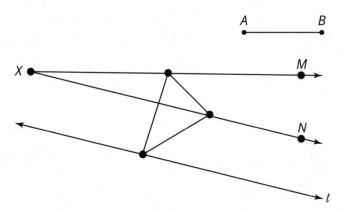

4. Compare the diagrams you created in Questions 1 through 3. Each set of three lines and/or rays makes up a transformation machine.

   a. Which transformation machine produces a translation of the triangle? Explain your reasoning.

   b. Which transformation machine produces a dilation of the triangle? Explain your reasoning.

2.1 Translation Functions

Transformations are used frequently in web design and game animation and are often written as functions, which take points, distances, and angles as inputs. The functions output a new set of points after applying a transformation. These transformations move objects around on the screen.

Think **about:**

A translation moves a set of points a specified distance in a specified direction along parallel lines.

Suppose you are designing a website banner for a new restaurant. The banner will show three congruent triangles animated from left to right, and then the name will fade in.

1. **Consider the translation of the first triangle, △SQR.**

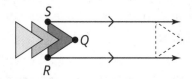

   a. **Label the points of the image, △S'Q'R'.**

   b. **What relationship is there between $\overline{SS'}$ and $\overline{RR'}$?**

   c. **Measure the lengths of the two line segments used in the translation. What do you notice?**

   d. **What do you know about the distance QQ'? What do you know about the line containing $\overline{QQ'}$?**

A translation can be measured as a directed line segment.

△MNP was translated to produce △M'N'P'. The triangle was translated a distance equal to the distance between points A and B. It was translated in the direction from point A to point B.

So, $\overline{AB}$ is the directed line segment used to measure this translation.

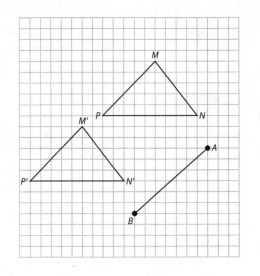

2. **Suppose each grid square is 1 unit × 1 unit.**

   a. **What is the distance from point A to point B?**

   b. **Compare the distance AB with the distances MM', NN', and PP'. What do you notice?**

   c. **Can you draw another directed line segment on the grid which defines the translation of △MNP to △M'N'P'? If so, draw the segment on the grid. Explain your thinking.**

Remember:

3. **Write equality and congruence statements to compare the corresponding sides and angles of the pre-image △MNP and the image △M'N'P'.**

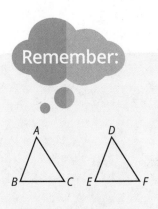

If △ABC ≅ △DEF, then:

$\overline{AB} \cong \overline{DE}$

$AB = DE$

$\angle ABC \cong \angle DEF$

$m\angle ABC = m\angle DEF$

Remember:

A function is a rule that assigns exactly one output to each input.

Inputs to functions do not have to be numbers. They can be points, too.

A **translation** is a function, *T*, which takes as its input a set of pre-image points and outputs a set of image points. The pre-image points are translated a distance of *AB* in the direction *AB*. For example, a translation of point *P* could be expressed as $T_{AB}(P)$, or *P'*. A translation is an example of an *isometry*. An **isometry** is a rigid motion transformation that preserves size and shape.

Worked Example

A translation function can represent the distance and direction of the translation using a line or line segment, or a parallel line or line segment.

$$T_{AB}(P) = P'$$

$$T_{AC}(P) = P''$$

---

4. **Identify how the distance and direction of the translation are specified in each of the functions.**

5. **Consider the translation of the website banner from Question 1.**

   a. **Use the notation from the worked example to describe the translation of △*SQR*.**

   b. **Explain how your function represents the translation of every point of △*SQR*.**

6. Greta says that the exact same function can be used for every triangle in the animated web banner. Is Greta correct? Explain your thinking, and then draw the translations to justify your answer.

7. Complete each translation using the given function.

   a. T_{AB}(Sun)

   b. $T_{L'M}$ (Moon)

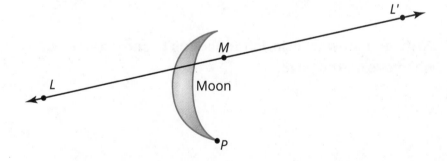

8. Explain why you can use parallel lines when describing translations.

ACTIVITY 2.2

Determining Congruence Using Translations

When users click on the menu of Bow Thai, copies of 3 triangles will move from the corners and top of the web page to the center to form the background behind the word "Menu" as shown.

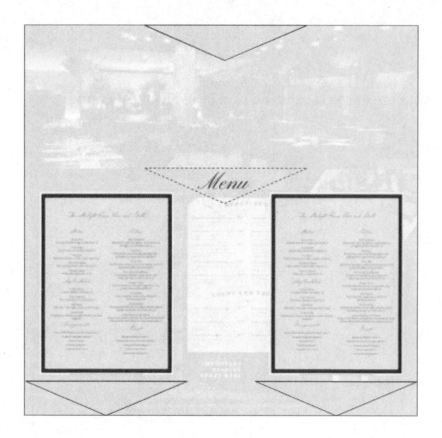

1. **Write and draw translation functions to show how each triangle will move on the page.**

2. **Are the triangles all congruent? Explain why or why not.**

The owner of Bow Thai is thinking about using smaller triangles on the sides of the menu web page. She still wants the triangles to move and merge to form the triangle background behind the word "Menu."

3. **Would these transformations be isometries? Demonstrate why or why not and explain your process.**

TALK the TALK

Isometries on the Menu

1. Describe how to distinguish between an isometry and a transformation that is not an isometry.

2. Write a function to describe each translation. Each solid figure is a pre-image, and each dashed figure is an image.

   a.

   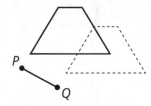

   b.

   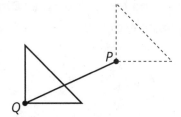

3. What similarities and differences are there between a geometric translation function and an algebraic equation which shows the translation of a function?

Assignment

Write

Determine whether each statement is true or false. If the statement is false, rewrite it so that it becomes a true statement.

1. A translation function along parallel lines is a type of geometric transformation that is non-rigid.
2. Isometries includes geometric transformations such as translations, rotations, and reflections.
3. A transformation is an isometry if it does not preserve size and shape.
4. A dilation is a non-rigid geometric transformation.

Remember

A translation is a function, *T*, which takes as its input a set of pre-image points and outputs a set of image points. The pre-image points are translated a distance of *AB* in the direction *AB*. For example, a translation of point *P* could be expressed as $T_{AB}(P)$, or *P′*.

Practice

1. Write a function to describe each translation. Each solid figure is a pre-image, and each dashed figure is an image.

a.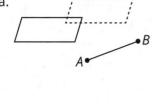

b.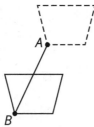

c.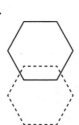

d.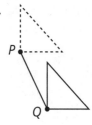

2. Complete each translation given the function.

a. T_{AB}(Rectangle) = Rectangle′

b. $T_{L'M}$(Triangle) = Triangle′

c. T_{BA}(Trapezoid) = Trapezoid′

d. $T_{L'M}$(Parallelogram) = Parallelogram′

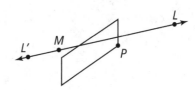

Stretch

1. A translation function for a trapezoid is given as T_{PQ} (Trapezoid *ABCD*) = Trapezoid *A'B'C'D'*. Trapezoid *ABCD* has vertices *A*(−7, −1), *B*(−5, −1), *C*(−4, −4), and *D*(−8, −4). If *P* is located at (−2, 3) and *Q* is located at (7, 5), determine the vertices of the translated trapezoid *A'B'C'D'*.

   a. Draw points *P* and *Q* and trapezoids *ABCD* and *A'B'C'D'* on a coordinate plane. Include a dashed line between points *P* and *Q*.

   b. Determine the distance traveled by each point of the trapezoid and the slope of the line along which the points moved.

Review

1. Construct a square inscribed in a circle using the given line segment.

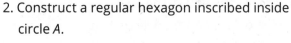

2. Construct a regular hexagon inscribed inside circle *A*.

3. Identify the mappings that are functions. If the mapping is not a function, explain why not.

   a. {(1, 1), (1, 3), (3, 1), (2, 2), (5, 5)}

   b. {(2, 4), (3, 5), (4, 6), (6, 8), (8, 10)}

   c. {(−1, 2), (0, 1), (1, 1), (2, 1), (3, 1), (4, 0)}

Staring Back at Me

Reflections as Functions

Warm Up

Each coordinate plane shows the graph of $f(x)$. Sketch the graph of $g(x)$.

1. $g(x) = -f(x)$

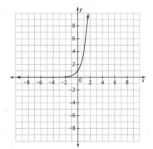

2. $g(x) = f(-x)$

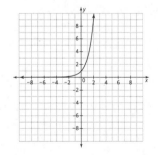

Learning Goals

- Represent reflections in the plane using patty paper and constructions.
- Describe reflection transformations as functions that take points as inputs and output reflected points.
- Identify reflections as points equidistant to the perpendicular bisector of line segments connecting the pre-image and image points of the reflection.
- Specify a sequence of translations and reflections that will carry a figure onto a congruent figure.

Key Terms

- reflection
- Perpendicular Bisector Theorem
- proof

You have learned how to represent the horizontal or vertical reflection of a function. How can you write geometric reflections of figures on the plane as functions?

Reflecting on Bisecting

In previous lessons, you constructed the perpendicular bisector of line segments.

1. Construct a perpendicular bisector of $\overline{RB}$.

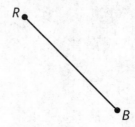

2. Use patty paper to trace the diagram you constructed. How can you use patty paper to map point R onto point B? Explain the transformation you used.

3. Can you draw two points in the plane that cannot be mapped onto each other by the same transformation you used in Question 2? Justify your answer.

You saw in the previous lesson that translations can be used in web design and are often written as functions, which take points, distances, and angles as inputs and outputs a new set of points after applying a transformation. The same is true for reflections.

To reveal a message during a game, you have to make two triangles fly open.

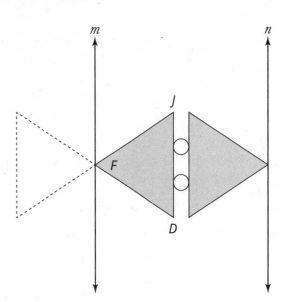

1. **Consider the reflection of the left triangle, △FJD, across line *m*.**

   a. **Label the points of the image, △F′J′D′.**

   b. **What relationship is there among $\overline{JJ'}$ and $\overline{DD'}$? Justify your answer.**

   c. **What relationship is there among $\overline{JJ'}$, $\overline{DD'}$, and line *m*? Justify your answer.**

   d. **Reflect the other triangle across line *n*. Label the points of the pre-image and image. Compare this reflection with the reflection of the first triangle.**

2. **Write equality and congruence statements to compare the corresponding sides of the pre-image and the image.**

A **reflection** is a function, R_ℓ, which takes as its input, P, the location of a point with respect to some line of reflection ℓ and outputs $R_\ell(P)$, or the opposite of the location of P with respect to the line of reflection.

3. **Consider the reflections from Question 1.**

   a. **Write a function of the form $R_\ell(P)$ to describe the reflection of $\triangle FJD$.**

   b. **Explain how your function represents the reflection of every point of $\triangle FJD$.**

4. **Describe the relationship between corresponding points of a reflection and the line of reflection.**

5. **Complete each reflection using the given function.**

   a. $R_m(STUV)$

b. $R_c(JTG)$

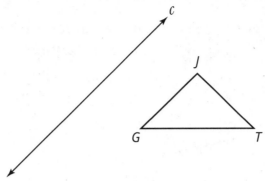

It is possible to construct the line of reflection when given two figures that are reflections of one another.

Worked Example

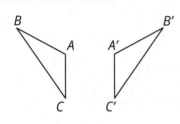

1. Label the vertices.

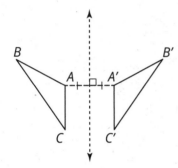

2. Connect two corresponding points. Construct the perpendicular bisector of the line segment connecting them.

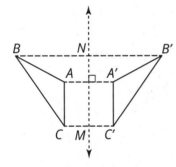

3. Connect remaining corresponding points. Label the intersection of each line segment with the perpendicular bisector.

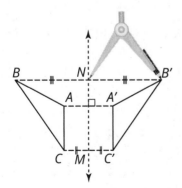

4. Use a compass to determine whether each intersection point is the midpoint of the line segment connecting corresponding vertices. If that is the case, the perpendicular bisector is the line of reflection. If not, the figures are not reflections of one another.

$\overline{CM} \cong \overline{C'M}$
$\overline{BN} \cong \overline{B'N}$
$\overleftrightarrow{MN}$ is the line of reflection.

6. **Determine whether the figures are reflections of one another. If so, identify the line of reflection.**

a.

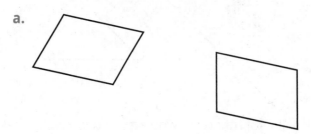

b.

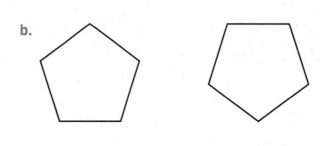

c.

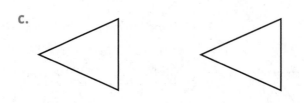

7. **How do you know whether two figures are not reflections of one another?**

Perpendicular Bisector Theorem

In the Getting Started, you saw that the perpendicular bisector of a line segment is the line of reflection between the endpoints of the segment. Consider $\overline{RB}$ with perpendicular bisector ℓ.

1. **Label point P anywhere on ℓ. What do you notice about the relationship between point P and points R and B?**

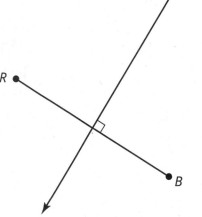

You can prove that the endpoints of a line segment are equidistant from any point on the perpendicular bisector.

> A **proof** is a series of statements and corresponding reasons forming a valid argument that starts with a hypothesis and arrives at a conclusion.

Worked Example

Given: Line ℓ is the perpendicular bisector of $\overline{RB}$.
    Point P is on ℓ.

Prove: $PR = PB$

The reflection of point P across line ℓ is point P by the definition of reflection.

Because line ℓ is the perpendicular bisector of $\overline{RB}$, the reflection of point R across line ℓ is point B.

Therefore, $PR = PB$.

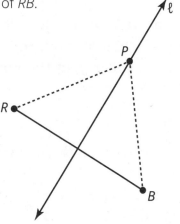

2. **Provide a reason why $PR = PB$.**

The **Perpendicular Bisector Theorem** states: "Any point on the perpendicular bisector of a segment is equidistant from the endpoints of that segment." Remember that a theorem is a statement that can be demonstrated to be true by accepted mathematical operations and arguments.

Let's consider the relationship between endpoints of a line segment and any point on the perpendicular bisector from another perspective.

Suppose you have two points that are equidistant from a third point. You can show that the third point lies on the perpendicular bisector of the segment connecting the points.

3. **Consider point Q, which is equidistant from points A and B.**

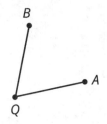

a. **Draw $\overrightarrow{QP}$ so that it bisects $\angle BQA$. This makes $\angle BQP$ and $\angle PQA$ congruent angles. Label the intersection of $\overrightarrow{QP}$ and $\overline{AB}$ as point C.**

b. **Describe the location of $\overline{QB'}$ if $\overline{QB}$ is reflected across $\overrightarrow{QP}$. What does this tell you about the distances BC and CA? Explain your thinking.**

c. **Explain how you know that $\overrightarrow{QP}$ is a perpendicular bisector of $\overline{AB}$.**

You have learned that reflections and translations are isometries, which means that they preserve distances and angle measures.

1. **Sunita made a conjecture about reflections. She said that you can always map one congruent line segment onto the other using at most two reflections.**

   Do you think Sunita is correct? Draw examples or counterexamples to justify your reasoning.

Remember:

Any point that is equidistant from two other points lies on the perpendicular bisector between the two points.

2. **Triangle *GHJ* is a reflection of △*MNP*. Describe the locations of the midpoints of $\overline{GM}$, $\overline{HN}$, and $\overline{JP}$.**

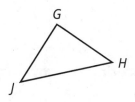

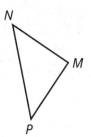

3. **Describe and sketch the sequence of translations and reflections that shows that the two figures in each pair are congruent. Images are shown with dashed lines.**

   a.

   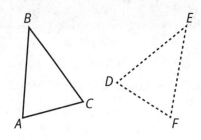

   b.

Sides that have the same number of arrowhead markings are parallel to one another.

   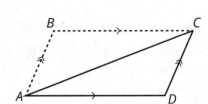

4. **Miguel was investigating a transformation of △ABC to △A'B'C' and discovered that the midpoints of the segments connecting corresponding points were collinear, but the line was not a perpendicular bisector of each segment. He thought that this must not be a reflection.**

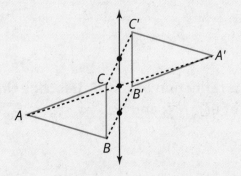

   Lina disagreed. She said that you can translate first to show that the midpoints lie on a perpendicular bisector.
   Who is correct? Explain your reasoning.

TALK the TALK

But We're Off the Grid

In this activity, you translated and reflected figures in the plane. Let's compare those transformations with the same ones performed on a coordinate plane.

1. **Describe the sequence of translations and reflections which maps the pre-image triangle, △PQR, to the image triangle, △ABC on the coordinate plane.**

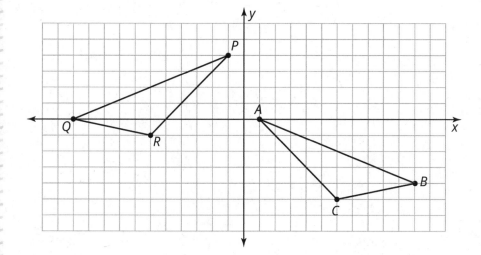

2. **How are translating and reflecting geometric figures in the plane different from performing these transformations on the coordinate plane? How are they the same?**

3. **What similarities and differences are there between a geometric reflection function and an algebraic equation that shows the reflection of a function?**

Write

Explain why a reflection of a figure is an isometry.

Remember

- A reflection is a function, R_ℓ, which takes as its input, P, the location of a point with respect to some line of reflection ℓ and outputs $R_\ell(P)$, or the opposite of the location of P with respect to the line of reflection.
- Any point that is equidistant from two other points lies on the perpendicular bisector between the two points.

Practice

1. Complete each reflection, given the function.

a. $R_m(ABCD)$

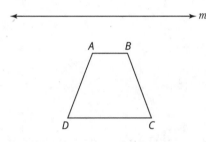

b. $R_p(JKL)$

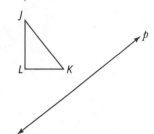

c. $R_b(QRSTU)$

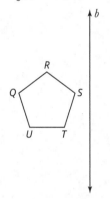

d. $R_k(ABCD)$

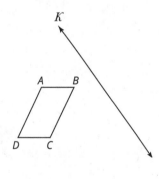

2. Describe the sequence of translations and reflections that show that the two figures in each pair are congruent. Images are shown with dashed lines.

a.

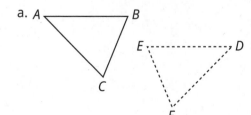

b.

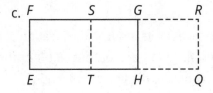

c.

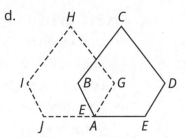

d.

Stretch

Describe the sequence of translations and reflections to each figure so that the word APPLE is shown in between the two lines with the figures in the same positions.

Review

1. Write a function to describe the translation. The solid figure is the pre-image, and the dotted figure is the image.

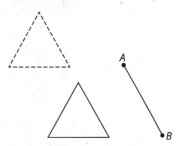

2. Complete the translation given the function T_{AB}(Trapezoid) = Trapezoid′

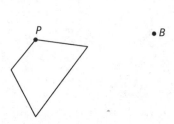

3. Construct the angle bisector of the given angle.

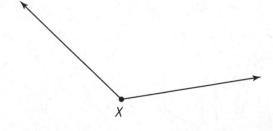

4. Construct a 22.5° angle using only a compass and straightedge. Summarize your steps.

Turn Yourself Around

Rotations as Functions

Warm Up

Identify each central angle measure.

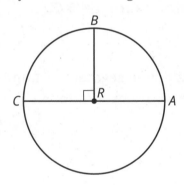

1. m∠ARC

2. m∠ARB

3. m∠CRB

Learning Goals

- Represent rotations in the plane.
- Describe rotation transformations as functions that take points as inputs and output rotated points.
- Specify a sequence of translations, reflections, and rotations that will carry a figure onto a congruent figure.

Key Term

- rotation

You have studied circles and rotations. How can you use circles to define and describe rotations on the plane?

Concentric Circles

Concentric circles are circles with a common center point.

You have constructed circles and identified parts of circles in previous lessons. Circles are important for understanding rotations.

1. Consider three concentric circles with center at point *E*.

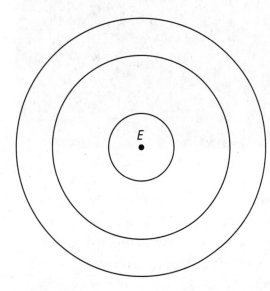

   a. Draw one point on each circle so that you can connect the points to form △*ABC*. Draw the sides of the triangle.

   b. Choose a positive or negative rotation angle, *t*.

   c. Draw *A'* as an endpoint of *EA'* such that ∠*AEA'* has a measure of *t* degrees.

   d. Repeat part (c) to draw points *B'* and *C'*. Connect the transformed points to form △*A'B'C'*.

2. What do you notice about the pairs of line segments $\overline{EA}$ and $\overline{EA'}$, $\overline{EB}$ and $\overline{EB'}$, and $\overline{EC}$ and $\overline{EC'}$? Explain your observations.

Remember:

An isometry preserves distances and angle measures.

3. Is the transformation you created an isometry? Explain your thinking.

A **rotation** is a function that maps its input, a point P, to another location, $f(P)$. This movement to a new location is defined by a center of rotation, E, and a rotation angle, t. For this reason, a rotation function is written as $R_{E,t}(P)$.

Because the rotation is defined about a point E, the movement of a specific point traces an arc that is part of the circumference of a circle with center E. The arc can be labeled by the starting point, P, and the endpoint P' or as $\overset{\frown}{PP'}$. The degree measure of this arc is equivalent to the degree rotation, t, that creates a central angle in Circle E.

Remember:

A circle is named by the point that is its center.

1. **Consider the rotation you created in the previous activity.**

   a. **Write a function of the form $R_{E,t}(\triangle ABC)$ to describe the rotation of $\triangle ABC$.**

Think

about:

   b. **Explain how your function represents the rotation of every point of $\triangle ABC$.**

A circle is a rotation of a point around a given center 360 degrees.

A circle is a locus of points that are all a given distance from a center point.

   c. **Do the arcs you created all have the same measure? Explain your answer.**

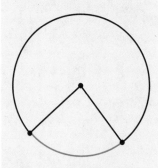

2. **Write equality and congruence statements to compare the corresponding sides of the pre-image and the image.**

An angle is the measure of the distance the point is rotated as measured by the central angle.

It is possible to apply the rotation function to a figure by using a protractor and ruler.

$R_{A,40}(\overline{JN})$

This means to rotate $\overline{JN}$ 40°, using point A as the center of rotation.

1. Draw a line segment from the center of rotation, A, to one endpoint of the line segment.

2. Using a protractor, draw a 40° angle. Use the center of rotation, A, as the vertex and the line segment drawn, $\overline{AJ}$ as one side of the angle.

   Since the angle measure is positive, place the angle in the counter-clockwise direction of the line segment drawn.

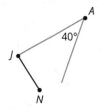

3. Use a ruler or compass to extend the side of the angle so that it is the same length as $\overline{AJ}$. Label the other endpoint J'.

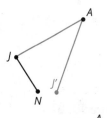

4. Repeat steps 1, 2, and 3 using the other endpoint of the original line segment.

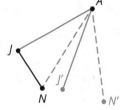

5. Connect endpoints J' and N'.

$R_{A,40}(\overline{JN}) = \overline{J'N'}$
Segment $\overline{J'N'}$ is the result of a 40° rotation of $\overline{JN}$ about point A.

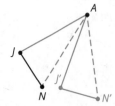

3. Complete each rotation using the given function.

a. $R_{E,\,75}(\overline{VH})$

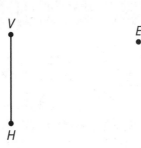

Remember:

When you construct, you use only a compass and straightedge. Here you are drawing, so you can use those tools as well as measuring tools, such as a protractor and ruler.

b. $R_{Q,\,-30}(\overline{MN})$

Q

M • ———————— • N

You have seen that corresponding points on rotated figures are equidistant from the center of rotation.

1. **Draw an example to explain why Tori is correct.**

> **Tori**
> If two points Q and Q′ are equidistant from the center, then the perpendicular bisector of QQ′ passes through the center.

2. **Use what you know to determine the center of rotation and rotation angle for the transformation of each figure. Write each rotation as a function.**

a.

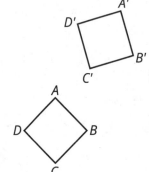

b.

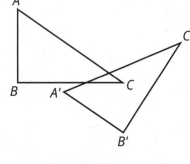

You have learned that translations, reflections, and rotations are isometries, which means that they preserve distances and angle measures.

1. **Describe and sketch the sequence of isometries that shows that the two figures in each pair are congruent. Images are shown with dashed lines.**

a.

b.

That's What It's All About!

1. Complete the graphic organizers to summarize the characteristics of each.

    a. Translation

    b. Reflection

    c. Rotation

Graphic Organizer

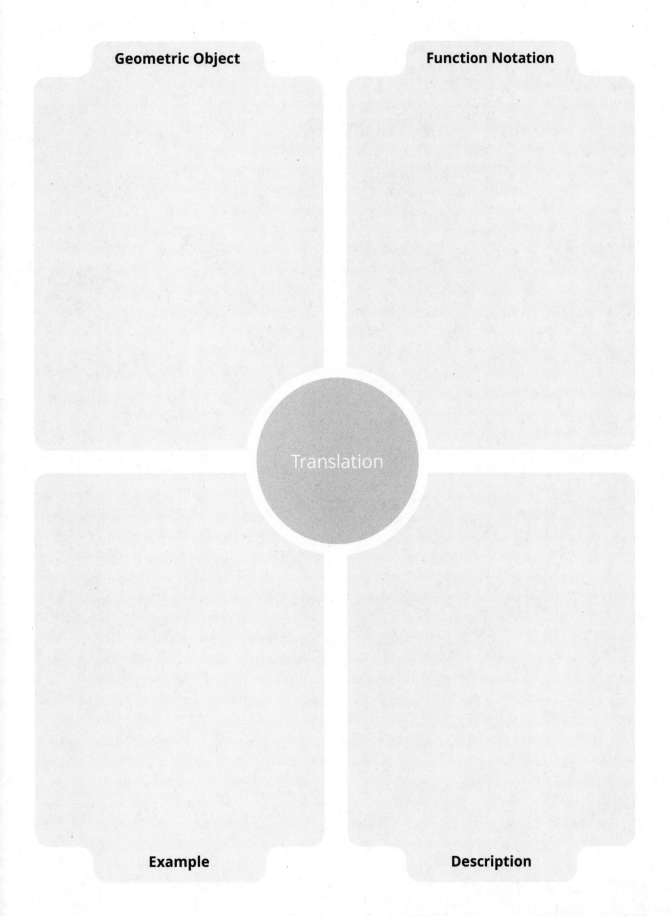

Geometric Object

Function Notation

Translation

Example

Description

Graphic Organizer

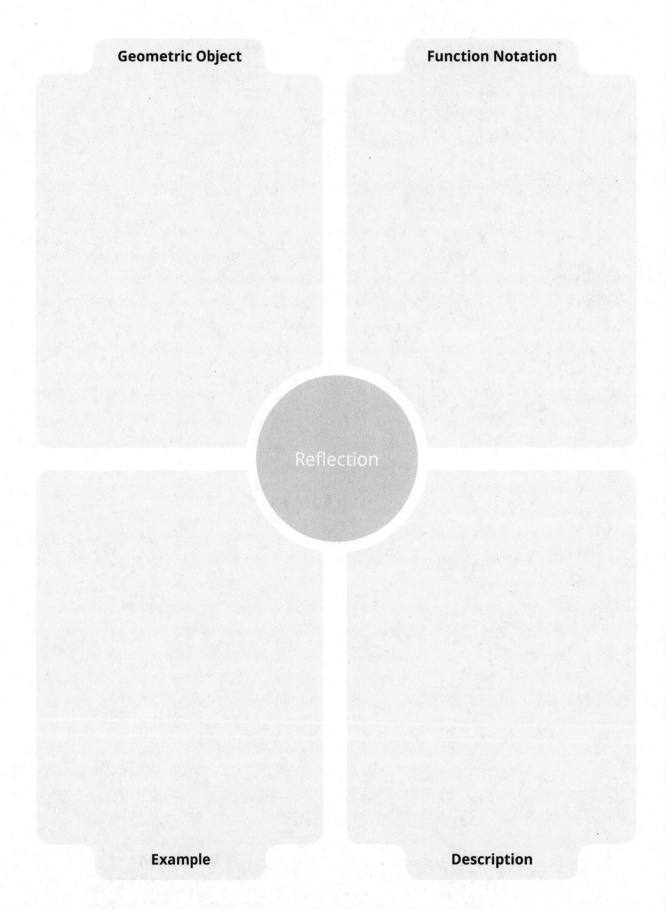

Geometric Object

Function Notation

Reflection

Example

Description

Graphic Organizer

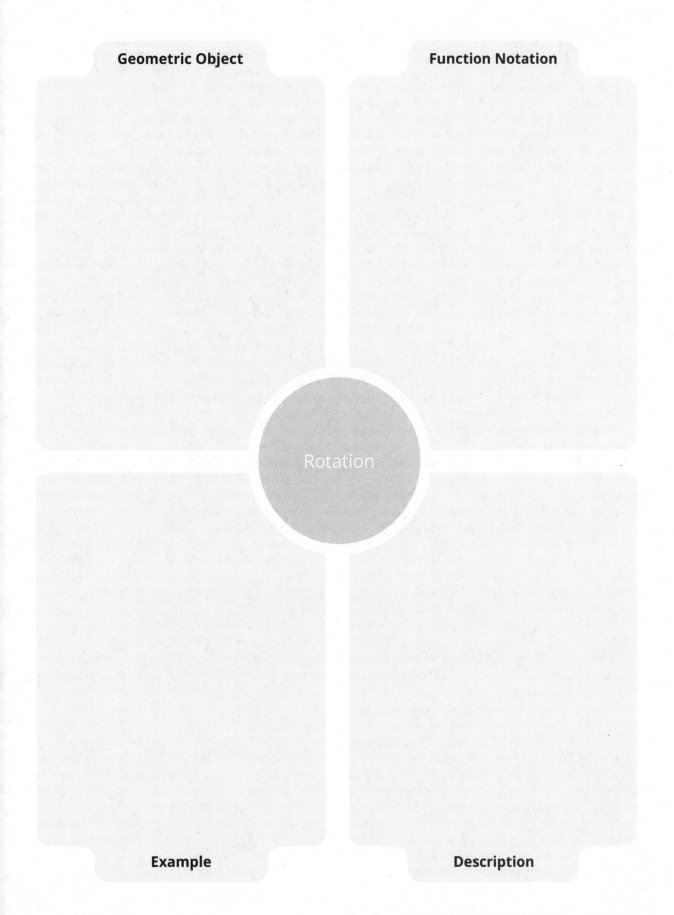

Geometric Object

Function Notation

Rotation

Example

Description

Assignment

Write

Complete each definition.

1. A function that rotates points around a center point through an angle is called a _____.

2. Concentric circles are circles with a common _____.

Remember

A rotation is a function that maps its input, a point P, to another location, $f(P)$. This movement to a new location is defined by a center of rotation, E, and a rotation angle, t. A rotation function is written as $R_{E,t}(P)$.

Practice

1. Complete each rotation given the function.

   a. $R_{D,45}(\overline{AB})$

   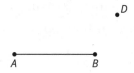

   b. $R_{X,-25}(\overline{MV})$

   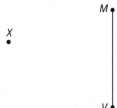

   c. $R_{A,125}(\overline{QR})$

   d. $R_{C,80}(\overline{TY})$

2. Use what you know to determine the center of rotation and rotation angle for the transformation of each figure. Write each rotation as a function.

   a.

   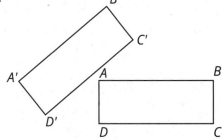

   b.

   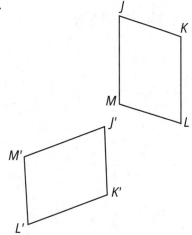

Stretch

Determine and draw the sequence of transformations that could be used to transform Trapezoid *ABCD* into Trapezoid *A'B'C'D'*. Include the locations of lines and points that the figure is reflected around, translated on, or rotated about. Also include the rotation angle.

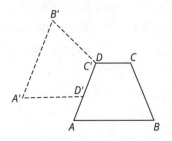

Review

1. Complete the reflection given the function $R_m(ABC)$.

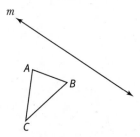

2. Describe the sequence of transformations that will map parallelogram *ABCD* onto parallelogram *GHEF*.

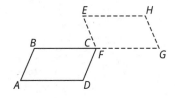

3. Construct a line perpendicular to line *AB* that passes through point *X*.

4. Duplicate ∠*Q*.

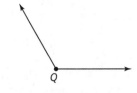

5

OKEECHOBEE
Reflectional and Rotational Symmetry

Warm Up

Identify the opposite of each number on the number line.

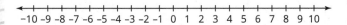

-10 -9 -8 -7 -6 -5 -4 -3 -2 -1 0 1 2 3 4 5 6 7 8 9 10

1. −8

2. −|−2|

3. 9

4. −(−7)

Learning Goals

- Identify geometric figures with line symmetry and rotational symmetry.
- Identify lines of symmetry for different geometric figures.
- Describe rotations that carry a figure onto itself.
- Describe reflections that carry a figure onto itself.

Key Terms

- reflectional symmetry
- rotational symmetry

You have learned that pre-images are congruent to images after rigid motion transformations. How can you use transformations to show that a figure can be carried onto itself?

WOW MOM

Consider the different shapes shown.

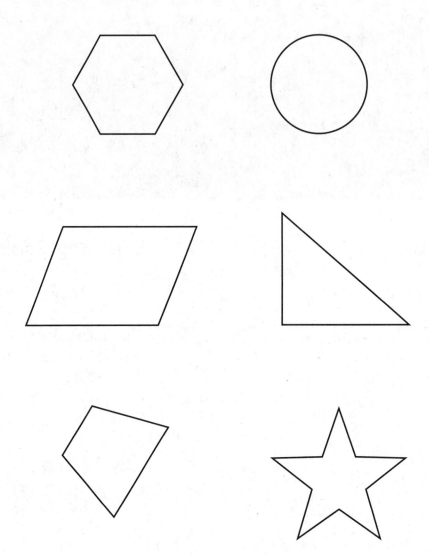

1. Copy each shape onto patty paper. For each shape:

   a. Determine whether you can fold the shape so that half of the figure lies exactly on the other half of the figure. If so, are there any other folds that will do this?

   b. Determine whether you can rotate the figure so that it looks exactly like it did before the rotation. If so, are there other rotations that will do this?

Consider the shapes from the Getting Started.

1. Name the shapes.

A plane figure has **reflectional symmetry** if you can draw a line so that the figure to one side of the line is a reflection of the figure on the other side of the line. Recall that the line that you drew on each shape is called the line of symmetry. A figure may have more than one line of symmetry.

2. Which shapes have reflectional symmetry?

3. Consider the equilateral triangle shown. It has 3 lines of symmetry. Draw these lines of symmetry.

4. How many lines of symmetry does the rectangle shown have? Explain your reasoning.

5. How many lines of symmetry are there in a square? Show the line(s) of symmetry.

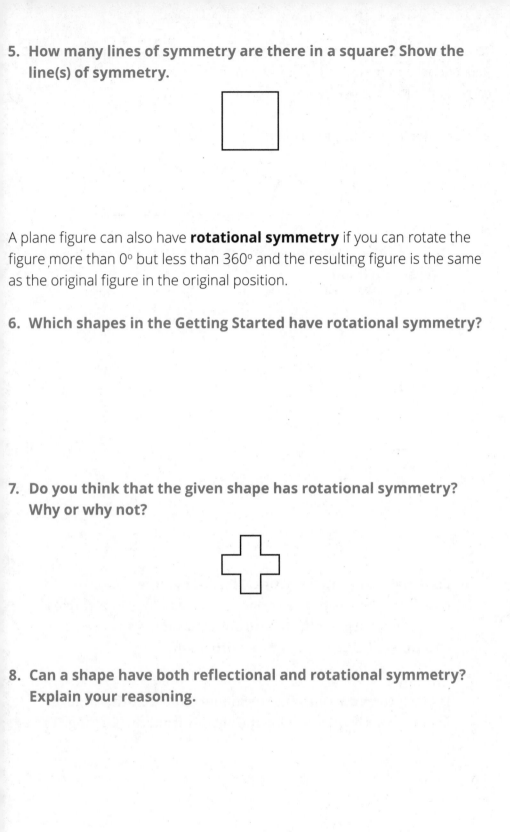

A plane figure can also have **rotational symmetry** if you can rotate the figure more than 0° but less than 360° and the resulting figure is the same as the original figure in the original position.

6. Which shapes in the Getting Started have rotational symmetry?

7. Do you think that the given shape has rotational symmetry? Why or why not?

8. Can a shape have both reflectional and rotational symmetry? Explain your reasoning.

You have also identified transformations that carry a figure onto itself. Reflectional and rotational symmetry are properties of figures that can be carried onto themselves by reflections and rotations.

9. Consider the 4 shapes shown.

   a. Describe the reflections and rotations that can carry each figure onto itself.

   b. Clark says that the horizontal line of symmetry in the rectangle means that a reflection across that line carries the figure onto itself. He also says that it means that a 180° rotation will carry the figure onto itself.

     Is Clark correct? Does his reasoning apply to other figures? Explain your thinking using the shapes from the Getting Started.

The standard alphabet has many letters that have a variety of symmetries, including reflectional and rotational symmetry. Some letters have a vertical line of symmetry. Other letters have a horizontal line of symmetry.

1. **Which letter(s) have a horizontal but not a vertical line of symmetry?**

        A   C   H   M

2. **Which letter(s) have a vertical but not a horizontal line of symmetry?**

        M   B   H   X

3. **Which letter(s) have both a horizontal and a vertical line of symmetry?**

        Z   E   H   M

4. **Which letter(s) have rotational symmetry?**

        Z   W   K   M

TALK the TALK

CHECK

The title of this lesson, OKEECHOBEE, is the name of a city, a county, and a lake in Florida. That title, along with the title of the Getting Started activity, WOW MOM, and the title of this activity, CHECK, all have rotational and/or reflectional symmetry.

1. **Identify the symmetries in each title. Explain your thinking.**

2. **Consider the rotational symmetries of an equilateral triangle, square, and regular hexagon.**

   a. **What relationship exists between the rotational symmetries of each figure and its interior angle measures?**

   b. **Test the pattern you noticed on a regular pentagon and regular hexagon. What do you notice?**

Assignment

Write

Explain the difference between reflectional symmetry and rotational symmetry in your own words.

Remember

A plane figure has reflectional symmetry if you can draw a line so that the figure to one side of the line is a reflection of the figure on the other side. A plane figure has rotational symmetry if you can rotate the figure more than 0° and less than 360° and the resulting figure is the same as the original figure.

There is a sequence of reflections and/or rotations that can carry any plane figure onto itself.

Practice

1. Determine how many lines of symmetry each figure has. Then draw all lines of symmetry for each figure.

   a. regular hexagon

   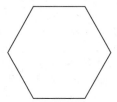

   b. isosceles right triangle

   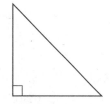

   c. rhombus

   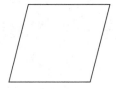

   d. regular pentagon

   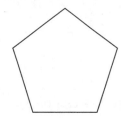

2. Identify a sequence of transformations that will carry each given pre-image onto the image shown with dashed lines.

   a.

   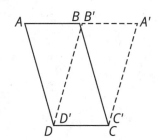

   b.

   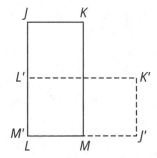

3. Describe the sequence of rotations and/or reflections that can carry each figure onto itself. Use the figure's reflectional and rotational symmetry, if any, to justify your answer.

a.

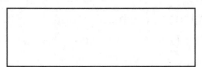

b.

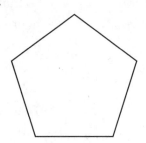

Stretch

Graph the figure with vertices at $A(2, 6)$, $B(5, 6)$, $C(5, 3)$, $D(-2, -1)$. Determine the equation(s) for all lines of symmetry for the figure. Draw the line(s) of symmetry using a dashed line.

Review

1. Locate the midpoint of the line segment using construction tools and label it point M.

2. Construct a line that is perpendicular to $\overleftrightarrow{AB}$ and passes through point X.

3. Construct the angle bisector of $\angle J$.

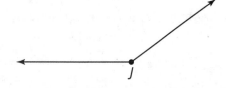

4. Determine the value of c^2.

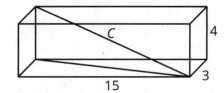

Rigid Motions on a Plane Summary

KEY TERMS

- collinear points
- angle
- ray
- rotation angle
- translation

- isometry
- reflection
- Perpendicular Bisector Theorem
- proof

- rotation
- reflectional symmetry
- rotational symmetry

LESSON 1

Put Your Input In, Take Your Output Out

Lines and circles form the basis of rigid motion transformations in geometry.

Points that lie along the same line are **collinear points**.

An **angle** is a set of points consisting of a vertex point and two rays extending from the vertex point. A **ray** is a portion of a line that begins with a single point and extends infinitely in one direction.

A **rotation angle** is a directed angle based on a circle. Positive rotation angles turn counterclockwise, and negative rotation angles turn clockwise.

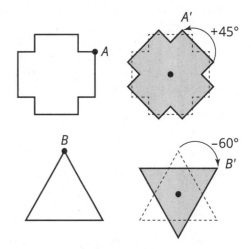

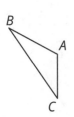

LESSON 2 · Bow Thai

Transformations are used frequently in web design and game animations and are often written as functions, which take points, distances, and angles as inputs. The functions output a new set of points after applying a transformation. These transformations move objects around on the screen.

A **translation** is a function, T, which takes as its input a set of pre-image points P and outputs a set of image points $T_{AB}(P)$, or P'. The set of image points is a translation of the set of pre-image points. The pre-image points are translated a distance of AB in the direction AB. A translation is a rigid motion transformation, or **isometry**. An isometry preserves distances and angle measures.

A translation function can represent the distance and direction of the translation using a line or line segment, or a parallel line or line segment:

$$T_{AB}(P) = P'$$
$$T_{AC}(P) = P''$$

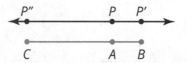

LESSON 3 · Staring Back at Me

A **reflection** is a function, R_ℓ, which takes as its input, p, the location of a point with respect to some line of reflection ℓ and outputs $R_\ell(p)$, or the opposite of the location of p with respect to the line of reflection. A reflection is an isometry.

It is possible to construct the line of reflection when given two figures that are reflections of one another.

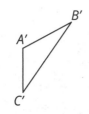

1. Label the vertices.

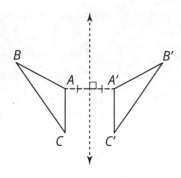

2. Connect two corresponding points. Construct the perpendicular bisector of the line segment connecting them.

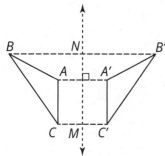

3. Connect remaining corresponding points. Label the intersection of each line segment with the perpendicular bisector.

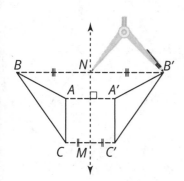

4. Use a compass to determine whether each intersection point is the midpoint of the line segment connecting corresponding vertices. If that is the case, the perpendicular bisector is the line of reflection. If not, the figures are not reflections of one another.

$\overline{CM} \cong \overline{C'M}$

$\overline{BN} \cong \overline{B'N}$

$\overline{MN}$ is the line of reflection.

You know that the perpendicular bisector of a line segment is the line of reflection between the endpoints of the segment. The **Perpendicular Bisector Theorem** states: "Any point on the perpendicular bisector of a segment is equidistant from the endpoints of that segment." A **proof** is a series of statements and corresponding reasons forming a valid argument that starts with a hypothesis and arrives at a conclusion.

A **rotation** is a function that maps its input, a point P, to another location, which is defined by a center of rotation, E, and a rotation angle, t. For this reason, a rotation function is written as $R_{E,t}(P)$. A rotation is an isometry.

Because the rotation is defined about a point E, the movement of a specific point traces an arc that is part of the circumference of a circle with center E. The arc can be labeled by the starting point, P, and the endpoint P' or as $\overset{\frown}{PP'}$. The degree measure of this arc is equivalent to the degree rotation, t, that creates a central angle in Circle E.

A circle is a rotation of a point around a given center 360 degrees. An angle is the measure of the distance the point is rotated as measured by the central angle.

It is possible to apply the rotation function to a figure by using a protractor and a straightedge.

$R_{A,\,40}(\overline{JN})$

This means to rotate JN 40°, using point A as the center of rotation.

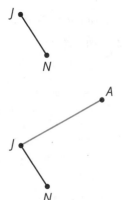

1. Draw a line segment from the center of rotation, A, to one endpoint of the line segment.

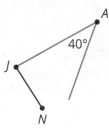

2. Using a protractor, draw a 40° angle. Use the center of rotation, *A*, as the vertex and the line segment drawn, $\overline{AJ}$, as one side of the angle. Since the angle measure is positive, place the angle in the counterclockwise direction of the line segment drawn.

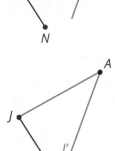

3. Use a straightedge to extend the side of the angle so that is the same length as $\overline{AJ}$. Label the other endpoint *J'*.

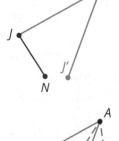

4. Repeat steps 1, 2, and 3 using the other endpoint of the original line segment.

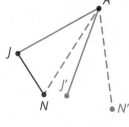

5. Connect endpoints *J'* and *N'*.

$R_{A,\,40}(\overline{JN}) = \overline{J'N'}$

Segment $\overline{J'N'}$ is the result of a 40° rotation of *JN* about point *A*.

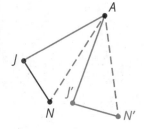

A plane figure has **reflectional symmetry** if you can draw a line so that the figure to one side of the line is a reflection of the figure on the other side of the line. So, both the octagon and the trapezoid have reflectional symmetry. The line that you can draw on each shape is called the line of symmetry. A figure can have more than one line of symmetry.

A plane figure can also have **rotational symmetry** if you can rotate the figure more than 0° but less than 360° and the resulting figure is the same as the original figure in the original position.

A shape, such as a square, can have both reflectional and rotational symmetry. The standard alphabet has many letters that have a variety of symmetries, including reflectional and rotational symmetry. Some letters have a vertical line of symmetry. Other letters have a horizontal line of symmetry.

MODULE 2

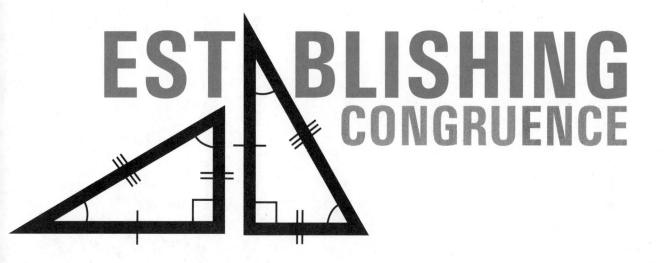

ESTABLISHING CONGRUENCE

The lessons in this module build on your experience with geometric relationships and congruence. In this module, you will continue to prove theorems and write formal proofs. You will prove theorems related to angle pairs and lines. You will prove theorems related to triangle congruence and then apply these insights to solve problems.

Topic 1 Congruence Through Transformations · · · · · · · · · · · · · · · **M2-3**

Topic 2 Justifying Line and Angle Relationships · · · · · · · · · · · · **M2-57**

Topic 3 Using Congruence Theorems · **M2-181**

TOPIC 1
Congruence Through Transformations

Congruent triangles have the same size and shape, while similar triangles have the same shape but may be different sizes. This skylight illustrates both.

Lesson 1
The Elements

Formal Reasoning in Euclidean Geometry. M2-7

Lesson 2
ASA, SAS, and SSS

Proving Triangle Congruence Theorems M2-23

Lesson 3
I Never Forget a Face

Using Triangle Congruence to Solve Problems. M2-39

Module 2: Establishing Congruence

TOPIC 1: CONGRUENCE THROUGH TRANSFORMATIONS

In this topic, students use formal reasoning to prove geometric theorems. They use what they know about rigid motions to prove triangle congruence theorems by construction. Students prove the Side-Side-Side, Side-Angle-Side, and Angle-Side-Angle Congruence Theorems by construction. Each proof involves a sequence of transformations that maps one triangle onto another, given the congruence of three corresponding parts. Integrating their knowledge of geometry and algebra, students encounter triangles on the coordinate plane that require them to use the Distance Formula to apply the congruence theorems to triangles with given measurements on the plane.

Where have we been?

In middle school, students constructed triangles from three measures of angles or sides, noticing when the conditions determine a unique triangle, more than one triangle, or no triangle. Through that hands-on exploration, they developed an intuition regarding the minimum criteria for determining whether triangles are congruent.

Where are we going?

In addition to proof by construction, students will learn to write two-column, flowchart, and paragraph proofs. They will develop their deductive reasoning skills as they prove conjectures that they have made through investigation. The triangle congruence theorems proven in this topic will be used in many of these upcoming proofs. They are used to prove the properties of quadrilaterals and other polygons, the relationships between chords, secants, and tangents in circles, and line and angle relationships in triangles and polygons.

Congruence Markers

Marks are used in geometric drawings to indicate when two or more line segments are congruent. The markers on the diagram indicate congruent line segments.

$$\overline{AB} \cong \overline{DF} \text{ and } \overline{BC} \cong \overline{ED}$$

$$\angle CAB \cong \angle EFD \text{ and } \angle ABC \cong \angle FDE$$

The Face That Launched a Thousand Triangles

How does chat software know where to apply the funny face filter, even as you move your face around on the screen? The software behind this face recognition may use congruent triangles, often in a mesh of triangles as shown. And, in order to work more quickly, the software wants to use the least amount of information it has to in order to identify congruent triangles.

Talking Points

Triangle congruence is an important topic to know about for college admissions tests. Here is a sample question:

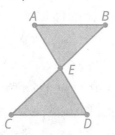

In the figure, $\overline{AB}$ and $\overline{CD}$ are 8 cm apart, congruent, and parallel. If AB = 4 cm, what is the shaded area?

$\angle AEB \cong \angle CED$ because they are vertical angles. Alternate interior angles are also congruent, so the two triangles are congruent by Angle-Side-Angle.

Since the triangles are congruent, they have congruent altitudes, so each has an altitude of 4 cm. Thus, each triangle's area is $\frac{1}{2}(4)(4)$ or 8 square cm. The total area shaded, then, is 16 square cm.

Key Terms

postulate
A postulate is a statement that is accepted without proof.

theorem
A theorem is a statement that can be proven.

proof
A proof is a series of statements and corresponding reasons forming a valid argument that starts with a hypothesis and arrives at a conclusion.

The Elements

Formal Reasoning in Euclidean Geometry

1

Warm Up

Solve for *x*.

1. $x + 4x = 90$

2. $0.5x + 2x = 90$

3. $x + 2x = 180$

4. $0.5x + 4x = 180$

Learning Goals

- Identify the hypothesis and conclusion of a conditional statement.
- Explore the truth values of conditional statements.
- Use a truth table.
- Differentiate between postulates and theorems.

Key Terms

- counterexample
- truth value
- truth table
- Euclidean geometry
- Linear Pair Postulate
- Segment Addition Postulate
- Angle Addition Postulate

You have created many conjectures in geometry. How can you reason more formally in Euclidean geometry with postulates and theorems?

If . . ., Then . . .

Decide whether each statement is true or false and explain your reasoning.

1. All rectangles are quadrilaterals.

2. All rectangles are squares.

3. If it rains today, then it will not rain tomorrow.

Counterexamples

In previous lessons—and in previous grades—you have used different kinds of reasoning to arrive at conclusions and to justify those conclusions. In this lesson and the next, you will start to use a more exact kind of reasoning commonly used in formal mathematics. When using this kind of reasoning, it is important to be able to identify false conclusions.

There are two reasons why a conclusion may be false. Either the assumed information is false, or the conclusion does not necessarily follow from the hypothesis.

1. **Derek tells his little brother that it will not rain for the next 30 days because he "knows everything." Why is this conclusion false?**

2. **The sum of the interior angles of a figure is 360°, so the figure must be a square. Why is this conclusion false?**

3. **Write an example of a conclusion that is false because the assumed information is false.**

4. **Write an example of a conclusion that is false because the argument is not valid.**

Think about:

If you are reading this sentence, then your first language must be English. This is an invalid argument. Both the assumed information and conclusion might be true, but the conclusion does not necessarily follow from the given.

To show that a statement is false, you can provide a *counterexample*. A **counterexample** is a specific example that shows that a general statement is not true.

5. **Provide a counterexample for each statement to demonstrate that they are not true.**

    a. **All prime numbers are odd.**

    b. **The sum of the measures of two acute angles is always greater than 90°.**

ACTIVITY 1.2

Conditional Statements and Truth Tables

A conditional statement is a statement that can be written in the form "If p, then q." It can be written using symbols as $p \rightarrow q$, which is read as "p implies q." The hypothesis of a conditional statement is the variable p. A hypothesis is the "if" part of an "if-then" statement. The conclusion of a conditional statement is the variable q. A conclusion is the "then" part of an "if-then" statement.

The **truth value** of a conditional statement is whether the statement is true or false. If a conditional statement could be true, then the truth value of the statement is considered true. The truth value of a conditional statement is either true or false, but not both.

Worked Example

You can identify the hypothesis and conclusion from a
conditional statement.

Conditional Statement

$$\underbrace{\text{If } x^2 = 36,}_{\textbf{Hypothesis}} \underbrace{\text{then } x = 6 \text{ or } x = -6.}_{\textbf{Conclusion}}$$

1. Consider the conditional statement.
   If the measure of an angle is 32°, then the angle is acute.

   a. Identify the hypothesis p.

   b. Identify the conclusion q.

Use the given conditional statement in Question 1 to answer Questions 2
through 5.

2. **If p is true and q is true, then the truth value of a conditional
   statement is true.**

   a. What does the phrase "If p is true" mean in terms of the
      conditional statement?

   b. What does the phrase "If q is true" mean in terms of the
      conditional statement?

   c. Explain why the truth value of the conditional statement is
      true if both p and q are true.

3. If *p* is true and *q* is false, then the truth value of a conditional statement is false.

   a. What does the phrase "If *p* is true" mean in terms of the conditional statement?

   b. What does the phrase "If *q* is false" mean in terms of the conditional statement?

   c. Explain why the truth value of the conditional statement is false if *p* is true and *q* is false.

Continue to use this conditional statement to respond to Questions 3 through 5.

If the measure of an angle is 32°, then the angle is acute.

4. If *p* is false and *q* is true, then the truth value of a conditional statement is true.

   a. What does the phrase "If *p* is false" mean in terms of the conditional statement?

   b. What does the phrase "If *q* is true" mean in terms of the conditional statement?

   c. Explain why the truth value of the conditional statement is true if *p* is false and *q* is true.

Think about:

If *p* is false and *q* is true, the truth value is always true. Can you think of other examples that show this?

5. **If p is false and q is false, then the truth value of a conditional statement is true.**

   a. **What does the phrase "If p is false" mean in terms of the conditional statement?**

   b. **What does the phrase "If q is false" mean in terms of the conditional statement?**

   c. **Explain why the truth value of the conditional statement is true if both p and q are false.**

A **truth table** is a table that summarizes all possible truth values for a conditional statement $p \rightarrow q$. The first two columns of a truth table represent all possible truth values for the variables p and q. The last column represents the truth value of the conditional statement $p \rightarrow q$.

The truth values for the conditional statement "If the measure of an angle is 32°, then the angle is acute" is shown.

Worked Example

The truth value of the conditional statement $p \rightarrow q$ is determined by the truth value of p and the truth value of q.

- If p is true and q is true, then $p \rightarrow q$ is true.
- If p is true and q is false, then $p \rightarrow q$ is false.
- If p is false and q is true, then $p \rightarrow q$ is true.
- If p is false and q is false, then $p \rightarrow q$ is true.

p	q	$p \rightarrow q$
the measure of an angle is 32°	the angle is acute	If the measure of an angle is 32°, then the angle is acute.
T	T	T
T	F	F
F	T	T
F	F	T

---

6. Consider the conditional statement.

If $m\overline{AB} = 6$ inches and $m\overline{BC} = 6$ inches, then $\overline{AB} \cong \overline{BC}$.

a. What is the hypothesis p?

b. What is the conclusion q?

c. If both p and q are true, what does that mean? What is the truth value of the conditional statement if both p and q are true?

d. If p is true and q is false, what does that mean? What is the truth value of the conditional statement if p is true and q is false?

e. If p is false and q is true, what does that mean? What is the truth value of the conditional statement if p is false and q is true?

f. If both p and q are false, what does that mean? What is the truth value of the conditional statement if both p and q are false?

g. Summarize your answers to parts (a) through (f) by completing a truth table for the conditional statement.

p	q	$p \rightarrow q$

7. Mr. David wrote the statement shown on the board.

If $\overline{AC} \cong \overline{BC}$, then point C is the midpoint of $\overline{AB}$.

He asked his students to discuss the truth of this conditional statement.

Susan said she believed the statement to be true in all situations. Marcus disagreed with Susan and said that the statement was not true all of the time.

What is Marcus thinking and who is correct?

ACTIVITY 1.3 Postulates and Theorems

Greek mathematician Euclid is sometimes referred to as the Father of Geometry.

A postulate is a statement that is taken to be true without proof. A theorem is a statement that can be demonstrated to be true by accepted mathematical operations and arguments.

The Elements is a book written by the Greek mathematician Euclid. He used a small number of undefined terms and postulates to systematically prove many theorems. As a result, Euclid was able to develop a complete system we now know as **Euclidean geometry**.

Euclid's first five postulates are:
1. A straight line segment can be drawn joining any two points.
2. Any straight line segment can be extended indefinitely in a straight line.
3. Given any straight line segment, a circle can be drawn that has the segment as its radius and one endpoint as center.
4. All right angles are congruent.
5. If two lines are drawn that intersect a third line in such a way that the sum of the inner angles on one side is less than two right angles, then the two lines inevitably must intersect each other on that side if extended far enough. (This postulate is equivalent to what is known as the parallel postulate.)

Euclid used only the first four postulates to prove the first 28 propositions or theorems of *The Elements,* but was forced to use the fifth postulate, the parallel postulate, to prove the 29th theorem.

The Elements also includes five "common notions."
1. Things that equal the same thing also equal one another.
2. If equals are added to equals, then the wholes are equal.
3. If equals are subtracted from equals, then the remainders are equal.
4. Things that coincide with one another equal one another.
5. The whole is greater than the part.

You have already used the three undefined terms *point, line,* and *plane* to define related terms such as *line segment* and *angle.* Now consider these three fundamental postulates.

- The Linear Pair Postulate
- The Segment Addition Postulate
- The Angle Addition Postulate

You will use these postulates to make various conjectures. If you are able to prove your conjectures, then the conjectures will become theorems. These theorems can then be used to make even more conjectures, which may also become theorems. Mathematicians use this process to create new mathematical ideas.

The **Linear Pair Postulate** states: "If two angles form a linear pair, then the angles are supplementary."

1. **Use the Linear Pair Postulate to complete each representation.**

   a. **Sketch and label a linear pair.**

   b. **Use your labeled sketch and the Linear Pair Postulate to write the hypothesis.**

   c. **Use your labeled sketch and the Linear Pair Postulate to write the conclusion.**

   d. **Use your conclusion and the definition of supplementary angles to write a statement about the measures of the angles in your figure.**

The **Segment Addition Postulate** states: "If point B is on $\overline{AC}$ and between points A and C, then $AB + BC = AC$."

2. **Use the Segment Addition Postulate to complete each representation.**

   a. Sketch and label collinear points D, E, and F with point E between points D and F.

   b. **Use your labeled sketch and the Segment Addition Postulate to write the hypothesis.**

   c. **Use your labeled sketch and the Segment Addition Postulate to write the conclusion.**

   d. **Write your conclusion using measure notation.**

The **Angle Addition Postulate** states: "If point *D* lies in the interior of ∠*ABC*, then m∠*ABD* + m∠*DBC* = m∠*ABC*."

3. **Use the Angle Addition Postulate to complete each representation.**

   a. **Sketch and label** ∠*DEF* **with** $\overrightarrow{EG}$ **drawn in the interior of** ∠*DEF*.

   b. **Use your labeled sketch and the Angle Addition Postulate to write the hypothesis.**

   c. **Use your labeled sketch and the Angle Addition Postulate to write the conclusion.**

TALK the TALK

While You Were Away...

1. Write a short note to a friend explaining conditional statements, truth values, and truth tables. Include definitions of all terms and examples that are easy to understand.

_____

_____

_____

_____

_____

_____

_____

_____

_____

_____

_____

_____

_____

_____

Assignment

Write

Define each term in your own words.

1. counterexample
2. conditional statement
3. truth value
4. truth table

Remember

A conditional statement is a statement that can be written in the form "if p, then q." Written as $p \rightarrow q$, it is read "p implies q." The variable p represents the hypothesis and the variable q represents the conclusion.

Truth tables are used to organize truth values of conditional statements. A postulate is a statement that is accepted without proof. A theorem is a statement that can be proven.

Practice

1. Write the postulate that confirms each statement.

   a. Angles *GFH* and *KFH* are supplementary angles.

   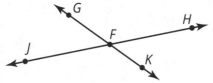

   b. $m\overline{RS} + m\overline{ST} = m\overline{RT}$

   c. $m\angle WXZ + m\angle ZXY = m\angle WXY$

   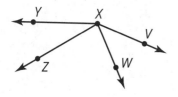

   d. $m\angle 1 + m\angle 2 = 180°$

   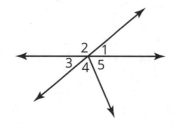

2. Complete a truth table for the conditional statements.

   a. If $\angle 1$ and $\angle 2$ are vertical angles, then $\angle 1 \cong \angle 2$.
   b. If $m\angle 1 = 90°$, then $\angle 1$ is a right angle.
   c. If $\overleftrightarrow{AB} \parallel \overleftrightarrow{CD}$, then $\overleftrightarrow{AB}$ does not intersect $\overleftrightarrow{CD}$.
   d. If a shape is a square, then the shape has four equal sides.

Stretch

Let the variable p represent the statement "the figure is a square" and let the variable q represent the statement "the figure is a quadrilateral". Complete a truth table for the statements, then determine if conditional statements are commutative, that is $p \rightarrow q$ is the same as $q \rightarrow p$, by completing a truth table for $q \rightarrow p$.

Review

1. Complete each rotation given the function.

   a. $R_{X,-65}(\overline{AB})$

   b. $R_{C,35}(\overline{PQ})$

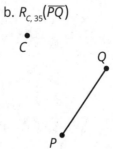

2. Determine how many lines of symmetry the equilateral triangle has. Then draw the lines of symmetry.

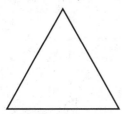

3. Write a function to describe the translation.

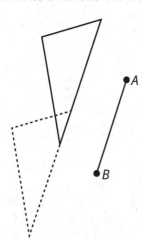

4. Write the equation of a line that passes through the point $(-8, 2)$ and is parallel to the line $3x - 2y = 12$.

5. Write the equation of a line that passes through the point $(5, -7)$ and is perpendicular to the line $-2x + 6y = -4$.

ASA, SAS, and SSS

Proving Triangle Congruence Theorems

Warm Up

Describe transformations that map Figure *A* onto the other figures shown.

1. Figure *B*

2. Figure *C*

3. Figure *D*

Learning Goals

- Use the definition of congruence in terms of rigid motions to show that two triangles are congruent.
- Prove the Side-Side-Side Congruence Theorem using rigid motion transformations.
- Prove the Side-Angle-Side Congruence Theorem using rigid motion transformations.
- Prove the Angle-Side-Angle Congruence Theorem using rigid motion transformations.

Key Terms

- Side-Side-Side Congruence Theorem (SSS)
- corresponding parts of congruent triangles are congruent (CPCTC)
- Side-Angle-Side Congruence Theorem (SAS)
- included angle
- Angle-Side-Angle Congruence Theorem (ASA)
- included side

You have defined the transformations that produce isometries. How can you use isometries to prove congruence theorems?

Necessary Conditions

Consider the two triangles shown. .

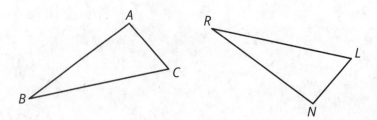

Each triangle pair has 6 relationships—3 pairs of sides and 3 pairs of angles. If the two triangles are congruent, all the corresponding side lengths and all the corresponding angle measures must be equal.

1. **Use a ruler and protractor to determine whether the two triangles are congruent. Explain your strategy.**

2. **What is the minimum number of measurements you could make to determine whether the two triangles are congruent? Explain your reasoning.**

Congruent Line Segments by Reflection

Congruent line segments and congruent angles are often denoted using special markers, rather than given measurements.

Slash markers can be used to indicate congruent line segments. When multiple line segments contain a single slash marker, this implies that all of those line segments are congruent . Double and triple slash markers can also be used to denote other line segment congruencies.

Arc markers can be used to indicate congruent angles. When multiple angles contain a single arc marker, this implies that those angles are congruent. Double and triple arc markers can also be used to denote other angle congruencies.

Think about:

Worked Example

The markers on the diagram indicate congruent line segments.
$\overline{AB} \cong \overline{FD}$ and $\overline{BC} \cong \overline{DE}$
$\angle BAC \cong \angle CBD \cong \angle DFE$
$\angle ABC \cong \angle FDE$

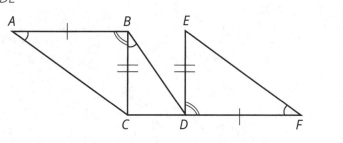

Although $\overline{DF}$ and $\overline{FD}$ represent the same line segment, when writing a congruence statement for segments that are part of a larger figure, think about how the sides and angles in the figure correspond to one another.

1. **Write the congruence statements represented by the markers in each diagram.**

Think about:

Make sure you are properly naming angles.

a.

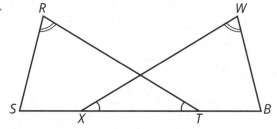

b.

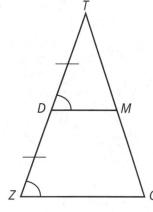

In previous lessons, you learned that:

(1) Isometries preserve distances and angle measures.
(2) Any point in the plane can be reflected across a line to map onto another point in the plane.
(3) A point is equidistant from two other points if and only if it lies on their perpendicular bisector.

You can use these facts to prove a conjecture that you have explored. Prove that you can always map one congruent line segment onto the other using at most two reflections.

Worked Example

Prove that a segment can be mapped onto itself in at most two reflections.

Suppose that $\overline{AB} \cong \overline{CD}$.

Since any point in the plane can be reflected across a line to map onto another point in the plane, you know that point C is a reflection of point A across line m. Reflect $\overline{AB}$ across line m, $R_m(\overline{AB})$.

Reflections preserve distances, so you know that $\overline{CB'} \cong \overline{CD}$, because $\overline{AB} \cong \overline{CD}$ and $\overline{AB} \cong \overline{CB'}$. Thus, point C is equidistant from point B' and from point D.

Since a point is equidistant from two other points if and only if it lies on their perpendicular bisector, this means that point C lies on the perpendicular bisector of $\overline{B'D}$ (line n).

Thus, one last reflection across the perpendicular bisector maps $\overline{CB'}$ onto $\overline{CD}$, $R_n(\overline{CB'}) \rightarrow (\overline{CD})$.

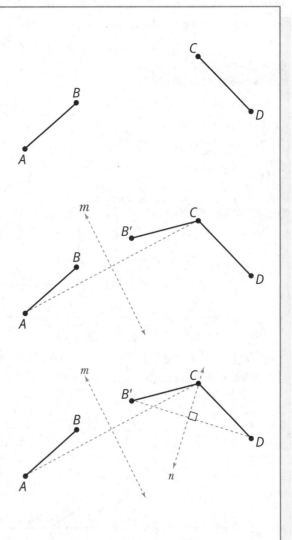

2. The proof in the worked example shows two reflections. Create an example in which $\overline{AB}$ maps onto $\overline{CD}$ in just one reflection. Explain your example.

3. Use the worked example to explain why you do not need more than two reflections to map a line segment onto a congruent line segment in the plane.

In previous courses, you investigated the conditions necessary for forming a triangle with different side lengths. Now you will prove that triangles are congruent given different minimal criteria.

> You can use the fact that a segment can be mapped onto itself in at most two reflections to prove △VAR is congruent to △BKF.

Consider two triangles such that the three sides of one triangle are congruent to the three sides of the second triangle. You can prove that this criteria is sufficient to demonstrate the two triangles are congruent.

Given two triangles △VAR and △BKF. Suppose VA = BK, VR = BF, and AR = KF.

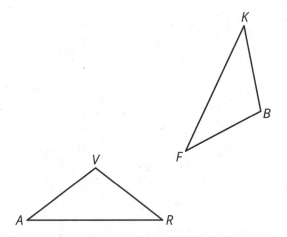

1. **Complete the steps to show the proof that △VAR ≅ △BKF.**

   a. **Draw the reflection of △VAR across a line that maps point V onto point B. Label the image as △V′A′R′. Give the reason(s) you can create this reflection.**

   b. **Draw the reflection of △V′A′R′ which maps $\overline{V'A'}$ onto $\overline{BK}$. Label the image as △V″A″R″. Give the reason(s) you can create this reflection.**

2. **Summarize the proof you completed in Question 1. Explain how knowing that the three corresponding sides of two triangles proves that the two triangles are congruent.**

Because this relationship has been proved to be true, you may now refer to it as a theorem. The **Side-Side-Side Congruence Theorem (SSS)** states: "If three sides of one triangle are congruent to the corresponding sides of another triangle, then the triangles are congruent."

> Any theorem can be used in the future as a reason in other proofs.

If two triangles are congruent, then each part of one triangle is congruent to the corresponding part of the other triangle. **Corresponding parts of congruent triangles are congruent**, abbreviated as **CPCTC**, is often used as a reason in proofs. CPCTC states that corresponding angles and sides in two congruent triangles are congruent. This reason can only be used after you have proven that the triangles are congruent.

3. **Write congruence statements for all corresponding side and angle relationships of the pre-image and the image.**

An **included angle** is the angle formed by two sides of a triangle.

Consider two triangles that have two sides and an included angle congruent. Analyze the proof using rigid motion transformations to demonstrate that this criteria is sufficient to prove the two triangles are congruent.

Worked Example

Given $\triangle CNF$ and $\triangle VRM$, $\overline{CN} \cong \overline{VR}$, $\overline{CF} \cong \overline{VM}$, and $\angle C \cong \angle V$. Prove $\triangle CNF \cong \triangle VRM$.

You know that you can map $\overline{CN}$ to $\overline{VR}$ in one or two reflections.

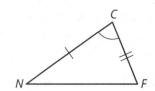

Since reflections preserve distance, this means that point F must be on the circle centered at V with radius CM, because $\overline{CF} \cong \overline{CM}$.

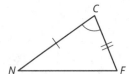

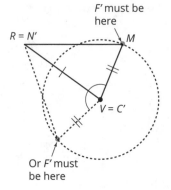

And since reflections preserve angle measures, there are only two possible locations for point F to be on the circle. If point F is not at M, then a reflection across $\overline{VR}$ will map point F onto point M, $R_{\overline{VR}}(F) \rightarrow M$.

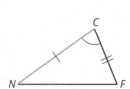

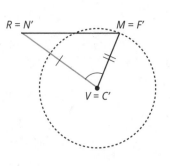

1. **Explain the final steps in the worked example.**

   a. **Why are there only two locations that point F' could be in relation to points V and R?**

   b. **Why will a reflection across $\overline{VR}$ map point F' onto point M?**

Because this relationship has been proved to be true, you may now refer to it as a theorem. The **Side-Angle-Side Congruence Theorem (SAS)** states: "If two sides and the included angle of one triangle are congruent to the corresponding two sides and the included angle of a second triangle, then the triangles are congruent."

2. **Consider the diagram shown where $\overline{AB} \cong \overline{DE}$, $\overline{AC} \cong \overline{DF}$, and $\angle A \cong \angle D$.**
   Prove $\triangle ABC \cong \triangle DEF$. Explain your steps.

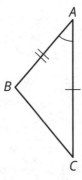
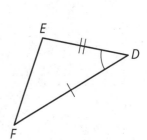

3. **Write congruence statements for all corresponding parts and angle relationships of the pre-image and the image.**

An **included side** is the side between two angles of a triangle.

Let's consider two triangles that have two angles and an included side congruent. Use this criteria to prove the two triangles are congruent. Use reasoning similar to that used for the Side-Angle-Side Theorem.

1. **Consider △FGH and △PQR where $\overline{FG} \cong \overline{PQ}$, ∠G ≅ ∠Q, and ∠F ≅ ∠P. Prove that △FGH ≅ △PQR.**

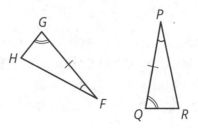

Because this relationship has been proved to be true, you may now refer to it as a theorem. The **Angle-Side-Angle Congruence Theorem (ASA)** states: "If two angles and the included side of one triangle are congruent to the corresponding two angles and the included side of another triangle, then the triangles are congruent."

2. **Write congruence statements for all corresponding parts and angle relationships of the pre-image and the image.**

Thus far, you have explored and proven each of the triangle congruence theorems:

- Side-Side-Side Congruence Theorem (SSS)
- Side-Angle-Side Congruence Theorem (SAS)
- Angle-Side-Angle Congruence Theorem (ASA)

1. **Juno wondered why AAA isn't on the list of congruence theorems. Provide a counterexample to show Juno why Angle-Angle-Angle (AAA) *is not* considered a triangle congruence theorem.**

2. **Juno also wondered why SSA isn't on the list of congruence theorems. Provide a counterexample to show Juno why Side-Side-Angle (SSA) *is not* considered a triangle congruence theorem.**

The Right Combination

1. Complete the graphic organizer to summarize what you have learned about the triangle congruence theorems.

Side-Side-Side Congruence Theorem

Side-Angle-Side Congruence Theorem

Triangle Congruence Theorems

Angle-Side-Angle Congruence Theorem

Non-Examples of Triangle Congruence Theorems

Write

Explain how you can list the six pairs of corresponding parts of congruent triangles by using the triangle congruence statement rather than a diagram.

Remember

The SSS Congruence Theorem states that if three sides of one triangle are congruent to the corresponding sides of another triangle, then the triangles are congruent.

The SAS Congruence Theorem states that if two sides and the included angle of one triangle are congruent to the corresponding sides and included angle of another triangle, then the triangles are congruent.

The ASA Congruence Theorem states that if two angles and the included side of one triangle are congruent to the corresponding angles and included side of another triangle, then the triangles are congruent.

Practice

1. Draw two triangles that correspond with each congruence statement. Then list the six pairs of congruent corresponding parts.

   a. $\triangle CGB \cong \triangle JMV$

   b. $\triangle LBR \cong \triangle MDS$

2. For each figure, determine whether there is enough information to conclude that the indicated triangles are congruent. If so, state the theorem you used.

   a. Given: $\overline{AC} \parallel \overline{BD}, \overline{AB} \parallel \overline{CD}$

   Is $\triangle ABD \cong \triangle DCA$?

   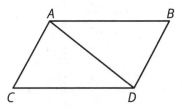

   b. Given: $\overline{EI} \cong \overline{GH}, \overline{EH} \cong \overline{GI}$

   Is $\triangle EHI \cong \triangle GIH$?

   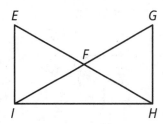

   c. Given: $\overline{TQ} \cong \overline{TP}$

   Is $\triangle TRQ \cong \triangle TRP$?

   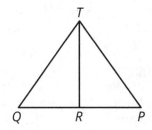

   d. Given: $\overline{TR}$ intersects $\overline{NP}, \overline{TU} \cong \overline{RU}, \overline{NU} \cong \overline{PU}$

   Is $\triangle TUN \cong \triangle RUP$?

   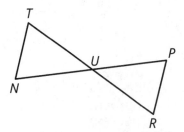

Stretch

Consider the given figure.

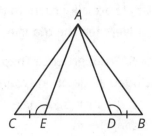

The table shows a series of statements that lead to a conclusion that shows that $\triangle CAD \cong \triangle BAE$. Fill in the table by writing sentences that give the reasoning for the truth of each statement.

Statement	Reasoning
$\overline{CE} \cong \overline{DB}$	
$\angle AEC \cong \angle ADB$	
$m\angle AEC + m\angle AED = 180°$	
$m\angle ADB + m\angle ADE = 180°$	
$\angle AED \cong \angle ADE$	
$\overline{AE} \cong \overline{AD}$	
$\overline{ED} \cong \overline{ED}$	
$\overline{CD} \cong \overline{EB}$	
$\triangle CAD \cong \triangle BAE$	

Review

1. Write the postulate that confirms the statement.

   $m\angle BCD + m\angle DCE = m\angle BCE$

2. Complete a truth table for the conditional statement.

   If $\angle A$ and $\angle B$ are supplementary angles, then $m\angle A + m\angle B = 180°$.

3. Complete the translation given the function.

   $T_{L'M}$ (Parallelogram) = Parallelogram'

   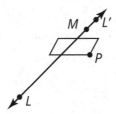

4. Identify a sequence of transformations that will carry each given pre-image onto the image shown with dashed lines.

   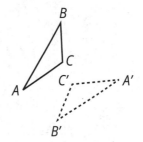

5. A composite figure is graphed on the coordinate plane shown. Round your answers to the nearest hundredth, if necessary.

   a. Determine the perimeter of the figure.

   b. Calculate the area of the figure.

   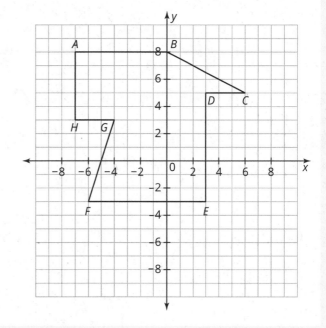

I Never Forget a Face

Using Triangle Congruence to Solve Problems

Warm Up

Determine the measure of the unknown angle in each triangle.

1.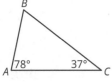

2.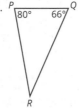

3.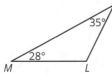

4.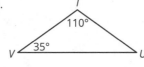

Learning Goals

- Use triangle congruence theorems to identify congruent triangles.
- Identify the information needed to conclude that two triangles are congruent by SSS, SAS, or ASA.

You have proven that Side-Side-Side, Side-Angle-Side, and Angle-Side-Angle Congruence Theorems are valid criteria to determine triangle congruence. How can you apply these theorems to problems?

A Bridge Too Far

Suppose you are planning to build a new bridge across a river to replace the old bridge, which has grown unusable. You need to know exactly how long to make the bridge, but you can't measure the width of the river. The only thing you know is the length of the old bridge.

Think about:

You can't assume that an angle is a right angle or that two figures are congruent, even if it seems like it.

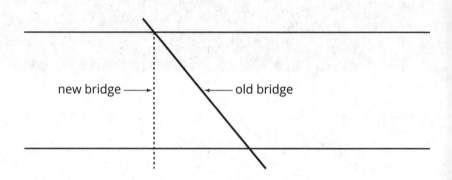

new bridge ⟶ ⟵ old bridge

1. **Explain how you could use congruent triangles to determine the exact length of the new bridge needed to cross the river. Explain your thinking.**

ACTIVITY 3.1 Using SSS, SAS, and ASA

You know that the Side-Side-Side, Side-Angle-Side, and Angle-Side-Angle Congruence Theorems can be used as valid reasons to demonstrate triangles are congruent. Consider each theorem as you analyze the given statements and diagrams.

1. **Suppose $\overline{AD}$ bisects $\angle A$, and $\overline{AD} \perp \overline{BC}$.**

   Are there congruent triangles in this diagram? Explain your reasoning.

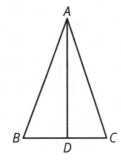

2. **Suppose $\angle DBC \cong \angle ECB$, and $\angle DCB \cong \angle EBC$.**

   Are there congruent triangles in this diagram? Explain your reasoning.

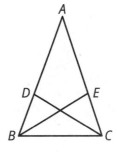

3. **Suppose $\overline{AB} \cong \overline{DF}$, $\angle A \cong \angle D$, and $\overline{BE} \cong \overline{FC}$.**

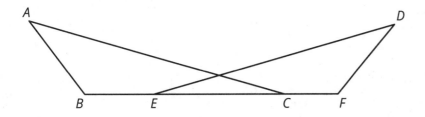

   Are there congruent triangles in this diagram? Explain your reasoning.

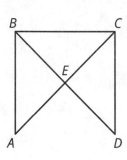

4. Suppose $\overline{AC} \cong \overline{DB}$, $\overline{AB} \perp \overline{BC}$, and $\overline{DC} \perp \overline{CB}$.

    a. What information would you need to conclude △CAB is congruent to △BDC using the ASA Congruence Theorem?

    b. What information would you need to conclude △ABE is congruent to △DCE using the ASA Congruence Theorem?

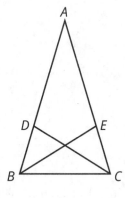

5. Suppose $\overline{AB} \cong \overline{AC}$.

    a. What additional information would be needed to conclude △ABE is congruent to △ACD using the ASA Congruence Theorem?

b. What additional information would be needed to conclude △*ABE* is congruent to △*ACD* using the SSS Congruence Theorem?

c. What additional information would be needed to conclude △*ABE* is congruent to △*ACD* using the SAS Congruence Theorem?

6. Simone says that since △*ABC* and △*DCB* have two pairs of congruent corresponding sides and congruent corresponding angles, then the triangles are congruent by SAS. Is Simone correct? Explain your reasoning.

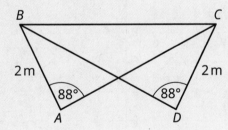

ACTIVITY 3.2 SSS, SAS, and ASA on the Coordinate Plane

1. **Use the Distance Formula and patty paper to show that the two triangles on the coordinate plane are congruent by SAS. Show your work.**

Think

How does your reasoning change when figures are represented on a coordinate plane?

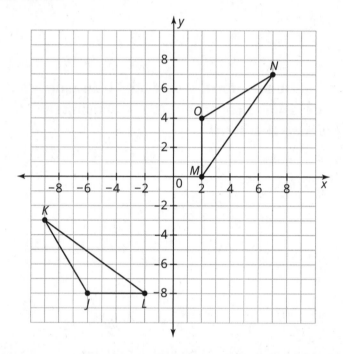

2. **Use the Distance Formula to show that the two triangles on the coordinate plane are congruent by SSS. Show your work.**

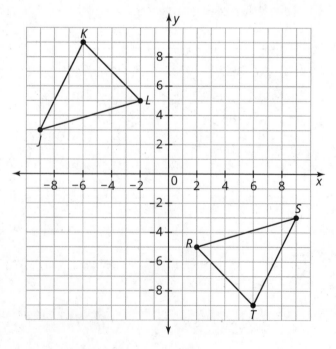

3. Emerson wants to translate △*ABC* and then reflect it across the *y*-axis to form a new triangle in Quadrant II. She uses what she knows about transformations to determine the vertices of △*A'B'C'* before performing the transformations.

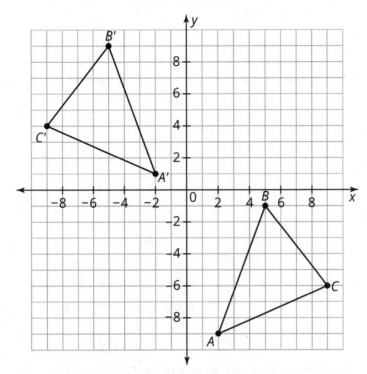

a. Describe how Emerson can use the ASA Congruence Theorem to determine whether or not she transformed △*ABC*, such that the image is congruent to the pre-image.

b. Did Emerson perform the transformations on △*ABC* so that the image is congruent to the pre-image? Explain your reasoning.

4. Describe how to prove the given triangles are congruent. Use the key terms *included angle* and *Side-Angle-Side Congruence Theorem* in your answer.

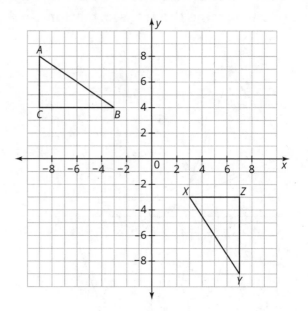

5. Describe how to prove the given triangles are congruent. Use the key terms *included side* and *Angle-Side-Angle Congruence Theorem* in your answer.

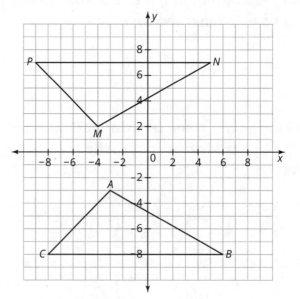

TALK the TALK

A Transformational Arteest

Congruence is an important concept, not only in technology but also in the world of art and design.

The image shown uses all three rigid motions—a rotation, a translation, and a reflection—and a single shape repeated to create a wallpaper design.

1. **Use the space on the next page to create your own wallpaper design using a single geometric figure and all three rigid motions.**

2. **Share your designs with your classmates. Determine the repeated pattern of transformations used to create each design.**

Assignment

Write

Explain in your own words how to determine which congruence theorem to use to identify congruent triangles.

Remember

The SSS, SAS, and ASA criteria for triangle congruence can be applied on and off the coordinate plane to solve real-world and mathematical problems.

Practice

1. State the theorem that proves the triangles are congruent. Then write a congruence statement.

a.

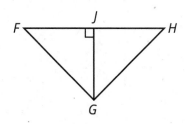

b.

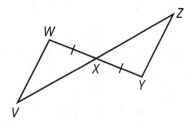

c.

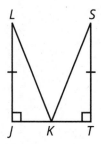

d.

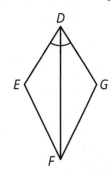

2. Determine the information that is needed to use the indicated theorem to show that the triangles are congruent.

a. △FJG ≅ △HJG by SAS

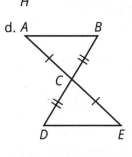

b. △VMX ≅ △ZYX by ASA

c. △KJL ≅ △KTS by SAS

d. △DEF ≅ △DGF by ASA

Stretch

Figure *ABCD* is a square. The line segments *AA'* and *BB'* are perpendicular to each other. Determine how it can be proven that △*ABB'* ≅ △*DAA'* using either SAS, SSS, or ASA.

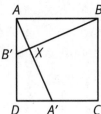

Review

1. Draw two triangles that correspond with the congruence statement △*MTA* ≅ △*BGC*. Then list the six pairs of congruent corresponding parts.

2. For the figure shown, determine whether there is enough information to conclude that the triangles are congruent. If so, state the theorem you used.

   Given: ∠*MOP* ≅ ∠*MON*

   Is △*POM* ≅ △*NOM*?

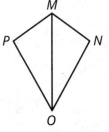

3. Describe the sequence of rotations and/or reflections that can carry each figure onto itself. Use the figure's reflectional and rotational symmetry, if any, to justify your answer.

   a.

   b.
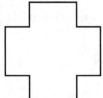

4. Use the dark points to determine the location of the vertices of a square.

Congruence Through Transformations Summary

KEY TERMS

- counterexample
- truth value
- truth table
- Euclidean geometry
- Linear Pair Postulate
- Segment Addition Postulate

- Angle Addition Postulate
- Side-Side-Side Congruence Theorem (SSS)
- corresponding parts of congruent triangles are congruent (CPCTC)

- Side-Angle-Side Congruence Theorem (SAS)
- included angle
- Angle-Side-Angle Congruence Theorem (ASA)
- included side

LESSON 1 · The Elements

When reasoning in mathematics, it is important to be able to identify false conclusions. There are two reasons why a conclusion may be false. Either the assumed information is false, or the conclusion does not necessarily follow from the hypothesis.

For example, consider the statement, "If you are reading this sentence, then your first language must be English." This is an invalid argument. Both the hypothesis and conclusion might be true, but the conclusion does not necessarily follow from the hypothesis.

To show that a statement is false, you can provide a counterexample. A **counterexample** is a specific example that shows that a general statement is not true.

The **truth value** of a conditional statement is whether the statement is true or false. If a conditional statement could be true, then the truth value of the statement is considered true. The truth value of a conditional statement is either true or false, but not both.

You can identify the hypothesis and conclusion from a conditional statement. For example:

conditional statement

$$\underbrace{\text{If } x^2 = 36,}_{\textbf{Hypothesis}} \ \underbrace{\text{then } x = 6 \text{ or } x = -6.}_{\textbf{Conclusion}}$$

A **truth table** is a table that summarizes all possible truth values for a conditional statement $p \rightarrow q$. The first two columns of a truth table represent all possible truth values for the propositional variables p and q. The last column represents the truth value of the conditional statement $p \rightarrow q$.

Euclid was a Greek mathematician who used a small number of undefined terms and postulates to systematically prove many theorems. As a result, Euclid was able to develop a complete system we now know as **Euclidean geometry**.

p	q	$p \rightarrow q$
true	true	true
true	false	false
false	true	true
false	false	true

Three fundamental postulates—the Linear Pair Postulate, the Segment Addition Postulate, and the Angle Addition Postulate—can be used to make various conjectures. If the conjectures are proven, then they will become theorems.

The **Linear Pair Postulate** states, "If two angles form a linear pair, then the angles are supplementary."

The **Segment Addition Postulate** states, "If point B is on $\overline{AC}$ and between points A and C, then $AB + BC = AC$."

The **Angle Addition Postulate** states, "If point D lies in the interior of $\angle ABC$, then m$\angle ABD$ + m$\angle DBC$ = m$\angle ABC$."

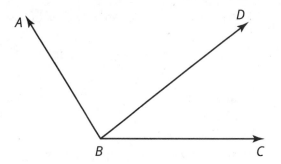

ASA, SAS, and SSS

It cannot be assumed that angles are right angles or that two figures are congruent, even if they appear to be. Labels and symbols indicate right angles and congruent figures.

Congruent line segments and congruent angles are often denoted using special markers rather than given measurements. Slash markers indicate congruent line segments. When multiple line segments contain a single slash marker, this implies that all of the line segments are congruent. Double and triple slash markers also denote other line segment congruencies. Arc markers indicate congruent angles. When multiple angles contain a single arc marker, this implies that those angles are congruent. Double and triple arc markers denote other angle congruencies.

The markers on the diagram indicate congruent line segments and angles.

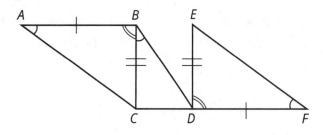

$\overline{AB} \cong \overline{DF}$ and $\overline{BC} \cong \overline{ED}$
$\angle BAC \cong \angle CBD \cong \angle DFE$
$\angle ABC \cong \angle FDE$

You can prove the conjecture that you can always map one congruent line segment onto the other using at most two reflections.

For example, suppose that $\overline{AB} \cong \overline{CD}$.

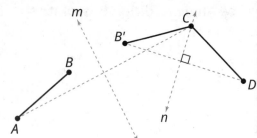

Since any point in the plane can be reflected across a line to map onto another point in the plane, point C is a reflection of point A across line m. Reflect $\overline{AB}$ across this line.

Reflections preserve distances, so $\overline{CB'} \cong \overline{CD}$, because $\overline{AB} \cong \overline{CD}$ and $\overline{AB} \cong \overline{CB'}$. Thus, point C is equidistant from point B' and from point D.

Since a point is equidistant from two other points if and only if it lies on their perpendicular bisector, point C lies on the perpendicular bisector of $\overline{B'D}$ (line n). Thus, one last reflection across the perpendicular bisector maps $\overline{CB'}$ to $\overline{CD}$.

You can prove that triangles are congruent given different minimal criteria.

The **Side-Side-Side Congruence Theorem (SSS)** states, "If three sides of one triangle are congruent to the corresponding sides of another triangle, then the triangles are congruent."

If two triangles are congruent, then each part of one triangle is congruent to the corresponding part of the other triangle. **Corresponding parts of congruent triangles are congruent**, abbreviated as **CPCTC**, is often used as a reason in proofs. CPCTC states that corresponding angles or sides in two congruent triangles are congruent. This reason can only be used after you have proven that the triangles are congruent.

The **Side-Angle-Side Congruence Theorem (SAS)** states, "If two sides and the included angle of one triangle are congruent to the corresponding two sides and the included angle of a second triangle, then the triangles are congruent." An **included angle** is the angle formed by two sides of a triangle. Consider this proof of the Side-Angle-Side Theorem:

Given △CNF and △VRM, $\overline{CN} \cong \overline{VR}$, $\overline{CF} \cong \overline{VM}$, and $\angle C \cong \angle V$.
You can map $\overline{CN}$ to $\overline{VR}$ in one or two reflections.

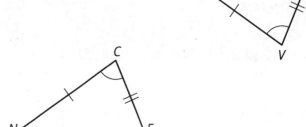

Since reflections preserve distance, this means that point *F* must be on the circle centered at *V* with radius *CM*, because $\overline{CF} \cong \overline{CM}$.

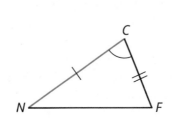

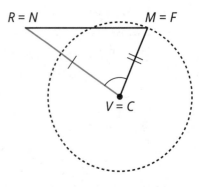

Since reflections preserve angle measures, there are only two possible locations for point *F* to be on the circle. If point *F* is not at *M*, then a reflection across $\overline{VR}$ will map point *F* to point *M*.

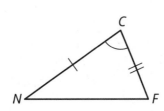

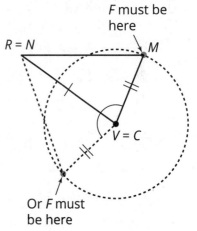

The **Angle-Side-Angle Congruence Theorem (ASA)** states, "If two angles and the included side of one triangle are congruent to the corresponding two angles and the included side of another triangle, then the triangles are congruent." An **included side** is a line segment between two consecutive angles of a figure. The proof of this theorem is similar to how the Side-Angle-Side Theorem is proven.

AAA and SSA are not triangle congruence theorems. Having these congruent parts of triangles does not mean that the triangles themselves are congruent.

Given $\overline{AD} \cong \overline{DC}$ and $\overline{DB}$ bisects $\overline{AC}$.

You can use the Side-Side-Side Congruence Theorem to demonstrate that △ADB is congruent to △CDB.

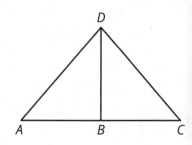

- Using the definition of a bisector, B is the midpoint of $\overline{AC}$ and therefore $\overline{AB} \cong \overline{BC}$.
- Since $\overline{DB}$ is the same side in each triangle, then $\overline{DB} \cong \overline{DB}$.
- Therefore, △ADB ≅ △CDB by SSS.

Given V is the midpoint of $\overline{UX}$ and V is the midpoint of $\overline{TW}$.

You can use the Side-Angle-Side Congruence Theorem to demonstrate that △UVT is congruent to △XVW.

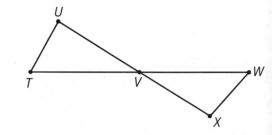

- By definition of a midpoint $\overline{UV} \cong \overline{XV}$ and $\overline{TV} \cong \overline{WV}$.
- Using the definition of vertical angles, ∠UVT ≅ ∠XVW.
- Therefore, △UVT ≅ △XVW by SAS.

Given $\overline{WZ} \parallel \overline{XY}$ and $\overline{WX} \parallel \overline{ZY}$.

You can use the Angle-Side-Angle Congruence Theorem to demonstrate that △WXY is congruent to △YZW.

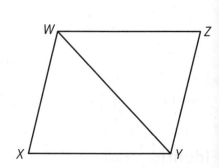

- Using the definition of alternate interior angles, ∠ZWY ≅ ∠XYW and ∠XWY ≅ ∠ZYW.
- Since $\overline{WY}$ is the same side in each triangle, then $\overline{WY} \cong \overline{WY}$.
- Therefore, △WXY ≅ △YZW by ASA.

Justifying Line and Angle Relationships

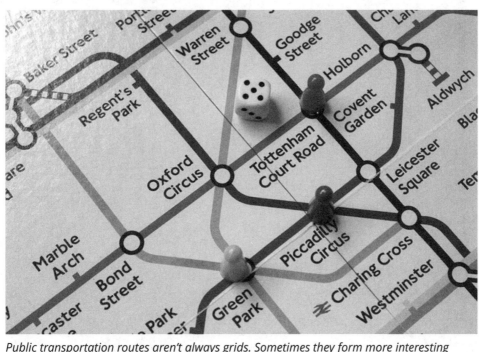

Public transportation routes aren't always grids. Sometimes they form more interesting shapes and angles.

Lesson 1
Proof Positive
Forms of Proof M2-61

Lesson 2
A Parallel Universe
Proving Parallel Line Theorems M2-83

Lesson 3
Ins and Outs
Interior and Exterior Angles of Polygons M2-103

Lesson 4
Identical Twins
Perpendicular Bisector and Isosceles Triangle Theorems M2-119

Lesson 5
Corners in a Round Room
Angle Relationships Inside and Outside Circles M2-141

Module 2: Establishing Congruence

TOPIC 2: JUSTIFYING LINE AND ANGLE RELATIONSHIPS

This topic moves from the conjectures made in the previous topic to formal proof. The development of proof-writing is slow and deliberate. In preparation for writing proofs independently, students engage with proofs on several levels: reading and analyzing completed proofs, finishing proofs that have been partially completed, supplying the reasons for given statements, and mirroring a two-column proof from a given flow-chart proof. Students have the opportunity to experience proofs before having to write them entirely on their own.

Where have we been?

In elementary and middle school, students investigated lines, angles, triangles, and quadrilaterals. They used informal arguments to establish facts about the angle sum and exterior angles of triangles, as well as the angles created when parallel lines are cut by a transversal. In the previous topic, students explored and conjectured about each of the concepts that they prove in this topic.

Where are we going?

As the theorems proven in this topic are used to prove other theorems in future topics, students are building a system of geometric relationships and seeing how these geometric ideas are connected. Seeing a system of relationships allows students to reason and generalize beyond the specificity of any given figure and prepares them to solve more complicated problems.

Analyzing Proofs

Proofs are at the heart of geometric reasoning. They are arguments which connect what you know to what you want to show. Diagrams are often essential when creating proofs.

In this topic, you will see a proof that a point equidistant from two other points must lie on their perpendicular bisector.

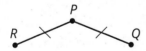

Points Q and R are equidistant from point P.

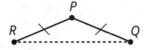

Draw $\overline{QR}$ to form isosceles triangle PQR.

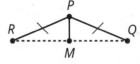

Draw the midpoint of $\overline{QR}$, point M. Then draw $\overline{PM}$.

Triangles PQM and PRM are congruent by SSS. And $\angle PMQ$ and $\angle PMR$ are a congruent linear pair that each measure 90°. So, point P lies on the perpendicular bisector of $\overline{QR}$.

Elementary, My Dear Watson

One of the most famous literary detectives is Sherlock Holmes. Created by author Sir Arthur Conan Doyle, Sherlock Holmes first appeared in print in 1887 in the novel *A Study in Scarlet*. The character has gone on to appear in four novels, 56 short stories, and over 200 films. The Guinness Book of World Records has listed Holmes as the most portrayed movie character, with more than 70 different actors playing the part.

Holmes is most famous for his keen powers of observation and logical reasoning, which always helped him solve the case. In many literary and film adaptations, Holmes is known to remark, "Elementary, my dear Watson," after explaining to his assistant how he solved the mystery. However, this well-known phrase doesn't actually appear in any of the stories written by Doyle.

Talking Points

It can be helpful to know geometric theorems for college admissions tests.

Here is an example of a sample question:

In the figure shown, ∠BED and ∠BCD are inscribed in circle A. What is the relationship between ∠BED and ∠BCD?

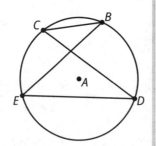

To solve this problem, you need to know the Inscribed Angle Theorem. Both of the inscribed angles are half the measure of the central angle, ∠BAD, because they intercept the same arc, $\overarc{BD}$. Since they are both half the measure of the same angle, the two inscribed angles must be congruent.

Key Terms

auxiliary line
An auxiliary line is a line that is drawn to help complete a geometric proof.

Hypotenuse-Angle Congruence Theorem
The Hypotenuse-Angle Congruence Theorem states that if the hypotenuse and an acute angle of a right triangle are congruent to the hypotenuse and an acute angle of another right triangle, then the triangles are congruent.

Angle-Angle-Side Congruence Theorem
The Angle-Angle-Side Congruence Theorem states that if two angles and the non-included side of one triangle are congruent to two angles and the non-included side of another triangle, then the triangles are congruent.

Inscribed Angle Theorem
The Inscribed Angle Theorem states that the measure of an inscribed angle is half the measure of its intercepted arc.

Proof Positive
Forms of Proof

Warm Up

Determine each unknown measure.

1.

97°
x°

2.
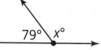
79° x°

3.
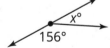
x°
156°

Learning Goals

- Recognize postulates as building blocks of proofs.
- Apply real number properties to angle measures, line segments, and distances.
- Prove theorems involving angles.
- Complete a flow chart proof.
- Complete a two-column proof.
- Complete a paragraph proof.

Key Terms

- Addition Property of Equality
- Subtraction Property of Equality
- Reflexive Property
- Substitution Property
- Transitive Property
- flow chart proof
- two-column proof
- Right Angle Congruence Postulate
- Congruent Supplement Theorem
- Vertical Angle Theorem
- paragraph proof

You have used observations to conjecture that vertical angles are congruent. How can you use definitions, properties, and postulates to prove your conjecture?

Infinite Regression

Think back on the conjecture you made in a previous topic that vertical angles are congruent. You made this conjecture based on the angle measures formed by two perpendicular diameters of a circle because you knew each angle measured 90°. What if you didn't know the angle measures formed by two intersecting lines? How do you prove that vertical angles are always congruent?

Consider $\overleftrightarrow{AB}$ and $\overleftrightarrow{CD}$ that intersect at point E.

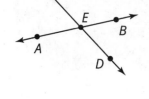

1. **What is the sum of m∠AEC and m∠CEB?**

2. **How do you know that these pairs of angles are supplementary?**

3. **How do you know that m∠AEC + m∠CEB = m∠AEB?**

4. **How do you know your reasoning to Question 3 is true?**

These questions can seem to never end. That's why mathematicians have agreed upon postulates in Euclidean geometry. There needs to be a starting point from which you can prove your conjectures.

You previously made conjectures about the sum of the measures of two angles and of two arcs. These conjectures are actually postulates. You were introduced to the following postulates in a previous topic, and they will come in handy as you begin to prove your conjectures.

Postulate	Statement
Angle Addition Postulate	If point D lies in the interior of $\angle ABC$, then m$\angle ABD$ + m$\angle DBC$ = m$\angle ABC$.
Linear Pair Postulate	If two angles form a linear pair, then the angles are supplementary.
Segment Addition Postulate	If point B is on $\overline{AC}$ and between points A and C, then $AB + BC = AC$ or m$\overline{AB}$ + m$\overline{BC}$ = m$\overline{AC}$.

Properties of Real Numbers in Geometry

Many properties of real numbers can be applied in geometry. These properties are important when making conjectures and proving new theorems.

Property	Statement
Addition Property of Equality	If a, b, and c are real numbers and $a = b$, then $a + c = b + c$.
Subtraction Property of Equality	If a, b, and c are real numbers and $a = b$, then $a - c = b - c$.
Reflexive Property	If a is a real number, then $a = a$.
Substitution Property	If a and b are real numbers and $a = b$, then a can be substituted for b.
Transitive Property	If a, b, and c are real numbers, $a = b$, and $b = c$, then $a = c$.

1. **Give algebraic examples of each property using numbers and variables.**

The Addition Property of Equality can be applied to angle measures, segment measures, and distances.

> ### Worked Example
>
> Angle measures:
> If $m\angle 1 = m\angle 3$,
> then $m\angle 1 + m\angle 2 = m\angle 3 + m\angle 2$.
>
>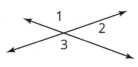
>
> Segment measures:
> If $m\overline{AB} = m\overline{CD}$,
> then $m\overline{AB} + m\overline{BC} = m\overline{BC} + m\overline{CD}$.
>
>
>
> Distances:
> If $AB = CD$, then $AB + BC = BC + CD$.

Notice the symbols used to represent measures of angles and segments. Distance is a numerical measurement that does not require the use of additional symbols.

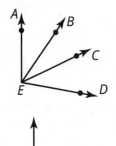

2. Consider each diagram and write a statement that applies each property to angle measures.

   a. Subtraction Property of Equality

   b. Reflexive Property

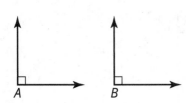

   c. Substitution Property

   d. Transitive Property

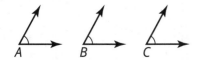

3. Consider each diagram and write a statement that applies each property to segment measures.

   a. Subtraction Property of Equality

   b. Reflexive Property

   c. Substitution Property

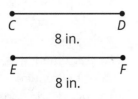

8 in.

8 in.

   d. Transitive Property

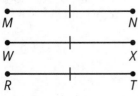

A proof is a logical series of statements and corresponding reasons that starts with a hypothesis and arrives at a conclusion. There is more than one way to organize a proof.

The diagram shows four collinear points A, B, C, and D such that point B lies between points A and C, point C lies between points B and D, and $\overline{AB} \cong \overline{CD}$.

Consider the conditional statement: If $\overline{AB} \cong \overline{CD}$, then $\overline{AC} \cong \overline{BD}$. When you begin the proof process, you take the parts of a conditional statement and organize them into "Given" and "Prove" statements.

1. **Kevin wrote the conditional statement shown. Explain how he decided which statement is given and which needs to be proved.**

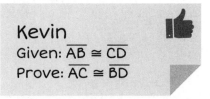

Kevin
Given: $\overline{AB} \cong \overline{CD}$
Prove: $\overline{AC} \cong \overline{BD}$

> You have used the Modeling Process to solve problems in previous courses. This structure can be used to guide your reasoning as you prove geometric theorems.

> **Notice and Wonder**
> What do you notice about the line segments in the diagram? Do you wonder if there are more pairs of congruent segments?

Organize and Mathematize

To organize your proof, analyze the conditional statement and what information is given and what information you need to prove.

2. For each conditional statement, write the hypothesis as the "Given" and the conclusion as the "Prove."

   a. m∠DEG + m∠GEF = 180°, if ∠DEG and ∠GEF are a linear pair.

      Given:

      Prove:

   b. If ∠ABD and ∠DBC are complementary, then $\overrightarrow{BA} \perp \overrightarrow{BC}$.

      Given:

      Prove:

   c. If ∠2 and ∠3 are vertical angles, then ∠2 ≅ ∠3.

      Given:

      Prove:

You can reason about the proof of conditional statements using constructions. Consider the conditional statement from Question 1:
If $\overline{AB} \cong \overline{CD}$, then $\overline{AC} \cong \overline{BD}$.

Predict and Analyze
Think about how you might reason from the given statement to the conclusion. Create or analyze diagrams and consider how they can be used to plan your proof. In geometry, this step of the modeling process can be thought of as **Draw and Deduce.**

3. **What constructions do you need to prove the conclusion of the conditional statement? Explain your reasoning.**

4. **Use the diagram and constructions to reason about the validity of the conditional statement.**

You can also use the postulates and properties you have learned so far to create different forms of proof. A **flow chart proof** is a proof in which the statement and reason for each step are written in boxes. Arrows connect the boxes and indicate how each step and reason is generated from one or more other steps and reasons.

A flow chart does not always fall in a straight line of reasoning.

Test and Interpret
Create a logical
sequence of
statements and
reasons to prove
the hypothesis.

Worked Example

You can complete a flow chart proof of the conditional statement:
If $\overline{AB} \cong \overline{CD}$, then $\overline{AC} \cong \overline{BD}$.

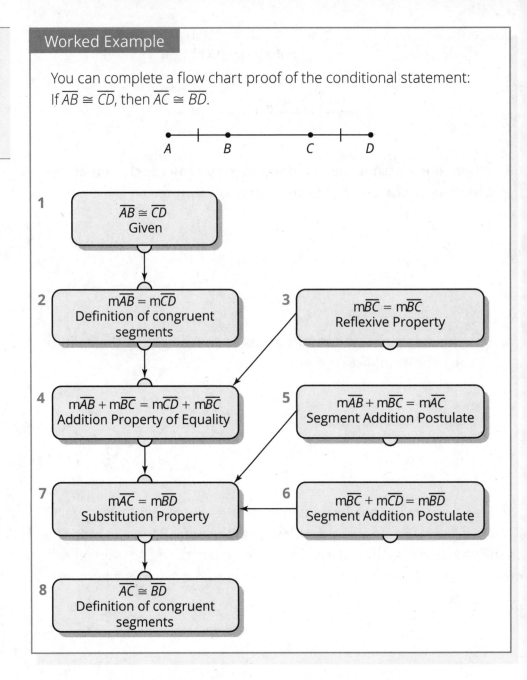

1 $\overline{AB} \cong \overline{CD}$
Given

2 $m\overline{AB} = m\overline{CD}$
Definition of congruent
segments

3 $m\overline{BC} = m\overline{BC}$
Reflexive Property

4 $m\overline{AB} + m\overline{BC} = m\overline{CD} + m\overline{BC}$
Addition Property of Equality

5 $m\overline{AB} + m\overline{BC} = m\overline{AC}$
Segment Addition Postulate

7 $m\overline{AC} = m\overline{BD}$
Substitution Property

6 $m\overline{BC} + m\overline{CD} = m\overline{BD}$
Segment Addition Postulate

8 $\overline{AC} \cong \overline{BD}$
Definition of congruent
segments

5. **Why is Step 2 of the flow chart proof critical in getting from the hypothesis to the conclusion?**

6. **Why does Step 8 follow Step 7?**

7. **Is there more than one correct way to order these statements and reasons? Explain your reasoning.**

A **two-column proof** is a proof in which the steps are written in the left column and the corresponding reasons are written in the right column. Each step and corresponding reason are numbered.

Worked Example

You can rewrite your flow chart proof in a two-column format.

Statements	Reasons
1. $\overline{AB} \cong \overline{CD}$	1. Given
2. $m\overline{AB} = m\overline{CD}$	2. Definition of congruent segments
3. $m\overline{BC} = m\overline{BC}$	3. Reflexive Property
4. $m\overline{AB} + m\overline{BC} = m\overline{CD} + m\overline{BC}$	4. Addition Property of Equality
5. $m\overline{AB} + m\overline{BC} = m\overline{AC}$	5. Segment Addition Postulate
6. $m\overline{BC} + m\overline{CD} = m\overline{BD}$	6. Segment Addition Postulate
7. $m\overline{AC} = m\overline{BD}$	7. Substitution Property
8. $\overline{AC} \cong \overline{BD}$	8. Definition of congruent segments

8. **How does the two-column proof relate to the flow chart proof?**

"Q.E.D." is an abbreviation for the Latin phrase *quod erat demonstrandum*, which means *that which was to be demonstrated*. It is a notation often placed at the end of a proof to indicate its completion.

9. **Khalil insists the angle in Figure 1 is larger than the angle in Figure 2. Roy disagrees and insists both angles are the same size.**

Figure 1   **Figure 2**

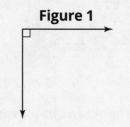

Who is correct? Justify your reasoning.

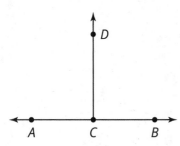

One of Euclid's first five postulates relates to right angles. The Right Angle Congruence Postulate states: "All right angles are congruent." While this statement is accepted without proof, definitions can be used to prove it.

Given: $\angle ACD$ and $\angle BCD$ are right angles.

Prove: $\angle ACD \cong \angle BCD$

10. **Complete the flow chart of the Right Angle Congruence Postulate by selecting a reason from the word bank for each statement shown and writing it in the correct step.**

Reasons
Definition of congruent angles

Definition of right angles

Given

Transitive Property of Equality

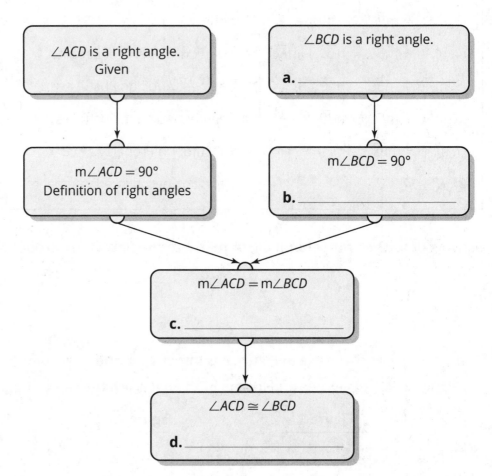

$\angle ACD$ is a right angle.
Given

$\angle BCD$ is a right angle.
a. _____

$m\angle ACD = 90°$
Definition of right angles

$m\angle BCD = 90°$
b. _____

$m\angle ACD = m\angle BCD$
c. _____

$\angle ACD \cong \angle BCD$
d. _____

11. **Why is the order of the steps important in a flow chart or two-column proof?**

ACTIVITY 1.3

Proofs of the Congruent Supplement Theorem

Considering what you know about angles, you might conjecture that if two angles are supplements of the same angle or of congruent angles, then the angles are congruent. Let's prove that this conjecture is true.

1. **Use the diagram to write the "Given" statements for the Congruent Supplement Theorem. The "Prove" statement is provided.**

   Given:

   Given:

   Given:

   Prove: ∠1 ≅ ∠3

2. **Cut out and use the statements and reasons located at the end of the lesson to complete the flow chart to prove the conjecture.**

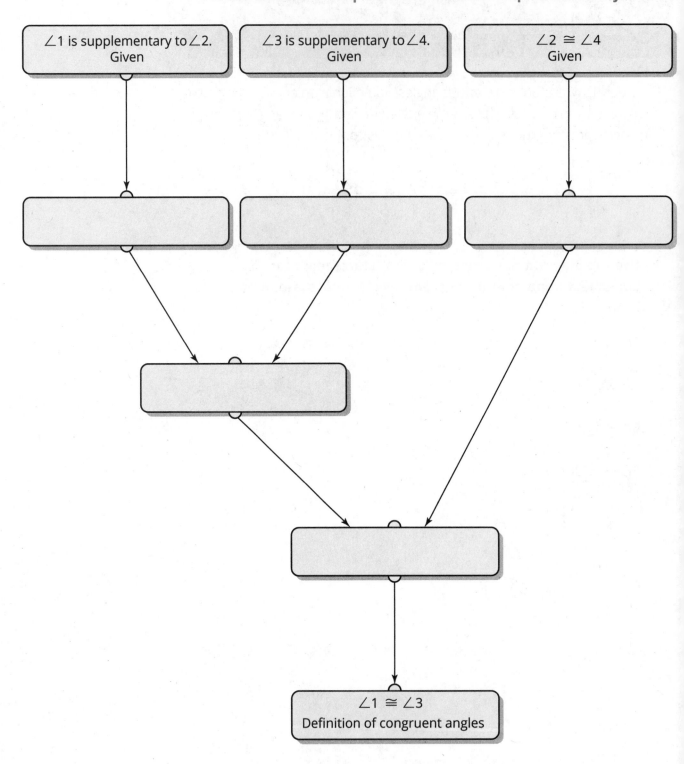

∠1 is supplementary to ∠2.
Given

∠3 is supplementary to ∠4.
Given

∠2 ≅ ∠4
Given

∠1 ≅ ∠3
Definition of congruent angles

3. **Create a two-column proof of the conjecture. Each box of the flow chart you completed should appear as a row in the two-column proof.**

Statements	Reasons
1. ∠1 is supplementary to ∠2.	1. Given
2. ∠3 is supplementary to ∠4.	2. Given
3. ∠2 ≅ ∠4	3. Given
4.	4.
5.	5.
6.	6.
7.	7.
8.	8.
9. ∠1 ≅ ∠3	9. Definition of congruent angles

Because you have proved that this conjecture is true, you may now refer to it as a theorem. The **Congruent Supplement Theorem** states: "If two angles are supplements of the same angle or of congruent angles, then the angles are congruent."

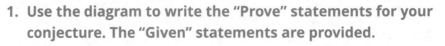

ACTIVITY 1.4
Proofs of the Vertical Angle Theorem

Now that you have studied different forms of proof, you can use the properties and postulates you know to prove the conjecture you made about vertical angles in a previous topic. You conjectured that vertical angles are congruent.

1. **Use the diagram to write the "Prove" statements for your conjecture. The "Given" statements are provided.**

Given: ∠1 and ∠2 are a linear pair.

Given: ∠2 and ∠3 are a linear pair.

Given: ∠2 and ∠3 are a linear pair.

Given: ∠3 and ∠4 are a linear pair.

Prove:

Prove:

Analyze the flow chart proof for one of the prove statements.

Worked Example

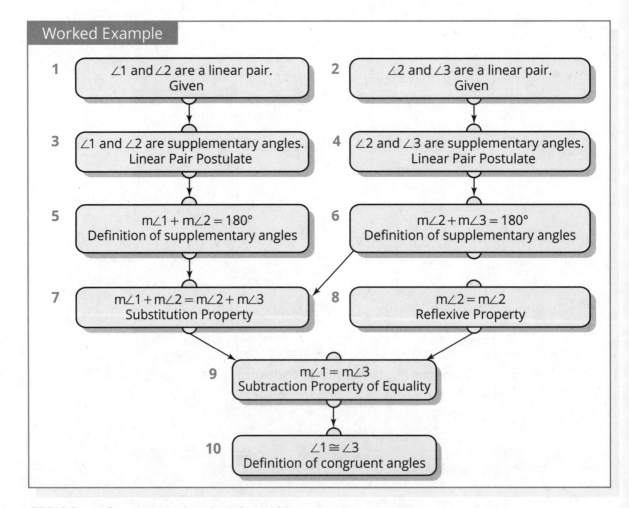

1. ∠1 and ∠2 are a linear pair.
   Given

2. ∠2 and ∠3 are a linear pair.
   Given

3. ∠1 and ∠2 are supplementary angles.
   Linear Pair Postulate

4. ∠2 and ∠3 are supplementary angles.
   Linear Pair Postulate

5. $m\angle 1 + m\angle 2 = 180°$
   Definition of supplementary angles

6. $m\angle 2 + m\angle 3 = 180°$
   Definition of supplementary angles

7. $m\angle 1 + m\angle 2 = m\angle 2 + m\angle 3$
   Substitution Property

8. $m\angle 2 = m\angle 2$
   Reflexive Property

9. $m\angle 1 = m\angle 3$
   Subtraction Property of Equality

10. $\angle 1 \cong \angle 3$
    Definition of congruent angles

2. Could Step 5 come before Step 3? Explain your reasoning.

3. What is the purpose of Step 8?

4. What steps would be different in a flow chart proof of the second prove statement of the Vertical Angle Theorem?

Because your conjecture has been proved to be true, you can now refer to it as a theorem. The **Vertical Angle Theorem** states: "Vertical angles are congruent."

Once a theorem has been proved, it can be used as a reason in another proof. Using theorems that have already been proved allows you to write shorter proofs.

5. Create a two-column proof for the other prove statement using the Congruent Supplement Theorem.

Statements	Reasons

Remember:

The Congruent Supplement Theorem states: "If two angles are supplements of the same angle, or of congruent angles, then the angles are congruent."

Keep a list of
theorems that you
prove throughout this
course. It will be an
excellent resource as
you continue to make
new conjectures and
expand your system
of geometry.

In this topic, you proved a postulate and two theorems.
- The Right Angle Congruence Postulate: "All right angles are congruent."
- The Congruent Supplement Theorem: "Supplements of congruent angles, or of the same angle, are congruent."
- The Vertical Angle Theorem: "Vertical angles are congruent."

Once you have proved a theorem, you know that it is true in all
instances. You can apply these theorems to determine unknown
geometric measures.

1. In the figure shown, $\overleftrightarrow{AB}$ intersects $\overleftrightarrow{CD}$ at point *E*. Determine
   m∠*AED*. Explain how you determined the angle measure.

Ask

yourself:

What is the name
of the angle whose
measure you want
to know?

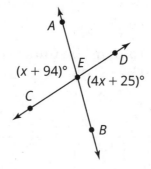

2. In the figure shown, $\overleftrightarrow{PQ}$ intersects $\overleftrightarrow{SR}$ at point *T*. Determine
   each angle measure. Explain how you determined the angle
   measure.

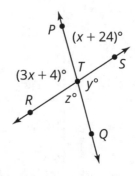

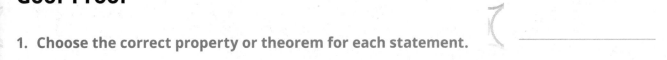

TALK the TALK 💬

Goof-Proof

1. Choose the correct property or theorem for each statement.

a. $\angle H \cong \angle K$
    $\angle K \cong \angle M$
    Therefore $\angle H \cong \angle M$

Property or Theorem
Addition Property of Equality
Congruent Supplement Theorem
Reflexive Property
Substitution
Transitive Property
Vertical Angle Theorem

b. $m\overline{MN} = m\overline{OP}$
    $m\overline{MN} + m\overline{RS} = m\overline{OP} + m\overline{RS}$

c. $m\angle T = 34°$
    $m\angle W = 34°$
    Therefore $m\angle T = m\angle W$

d. $m\angle A + m\angle B = 180°$
    $m\angle A + m\angle C = 180°$
    Therefore $\angle B \cong \angle C$

e. $m\angle V = m\angle V$

f. $\angle 1 \cong \angle 2$

Consider circle O with diameters $\overline{AC}$ and $\overline{BD}$.

2. What do you know about $\overset{\frown}{AB}$ and $\overset{\frown}{CD}$?

You have used reasoning through constructions, flow chart proofs, and two-column proofs to prove theorems. Another type of proof is a **paragraph proof,** in which the statements and corresponding reasons are written in complete sentences.

3. Use a paragraph proof to prove $\overset{\frown}{AB} \cong \overset{\frown}{CD}$.

Statements and Reasons for the Congruent Supplement Theorem Proof

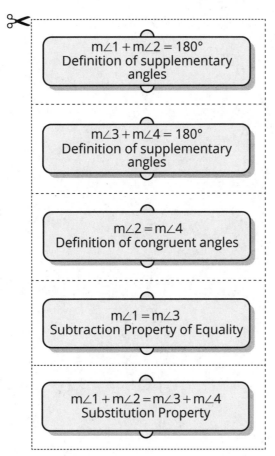

$m\angle 1 + m\angle 2 = 180°$
Definition of supplementary angles

$m\angle 3 + m\angle 4 = 180°$
Definition of supplementary angles

$m\angle 2 = m\angle 4$
Definition of congruent angles

$m\angle 1 = m\angle 3$
Subtraction Property of Equality

$m\angle 1 + m\angle 2 = m\angle 3 + m\angle 4$
Substitution Property

Assignment

Write

Describe the differences between a flow chart proof, a two-column proof, and a paragraph proof in your own words.

Remember

A proof is a logical series of statements and corresponding reasons that starts with a hypothesis and arrives at a conclusion. There is more than one way to organize a proof.

Practice

1. Identify the property that justifies each statement.
    a. If $\overline{AB} \cong \overline{PR}$ and $\overline{PR} \cong \overline{ST}$, then $\overline{AB} \cong \overline{ST}$.
    b. If $JK = 6$ centimeters and $CD = 6$ centimeters, then $JK = CD$.
    c. $\angle ABC \cong \angle ABC$
    d. If $m\angle 3 = m\angle 1$, then $m\angle 3 + m\angle 2 = m\angle 1 + m\angle 2$.

2. Enter the reasons to complete the two-column proof.

    Given: $\angle 1 \cong \angle 4$
    Prove: $\angle 2 \cong \angle 3$

    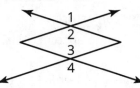

Statements	Reasons
1. $\angle 1 \cong \angle 4$	1. Given
2. $\angle 4 \cong \angle 3$	2.
3. $\angle 1 \cong \angle 2$	3.
4. $\angle 1 \cong \angle 3$	4.
5. $\angle 2 \cong \angle 3$	5. Transitive Property

3. Write a paragraph proof to prove the statement.

    Given: $m\angle QRS = 90°$
    Given: $\angle RTS \cong \angle QRT$
    Prove: $\angle RTS$ and $\angle TRS$ are complementary.

    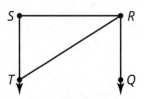

4. In the figure, $\angle GXF \cong \angle CXD$.

    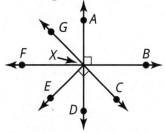

    a. What theorem tells you that $\angle AXG \cong \angle CXD$?
    b. What theorem tells you that $\angle EXF \cong \angle EXD$?
    c. What theorem tells you that $\angle GXD \cong \angle CXF$?

Stretch

Create a two-column proof.

Given: $\angle A$ and $\angle B$ are complementary.

Prove: $\angle C$ and $\angle D$ are complementary.

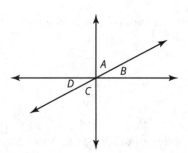

Review

1. Use a compass and straightedge to construct the incenter of $\triangle ABC$.

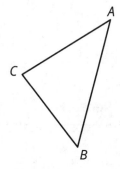

2. Use a compass and straightedge to construct the circumcenter of $\triangle XY\,Z$.

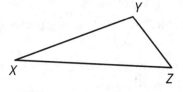

3. Write a conjecture about corresponding angles. Draw an example to test your conjecture.

4. Draw an example of an inscribed angle and a central angle that intercepts the same arc of a circle. What conjecture can you make about the measure of the inscribed angle?

5. Determine whether each pair of triangles is congruent. If so, state whether they are congruent by SSS, SAS, or ASA. If not, explain why.

a.

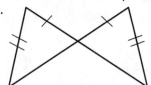

b.

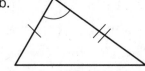

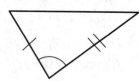

A Parallel Universe

Proving Parallel Line Theorems

Warm Up

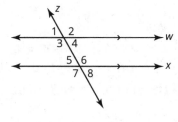

1. Identify the corresponding angles.

2. Identify the alternate interior angles.

3. Identify the vertical angles.

4. Identify the linear pairs.

Learning Goals

- Prove the Corresponding Angles Theorem, the Same-Side Interior Angles Theorem, the Alternate Interior Angles Theorem, and their converses.
- Demonstrate understanding of the Alternate Exterior Angles Theorem, the Same-Side Exterior Angles Theorem, and their converses.
- Prove the Perpendicular/Parallel Line Theorem.
- Write a proof plan to help connect mathematical statements using deductive reasoning.

Key Terms

- Corresponding Angles Theorem
- Corresponding Angles Converse Theorem
- Same-Side Interior Angles Theorem
- Alternate Interior Angles Theorem
- Alternate Exterior Angles Theorem
- Same-Side Exterior Angles Theorem
- Alternate Interior Angles Converse Theorem
- Same-Side Interior Angles Converse Theorem
- Alternate Exterior Angles Converse Theorem
- Perpendicular/Parallel Line Theorem

You already know about special angle pairs produced by parallel lines cut by a transversal. How do you know that these relationships are true in all cases?

Criss Cross Applesauce

You may recall that you can use translations to show that corresponding angles are congruent.

1. **Consider parallel lines *m* and *n* with a pair of corresponding angles, ∠A and ∠B.**

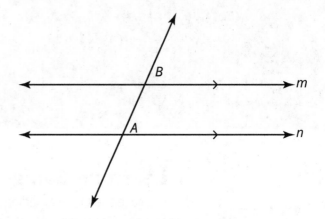

   a. **Use patty paper to translate one of the corresponding angles so that it lies on top of the other corresponding angle. Identify the line of translation and describe the distance and direction of the translation.**

   b. **What does this translation demonstrate about corresponding angles?**

2. **Describe how you can use a patty paper translation and what you know about vertical angles to demonstrate that alternate interior angles are congruent.**

Let's use translations to prove the conjecture that when parallel lines are cut by a transversal, corresponding angles are congruent. Consider these three properties of translations when formulating a proof:

- Line segments are taken to line segments of the same length.
- Angles are taken to angles of the same measure.
- A translated line is either identical to the original line or parallel to it.

1. **The given diagram shows ∠ABC.**

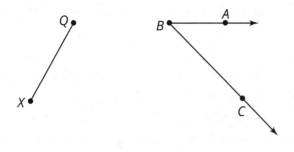

a. **Draw the translation T_{QX}(∠ABC). Label points A', B', and C'.**

b. **Identify a pair of parallel lines. How do you know the lines are parallel?**

c. **Draw transversal $\overline{BB'}$. Identify a pair of corresponding angles. How do you know the corresponding angles are congruent?**

Remember:

The notation T_{QX}(∠ABC) means to translate ∠ABC along a line parallel to $\overline{QX}$ in the direction and distance from point Q to point X.

2. **Use your work in Question 1 and the properties of translations to write a paragraph proof to demonstrate that two parallel lines intersected by a transversal create corresponding angles that are congruent.**

Because your conjecture has been proved to be true, you can now refer to it as a theorem. The **Corresponding Angles Theorem** states: "If two parallel lines are intersected by a transversal, then corresponding angles are congruent."

Recall that the converse of a theorem is created by interchanging the hypothesis and conclusion of the original theorem. Let's conjecture that the converse is also true. In other words, if two lines intersected by a transversal form congruent corresponding angles, then the lines are parallel.

3. **Show how you can use translations to demonstrate that the converse conjecture is true.**

Remember:

When a conditional statement and its converse are both true, this is called a biconditional statement. A biconditional statement is a statement written in the form "if and only if p, then q."

Because your conjecture has been proved to be true, you can now refer to it as a theorem. The **Corresponding Angles Converse Theorem** states: "If two lines intersected by a transversal form congruent corresponding angles, then the lines are parallel."

Now that you have proved the Corresponding Angles Theorem, you can use this theorem in future reasoning. The theorem can be used, for example, to prove other relationships regarding angles formed by parallel lines and a transversal. Let's prove your conjecture that if two parallel lines are intersected by a transversal, then the interior angles on the same side of the transversal are supplementary.

Consider the Given and Prove statements and the diagram.

Given: $w \parallel x$ and z is a transversal.

Prove: Same-side interior angles are supplementary angles.

1. **Cut out and use the statements and reasons located at the end of the lesson to prove your conjecture. Organize the statements and reasons to form a flow-chart proof of this theorem.**

Because your conjecture has been proved to be true, you can now refer to it as a theorem. The **Same-Side Interior Angles Theorem** states, "If two parallel lines are intersected by a transversal, then the interior angles on the same side of the transversal are supplementary."

ACTIVITY 2.3 | Alternate Interior Angles Theorem

A helpful technique you can use to write proofs is to start by writing a proof plan. When you write a proof plan, you use a combination of your own words and mathematical language to describe how you connect the given statement to the prove statement using postulates and theorems you have already proved. When you write a proof plan, you can test it and fill in missing steps before you write the actual proof.

Consider, for example, the conjecture you made earlier regarding alternate interior angles. You conjectured that if two parallel lines are intersected by a transversal, then the alternate interior angles are congruent.

Given: $w \parallel x$ and z is a transversal.
Prove: Alternate interior angles are congruent.

1. **Analyze Abelina's and Madison's proof plans.**

Abelina	Madison
I'll show that alternate interior angles 4 and 5 are congruent. It's given that the two lines are parallel and are cut by a transversal, so I know that angles 4 and 6 are supplementary, because they are same-side interior angles. And angles 5 and 6 are supplementary, because they are a linear pair. So, $m\angle 4 + m\angle 6 = 180°$. But $m\angle 5 + m\angle 6$ is also equal to 180°. That means that angles 4 and 5 have to have the same measure.	I need to prove that angles 3 and 6 are congruent, which means they have the same measure. The Given states that the lines are parallel and cut by a transversal, so angles 2 and 6 are congruent, because they are corresponding. But angles 2 and 3 are congruent too, because they are vertical angles. If $\angle 3$ and $\angle 6$ are both congruent to the same angle $\angle 2$, then they must be congruent to each other.

a. **Which proof plan is correct? Justify your answer.**

b. **List the definitions, postulates, and theorems Abelina and Madison use in their proof plans. Explain your reasoning.**

c. **Use Madison's proof plan to complete the flow chart proof of the Alternate Interior Angle Theorem by writing the reason for each statement in the boxes.**

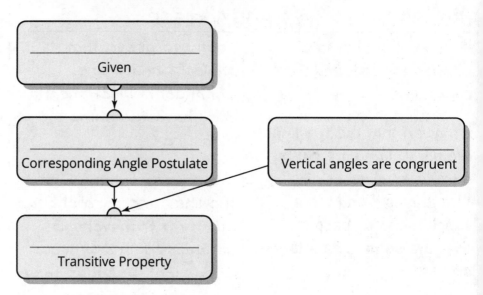

d. **Use Abelina's proof plan to create a two-column proof.**

Statements	Reasons

Because your conjecture has been proved to be true, you can now refer to it as a theorem. The **Alternate Interior Angles Theorem** states: "If two parallel lines are intersected by a transversal, then the alternate interior angles are congruent."

You also conjectured about other relationships regarding angles formed by parallel lines and a transversal.

You conjectured that if two parallel lines are intersected by a transversal, then the alternate exterior angles are congruent.

You also conjectured that if two parallel lines are intersected by a transversal, then the same-side exterior angles are supplementary.

2. **Draw diagrams for these theorems and then write a proof plan for each.**

Because your proof plans demonstrate that the statements can be proved true, you can now refer to these as theorems. The **Alternate Exterior Angles Theorem** states: "If two parallel lines are intersected by a transversal, then the alternate exterior angles are congruent." The **Same-Side Exterior Angles Theorem** states: "If two parallel lines are intersected by a transversal, then the same-side exterior angles are supplementary."

ACTIVITY 2.4 Parallel Line Converse Theorems

Earlier, you proved the Corresponding Angles Converse Theorem. You can use that theorem to prove the converse of other parallel line theorems.

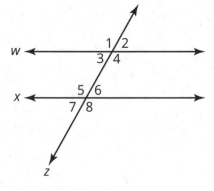

1. **Write the converse of the Alternate Interior Angle Theorem.**

2. **Use the diagram to write the given and prove statements for your converse statement. Then prove that this relationship exists in all cases.**

Because your converse statement has been proved to be true, you can now refer to it as a theorem. The **Alternate Interior Angles Converse Theorem** states: "If two lines intersected by a transversal form congruent alternate interior angles, then the lines are parallel."

3. **Write the converse of the Same-Side Interior Angles Theorem.**

4. **Use the diagram to write the given and prove statements for your converse statement. Then prove that this relationship exists in all cases.**

Because your converse statement has been proved to be true, you can now refer to it as a theorem. The **Same-Side Interior Angles Converse Theorem** states: "If two lines intersected by a transversal form supplementary same-side interior angles, then the lines are parallel."

5. Consider the exterior angles theorems.

   a. Write the converse of the Alternate Exterior Angles Theorem. Draw a diagram and write a proof plan.

   b. Write the converse of the Same-Side Exterior Angles Theorem. Draw a diagram and write a proof plan.

Because your proof plan demonstrates that the converse statement can be proved true, you can now refer to it as a theorem. There are other converse theorems that you can show to be true using what you know. The **Alternate Exterior Angles Converse Theorem** states: "If two lines intersected by a transversal form congruent alternate exterior angles, then the lines are parallel." The **Same-Side Exterior Angles Converse Theorem** states: "If two lines intersected by a transversal form supplementary same-side exterior angles, then the lines are parallel."

You can extend what you have proven about parallel line converse theorems to prove a theorem about parallel lines cut by a perpendicular transversal.

1. **Ramira says that if two lines are perpendicular to the same line, then the two lines are parallel to each other. Is Ramira correct? If she is correct, complete the proof to justify the reasoning, or state why she is not correct.**

   Given: $\ell_1 \perp \ell_3$ and $\ell_2 \perp \ell_3$
   Prove: $\ell_1 \parallel \ell_2$

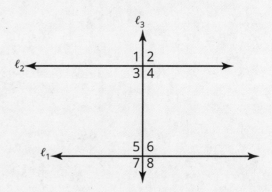

Because Ramira's conjecture has been proved to be true, you can now refer to it as a theorem. The **Perpendicular/Parallel Line Theorem** states: "If two lines are perpendicular to the same line, then the two lines are parallel to each other."

TALK the TALK

If 'N' Then Again

In this lesson you proved theorems about lines and angles.
- Corresponding Angles Theorem
- Corresponding Angles Converse Theorem
- Same-Side Interior Angles Theorem
- Same-Side Interior Angles Converse Theorem
- Alternate Interior Angles Theorem
- Alternate Interior Angles Converse Theorem
- Same-Side Exterior Angles Theorem
- Same-Side Exterior Angles Converse Theorem
- Alternate Exterior Angles Theorem
- Alternate Exterior Angles Converse Theorem
- Perpendicular/Parallel Line Theorem

1. Determine the theorem that justifies each if-then statement.

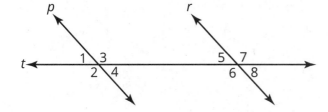

a. **If line *p* is parallel to line *r*, then ∠2 ≅ ∠7.**

b. **If line *p* is parallel to line *r*, then ∠4 ≅ ∠5.**

c. **If ∠3 ≅ ∠6, the line *p* is parallel to line *r*.**

d. **If line *p* is parallel to line *r*, then ∠1 ≅ ∠5.**

e. **If line *p* is parallel to line *r*, then m∠4 + m∠6 = 180°.**

f. **If line *p* is parallel to line *r*, then m∠1 + m∠7 = 180°.**

g. **If ∠3 + ∠5 = 180°, then line *p* is parallel to line *r*.**

NOTES

2. Gail determined the measures of all eight angles labeled using the given information. Stu said she could only calculate the measure of four angles with certainty.

Given: m∠4 = 37°

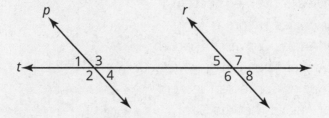

Who is correct? Explain your reasoning.

Statements and Reasons for the Same-Side Interior Angles Theorem Proof

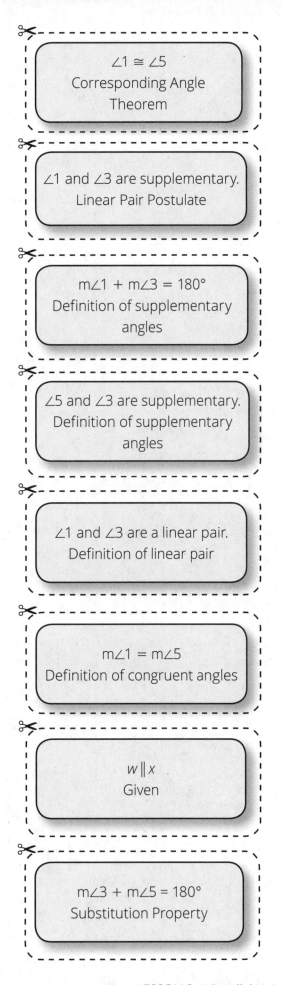

∠1 ≅ ∠5
Corresponding Angle Theorem

∠1 and ∠3 are supplementary.
Linear Pair Postulate

m∠1 + m∠3 = 180°
Definition of supplementary angles

∠5 and ∠3 are supplementary.
Definition of supplementary angles

∠1 and ∠3 are a linear pair.
Definition of linear pair

m∠1 = m∠5
Definition of congruent angles

$w \parallel x$
Given

m∠3 + m∠5 = 180°
Substitution Property

Assignment

Write

Write the converse of each postulate or theorem.

1. Alternate Interior Angle Theorem:

   "If two parallel lines are intersected by a transversal, then alternate interior angles are congruent."

2. Alternate Exterior Angle Theorem:

   "If two parallel lines are intersected by a transversal, then alternate exterior angles are congruent."

3. Same-Side Interior Angle Theorem:

   "If two parallel lines are intersected by a transversal, then same-side interior angles are supplementary."

4. Same-Side Exterior Angle Theorem:

   "If two parallel lines are intersected by a transversal, then same-side exterior angles are supplementary."

Remember

If two parallel lines are intersected by a transversal, then:

- Corresponding angles are congruent.
- Alternate interior angles are congruent.
- Alternate exterior angles are congruent.
- Same-side interior angles are supplementary.
- Same-side exterior angles are supplementary.

Practice

1. Consider the diagram shown. Determine which theorem leads to the conclusion that $c \parallel w$ for each statement.

   a. $\angle 3 \cong \angle 7$

   b. $\angle 5$ and $\angle 8$ are supplementary

   c. $\angle 4 \cong \angle 8$

   d. $\angle 2$ and $\angle 3$ are supplementary

Given: $\angle 2 \cong \angle 7 \cong \angle 19$, $m\angle 2 = 125°$

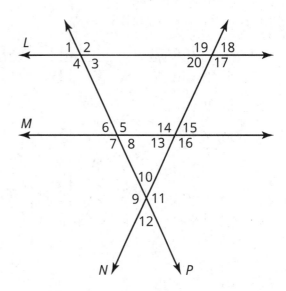

2. Using the diagram in conjunction with postulates and theorems, determine the measure of all unknown angles.

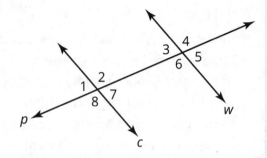

Stretch
Prove the conditional statement using any method you choose.

Given: $\angle DEG \cong \angle HEF$

Prove: $\angle DEH \cong \angle GEF$

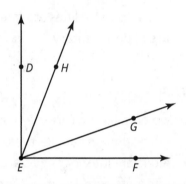

Review
1. Identify the property that justifies the statement: If $m\angle A = m\angle B$, then $m\angle A + m\angle C = m\angle B - m\angle C$.
2. Enter the reasons to complete the two-column proof.

   Given: $m\angle 1 = m\angle 3$

   Prove: $m\angle WXZ = m\angle YXV$

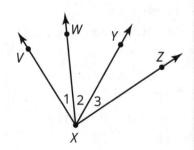

Statement	Reasons
1. $m\angle 1 = m\angle 3$	1. Given
2. $m\angle WXZ = m\angle 3 + m\angle 2$	2.
3. $m\angle WXZ = m\angle 1 + m\angle 2$	3.
4. $m\angle 1 + m\angle 2 = m\angle YXV$	4.
5. $m\angle WXZ = m\angle YXV$	5. Substitution Property

3. State as many properties as you can about a rhombus.

4. Describe how to construct rhombus *JKLM* given diagonal *JL*.

5. Determine whether each pair of triangles is congruent. If so, state whether they are congruent by SSS, SAS, or ASA. If not, explain why.

a.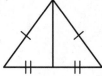

b.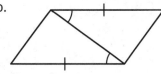

Ins and Outs

Interior and Exterior Angles of Polygons

Warm Up

Determine each unknown angle measure.

1.

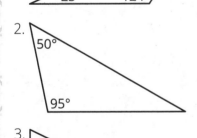

2.

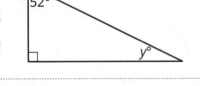

3.

Learning Goals

- Prove that the measures of interior angles of a triangle sum to 180°.
- Derive a formula for the sums of the measures of interior angles of a polygon.
- Derive a formula for the sums of the measures of exterior angles of a polygon.

Key Terms

- Triangle Sum Theorem
- Exterior Angle Theorem

You have made conjectures about the measures of the interior angles of triangles. How can you prove theorems about interior and exterior angle measures in polygons with any number of sides?

Rippy Bits

You have made conjectures about the angles of triangles and quadrilaterals. Let's start with an informal proof about the interior angles of a triangle.

1. **Draw any triangle on a piece of paper and cut it out. Tear off the triangle's three angles. Arrange the angles so that they are adjacent angles.**

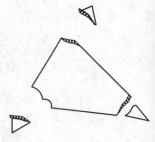

2. **What do you notice about the sum of these three angles?**

Triangle Sum and Exterior Angle Theorems

The angles you tore off of the triangle form a straight angle, or a line. Let's use a line to help prove that the sum of the interior angles of a triangle is equal to 180°.

1. Consider the diagram shown.

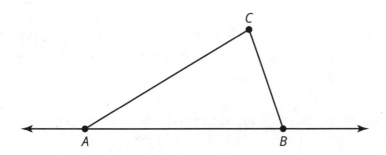

a. **Draw an auxiliary line parallel to $\overleftrightarrow{AB}$ through point C. Identify the three adjacent angles at point C that form a line.**

> Remember, an auxiliary line is a line that is drawn to help complete a geometric proof.

b. **Write a plan to prove that the sum of the interior angles of a triangle is 180°. Then write a paragraph proof regarding this relationship.**

Think
.● about:

You can now use the Corresponding Angles Theorem and Alternate Interior Angles Theorem as reasons in your proofs because you have proved them!

Because you have proved this relationship is true, you can now refer to it as a theorem. The **Triangle Sum Theorem** states: "The sum of the measures of the interior angles of a triangle is equal to 180°.

Consider another diagram which can be used to prove the Triangle Sum Theorem.

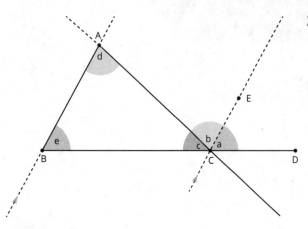

2. **Explain how the diagram demonstrates the Triangle Sum Theorem.**

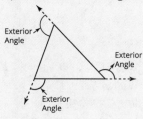

The remote interior angles of a triangle are the two angles that are not adjacent to the specified exterior angle.

It appears that a relationship exists among the angles of a triangle such that the measure of an exterior angle of a triangle is equal to the sum of the measures of the two remote interior angles.

3. **Explain how the diagram demonstrates that this relationship exists.**

Because you have demonstrated this relationship is true, you can now refer to it as a theorem. The **Exterior Angle Theorem** states: "The measure of an exterior angle of a triangle is equal to the sum of the measures of the two remote interior angles."

The Sum of the Measures of the Interior Angles of a Polygon

You have proved a theorem about the interior angles of a triangle. An interior angle of a polygon faces the inside of a polygon and is formed by consecutive sides of the polygon.

1. **Ms. Lambert asked her class to determine the sum of the measures of the interior angles of a quadrilateral. Carson drew a quadrilateral and added one diagonal as shown. He concluded that the sum of the measures of the interior angles of a quadrilateral must be equal to 360°.**

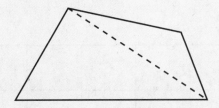

   Juno drew a quadrilateral and added two diagonals as shown. She concluded that the sum of the measures of the interior angles of a quadrilateral must be equal to 720°.

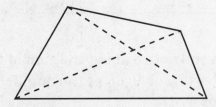

   Who is correct? Who is incorrect? Explain your reasoning.

You can use the Triangle Sum Theorem to calculate the sum of the measures of the interior angles of other polygons.

2. **Draw each polygon. Then calculate the sum of the measures of the interior angles of each polygon by drawing all possible diagonals from one vertex of the polygon. Complete the table for 3-, 4-, 5-, and 6-sided polygons.**

   a. **quadrilateral**

   b. **pentagon**

   c. **hexagon**

Number of Sides of the Polygon	3	4	5	6	7	8	9	16
Number of Diagonals Drawn	0							
Number of Triangles Formed	1							
Sum of the Measures of the Interior Angles								

3. **What pattern do you notice about the sum of the measures of the interior angles of a polygon as the number of sides of each polygon increases by 1?**

4. **Predict the number of possible diagonals drawn from one vertex and the number of triangles formed for 7-, 8-, 9-, and 16-sided polygons. Then, complete the table in Question 2. Explain your predictions.**

5. If a polygon has *n* sides, how many triangles are formed by drawing all diagonals from one vertex? Explain your reasoning.

6. What is the sum of the measures of the interior angles of an *n*-sided polygon? Explain your reasoning.

7. Use a formula to calculate the sum of the measures of the interior angles of a polygon with 32 sides.

8. If the sum of the measures of the interior angles of a polygon is 9540°, how many sides does the polygon have? Explain your reasoning.

9. Use the formula you developed to calculate the sum of the measures of the interior angles of a decagon.

10. Calculate the measure of each interior angle of a decagon if each interior angle is congruent. How did you calculate your answer?

11. Complete the table.

Number of Sides of the Regular Polygon	3	4	5	6	7	8
Sum of the Measures of the Interior Angles						
Measure of Each Interior Angle						

12. If a regular polygon has *n* sides, write a formula to calculate the measure of each interior angle.

13. Use the formula to calculate the measure of each interior angle of a regular 100-sided polygon.

14. If the measure of each interior angle of a regular polygon is equal to 150°, determine the number of sides. How did you calculate your answer?

ACTIVITY

3.3

The Sum of the Measures of the Exterior Angles of a Polygon

You wrote a formula for the sum of the measures of the interior angles of a polygon. Now let's write a formula for the sum of the measures of the exterior angles of a polygon.

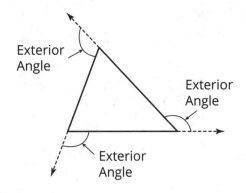

Exterior Angle

Exterior Angle

Exterior Angle

Think about:

These formulas work for convex polygons, not for concave polygons. Can you figure out why?

1. **Use the diagram, your formula for the sum of the measures of the interior angles of a polygon, and the Linear Pair Postulate to calculate the sum of the measures of the exterior angles of a triangle.**

Let's explore the sum of the measures of the exterior angles of other polygons.

2. **Draw each polygon. Then calculate the sum of the measures of the exterior angles of each polygon by extending each side of the polygon to locate an exterior angle at each vertex. Complete the table for 3-, 4-, 5-, and 6-sided polygons.**

   a. **quadrilateral**

   b. **pentagon**

   c. **hexagon**

Number of Sides of the Polygon	3	4	5	6	7	15
Number of Linear Pairs Formed						
Sum of the Measures of the Linear Pairs						
Sum of the Measures of the Interior Angles						
Sum of the Measures of the Exterior Angles						

3. What patterns do you notice?

4. Make predictions about the sum of the measures of the exterior angles of 7- and 15-sided polygons. Complete the table in Question 2.

5. What is the sum of the measures of the exterior angles of an *n*-sided polygon?

6. If the sum of the measures of the exterior angles of a polygon is 360°, how many sides does the polygon have? Explain your reasoning.

7. Calculate the measure of each angle and explain your reasoning.

    a. each exterior angle of an equilateral triangle

    b. each exterior angle of a square

    c. each exterior angle of a regular pentagon

    d. each exterior angle of a regular hexagon

8. If the measure of each exterior angle of a regular polygon is 18°, how many sides does the polygon have? Explain how you calculated your answer.

TALK the TALK

Peace Out

1. Adreene announced to the class that she could calculate the sum of the measures of the starred angles in this diagram without knowing the measure of any specific angle. How is this possible? Using theorems or postulates, explain what Adreene is thinking.

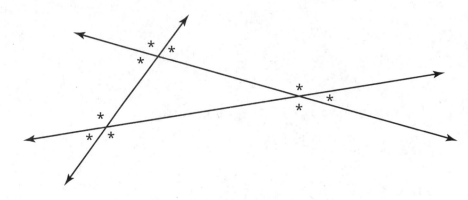

2. *PENTA* is a regular pentagon. Solve for *x*.

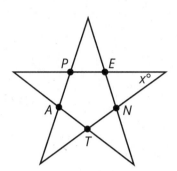

3. The Susan B. Anthony dollar coin minted in 1999 features a regular 11-gon, or hendecagon, inside a circle on both sides of the coin.

   What is the measure of each interior angle of the regular hendecagon?

4. Solve for *x* in each diagram.

a.

b.

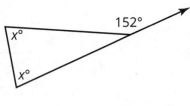

c.

d.

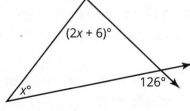

Write

Complete each statement with the correct term.

1. The _____ states that the sum of the measures of the exterior angles of a triangle is equal to 180°.
2. The sum of the measures of the _____ of a triangle is equal to the corresponding exterior angle.
3. A(n) _____ is a line drawn to help complete a proof.

Remember

The sum of the measures of the interior angles of a triangle is equal to 180°, and the sum of the measures of the interior angles of a quadrilateral is equal to 360°.

For a polygon with n sides, the sum of the measures of the interior angles is equal to $180(n - 2)$ degrees, and the sum of the measures of the exterior angles is equal to 360°.

Practice

1. Determine the measure of an interior angle of the given regular polygon.

   a. regular nonagon   b. regular 15-gon
   c. regular decagon   d. regular 47-gon

2. Determine the measure of the unknown angle in each figure.

   a.

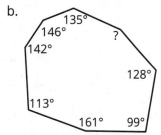

   b.

3. If a regular polygon has 30 sides, what is the measure of each exterior angle? Explain your reasoning.

4. The degree measure of each exterior angle of a regular octagon is represented by the expression $7x - 4$. Solve for x.

Stretch

1. Consider the nonagon shown.
   a. Determine the value of x.
   b. Determine the value of all the interior angles of the nonagon.

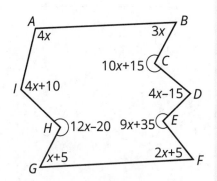

Review

1. Given: $\angle 12 \cong \angle 7$, $m\angle 12 = 65°$, $m\angle 8 = 50°$
   Using the diagram in conjunction with postulates and theorems, determine the measures of the unknown angles.

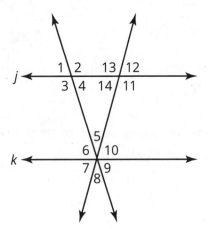

2. If $\angle 1$ and $\angle 4$ are supplementary, which theorem leads to the conclusion that $q \parallel s$?

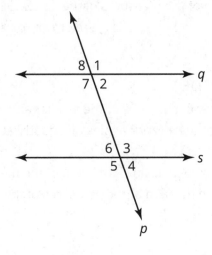

3. Write a conjecture about the angle measures of an equilateral triangle. Then, write the converse of the conjecture.

4. Use a compass and straightedge to construct the orthocenter of $\triangle ABC$.

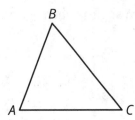

5. Determine whether each pair of triangles is congruent. If so, state whether they are congruent by SSS, SAS, or ASA. If not, explain why.

   a.

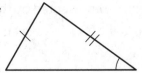

   b.

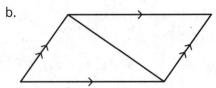

Identical Twins

Perpendicular Bisector and Isosceles Triangle Theorems

4

Warm Up

Determine each unknown measure.

1.
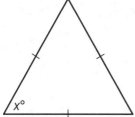

2.
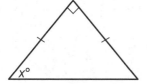

3.
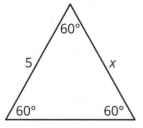

Learning Goals

- Prove that points on a perpendicular bisector of a line segment are exactly those equidistant from the segment's endpoints.
- Prove that the base angles of isosceles triangles are congruent.
- Demonstrate the 30°-60°-90° Triangle Theorem and the 45°-45°-90° Triangle Theorem using algebraic reasoning.

Key Terms

- Perpendicular Bisector Converse Theorem
- Isosceles Triangle Base Angles Theorem
- Isosceles Triangle Base Angles Converse Theorem
- 30°-60°-90° Triangle Theorem
- 45°-45°-90° Triangle Theorem
- Extract the roots
- Rationalize the denominator
- Hypotenuse-Angle (HA) Congruence Theorem
- Angle-Angle-Side (AAS) Congruence Theorem

You have conjectured about points on a perpendicular bisector and relationships between angles and sides of various triangles. How can you use definitions and theorems to prove these conjectures?

Mappings Matter

You have proven theorems related to triangle congruence. You know that two triangles are congruent when:

- Three corresponding sides are congruent (SSS).
- Two corresponding sides and the included angle are congruent (SAS).
- Two corresponding angles and the included side are congruent (ASA).

1. **Use Side-Angle-Side (SAS), Side-Side-Side (SSS), or Angle-Side-Angle (ASA) to explain why the triangles in each pair are congruent. Explain your reasoning.**

   a.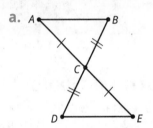

   b.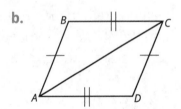

   c.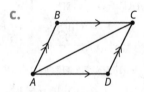

You know that if two triangles are congruent, then each part of one triangle is congruent to the corresponding part of the other triangle. Corresponding parts of congruent triangles are congruent, abbreviated CPCTC, is often used as a reason in proofs. CPCTC states that corresponding angles or sides in two congruent triangles are congruent. This reason can be used only after you have proved that the triangles are congruent.

1. **Consider △CPS and △WPD in the figure shown. Suppose $\overline{CW}$ and $\overline{SD}$ bisect each other.**

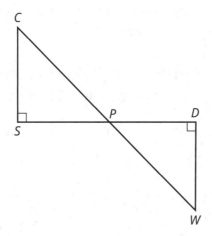

> **Draw and Deduce**
> How can you mark the diagram to reflect the given information?

   a. **Explain how you can demonstrate that the triangles are congruent.**

   b. **Use CPCTC to identify the congruent corresponding parts of the two triangles.**

You can use the triangle congruence theorems and the concept that corresponding angles and sides in two congruent triangles are congruent as key strategies to prove other geometric relationships.

You have already proved that any point on a perpendicular line segment is equidistant from the segment's endpoints using transformations. You can also prove this relationship using congruent triangles.

2. Consider $\overline{AB}$.

a. **Construct the perpendicular bisector of $\overline{AB}$. Then, draw a line segment from any one point on the bisector to each endpoint of the line segment, A and B.**

b. **Use your construction to write a proof plan to prove the Perpendicular Bisector Theorem. Then complete the proof.**

Remember:

The perpendicular bisector of a line segment is the line that divides the line segment into 2 congruent parts and that intersects the line segment at a right angle.

Draw and Deduce

Can you first prove that the two triangles are congruent?

The Perpendicular Bisector Theorem states: "Points on a perpendicular bisector of a line segment are equidistant from the segment's endpoints."

3. Consider the converse of the Perpendicular Bisector Theorem.

   a. State the Perpendicular Bisector Theorem as a conditional statement using if-then.

   b. State the converse of Perpendicular Bisector Theorem.

Analyze the proof of the converse of the Perpendicular Bisector Theorem.

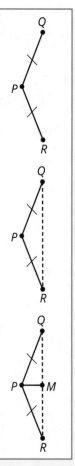

Worked Example

Given: Points Q and R are equidistant from point P.

An auxiliary line segment, $\overline{QR}$, can be drawn to form an isosceles triangle, $\triangle RPQ$.

Construct the midpoint of $\overline{QR}$, point M. Another auxiliary line segment, $\overline{PM}$, can be drawn, connecting the midpoint with point P.

The two triangles, $\triangle PQM$ and $\triangle PRM$ are congruent triangles by SSS Congruence.

This means that $\angle PMQ$ and $\angle PMR$ are congruent by CPCTC. And since these two angles are congruent and form a linear pair, they are both 90° angles.

Thus, point P lies on the perpendicular bisector of $\overline{QR}$.

4. **Consider the worked example. How would you know that point P lies on the perpendicular bisector of $\overline{QR}$? Explain your reasoning.**

Because this relationship has been proved true, you can now refer to it as a theorem. The **Perpendicular Bisector Converse Theorem** states: If a point is equidistant from the endpoints of a line segment, then the point lies on the perpendicular bisector of the segment." This theorem can be useful when proving theorems about right triangles.

ACTIVITY
4.2

Isosceles Triangle
Base Angles Theorem

CPCTC makes it possible to prove other theorems.

You have explored the relationship between the sides and angles of an isosceles triangle. Specifically, you conjectured that if the two sides of a triangle are congruent, then the angles opposite these sides are congruent. The Isosceles Triangle Base Angles Theorem states: "If two sides of a triangle are congruent, then the angles opposite these sides are congruent.""

Think
about:

You may want to draw a perpendicular bisector for these proofs. When you draw an auxiliary line, use the reason "construction."

1. **Consider the diagram to prove your conjecture using a paragraph proof.**

   Given: $\overline{GB} \cong \overline{GD}$
   Prove: $\angle B \cong \angle D$

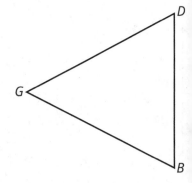

Because you have proved this relationship is true, you can now refer to it as a theorem. The **Isosceles Triangle Base Angles Theorem** states: "If two sides of a triangle are congruent, then the angles opposite these sides are congruent."

2. **Consider the converse of the Isosceles Triangle Base Angles Theorem.**

    a. State the converse as a conjecture.

    b. Consider the diagram to prove your conjecture using a paragraph proof.

    Given: $\angle B \cong \angle D$
    Prove: $\overline{GB} \cong \overline{GD}$

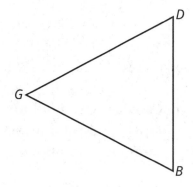

Think about:

You can draw an auxiliary line which bisects angle *G* and passes through a point somewhere on line segment *DB*.

Because you have proved this relationship is true, you can now refer to it as a theorem. The **Isosceles Triangle Base Angles Converse Theorem** states: "If two angles of a triangle are congruent, then the sides opposite these angles are congruent."

When proving the Perpendicular Bisector Theorem and theorems about isosceles triangles, you used auxiliary lines to create right triangles. There are geometric theorems specifically related to right triangles. Let's determine the relationship that exists among the measures of the angles and sides of a 30°-60°-90° triangle.

Remember:

You created this diagram in the last topic.

1. **Consider the equilateral triangle constructed in the diagram. A perpendicular bisector of $\overline{AB}$ is also constructed, which intersects $\overline{AB}$ at point D.**

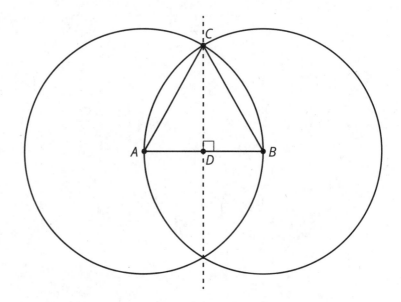

a. **Explain how you know that △ACB is an equilateral triangle.**

b. **Explain how you know that △CDB is a 30°-60°-90° triangle. Label the angle measures in the diagram.**

c. **Explain how you know that point C lies on the perpendicular bisector of $\overline{AB}$.**

d. **What do you know about the lengths of $\overline{DB}$ and $\overline{CB}$?**

2. Use what you know and the Pythagorean Theorem to demonstrate the 30°-60°-90° Triangle Theorem algebraically. Let a represent the length of the shorter leg, $\overline{DB}$.

3. Label the side measures in the diagram.

Because you have demonstrated this relationship to be true, you can now refer to it as a theorem. The **30°-60°-90° Triangle Theorem** states: "The length of the hypotenuse in a 30°-60°-90° triangle is 2 times the length of the shorter leg, and the length of the longer leg is √3 times the length of the shorter leg."

Let's determine the relationship that exists among the measures of the angles and sides of a 45°-45°-90° triangle.

4. Consider the isosceles right triangle constructed in the diagram. Line *MP* is a perpendicular bisector of diameter $\overline{QN}$.

   a. Explain how you know that △*MPN* is an isosceles right triangle.

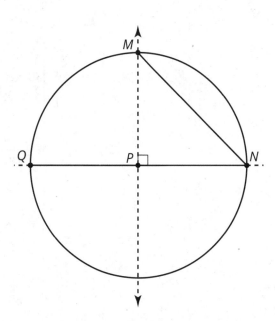

   b. Explain how you know that ∠*PMN* and ∠*PNM* are congruent angles. Label the angle measures in the diagram.

5. **Use what you know and the Pythagorean Theorem to demonstrate the 45°-45°-90° Triangle Theorem algebraically. Let *a* represent the length of each congruent leg.**

6. **Label the side measures in the diagram.**

Because you have demonstrated this relationship to be true, you can now refer to it as a theorem. The **45°-45°-90° Triangle Theorem** states: "The length of the hypotenuse in a 45°-45°-90° triangle is $\sqrt{2}$ times the length of a leg."

7. **Determine the length of sides *x* and *y* in each triangle.**

a.

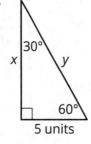

b.

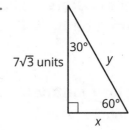

c.

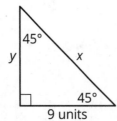

d.

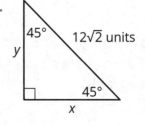

Now that you have practiced identifying the unknown lengths based on the special relationships among the sides of the triangle, consider when the given side lengths are expressed in a different form.

Worked Example

Determine the unknown side lengths in each triangle.

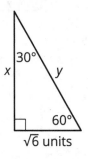

$x = \sqrt{3} \cdot \sqrt{6}$ $y = 2\sqrt{6}$ units

$x = \sqrt{3 \cdot 6}$

$x = \sqrt{3 \cdot 3 \cdot 2}$

$x = \sqrt{3^2 \cdot 2}$

$x = 3\sqrt{2}$ units

A standard procedure involving radicals is to **extract the roots**, which is the process of removing all perfect square numbers from under the radical symbol.

The Product Property of Radicals states that $\sqrt{a} \cdot \sqrt{b} = \sqrt{a \cdot b}$ when a and b are greater than 0.

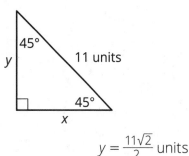

$x = \dfrac{11}{\sqrt{2}}$ $y = \dfrac{11\sqrt{2}}{2}$ units

$x = \dfrac{11}{\sqrt{2}} \cdot \dfrac{\sqrt{2}}{\sqrt{2}} = \dfrac{11\sqrt{2}}{2}$ units

A standard math convention is to **rationalize the denominator**, which is the process of rewriting a fraction with no irrational numbers in the denominator.

To rationalize the denominator of a fraction involving radicals, multiply a fraction by a form of 1 so that the product in the denominator includes a perfect square radicand. Then rewrite, if possible.

---

8. **Calculate the length of the legs of the isosceles triangle shown.**

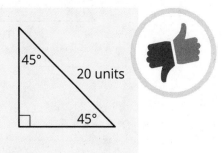

David says that the length of each side is $\sqrt{10}$ units.

$\dfrac{20}{\sqrt{2}} = \sqrt{\dfrac{20}{2}}$

$\quad = \sqrt{10}$

Brien says that the length of each side is $10\sqrt{2}$ units.

$\dfrac{20}{\sqrt{2}} \cdot \dfrac{\sqrt{2}}{\sqrt{2}} = \dfrac{20\sqrt{2}}{2}$

$\qquad = 10\sqrt{2}$

Determine who's correct and explain the error in the other student's work.

9. **Solve for the unknown side lengths of each figure.**

a.

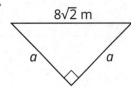

8√2 m

a   a

b.

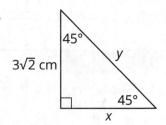

45°

3√2 cm

y

45°

x

c.

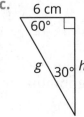

6 cm

60°

g   30° h

d.

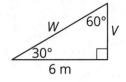

W   60° V

30°

6 m

e.

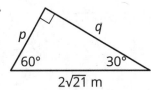

p

q

60°   30°

2√21 m

f. The perimeter of a square measures 32 cm.

k

More Triangle Congruence Theorems

Let's explore whether other combinations of side and angle measurements can be used to determine whether triangles are congruent.

Let's conjecture that two right triangles can be determined to be congruent by demonstrating that the hypotenuse and acute angle of one triangle are congruent to the hypotenuse and acute angle of the other triangle.

Also, let's conjecture that two triangles can be determined to be congruent by demonstrating that two angles and the non-included side of one triangle are congruent to two angles and the non-included side of another triangle.

Felipe

I can prove both conjectures by using the Triangle Sum Theorem and the ASA Congruence Theorem.

---

1. **Explain why Felipe is correct. Draw examples to demonstrate your reasoning.**

Because you have demonstrated these relationships are true, you can now refer to them as a theorems. The **Hypotenuse-Angle (HA) Congruence Theorem** states: "If the hypotenuse and an acute angle of one right triangle are congruent to the hypotenuse and an acute angle of another right triangle, then the two triangles are congruent." The **Angle-Angle-Side (AAS) Congruence Theorem** states: "If two angles and the non-included side of one triangle are congruent to two angles and the non-included side of another triangle, then the two triangles are congruent."

Use any theorems you have proven to solve each problem.
Explain each answer.

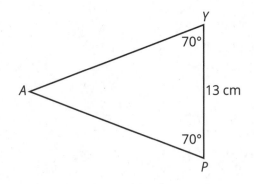

1. Calculate *AP* if the perimeter of △*AYP* is 43 cm.

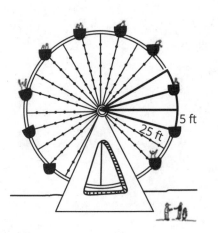

2. **Lighting booms on a Ferris wheel consist of four steel beams that have cabling with light bulbs attached. These beams, along with three shorter beams, form the edges of three congruent isosceles triangles, as shown. Maintenance crews are installing new lighting along the four beams. Calculate the total length of lighting needed for the four beams.**

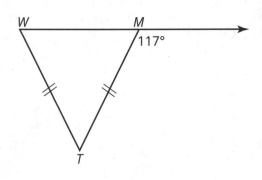

3. **Calculate m∠*T*.**

4. What is the width of the river?

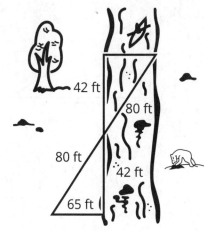
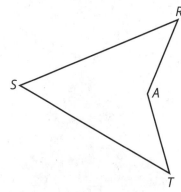

5. Given: $\overline{ST} \cong \overline{SR}$, $\overline{TA} \cong \overline{RA}$

Explain why $\angle T \cong \angle R$.

6. This stamp was issued in Mongolia. Suppose the longest side of this stamp is 50 millimeters.

a. Use the Pythagorean Theorem to determine the approximate length of the other sides of this stamp. Round your answer to the nearest tenth of a millimeter.

b. Use the 45°-45°-90° Triangle Theorem to determine the approximate length of the other sides of this stamp. Round your answer to the nearest tenth of a millimeter.

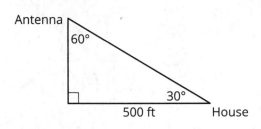

Antenna
60°
30°
500 ft
House

7. **A broadcast antenna is situated on top of a tower. The signal travels from the antenna to your house so you can watch TV. Consider the diagram to calculate the height of the tower and the distance the signal travels.**

8. **This stamp was issued in the Netherlands. Suppose the length of each side of the Netherlands stamp is 40 millimeters. Use the 30°-60°-90° Triangle Theorem to determine the height of the stamp.**

9. **In 1929, Uruguay issued a triangular parcel post stamp with sides equal in measure. Suppose the height of the Uruguay stamp is 30 millimeters. Use the 30°-60°-90° Triangle Theorem to determine the length of the three sides of the stamp.**

City of Bridges

1. Label the remaining sides of each triangle in terms of *x*.

   a. 45°-45°-90° triangle

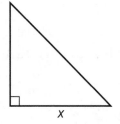

   b. 30°-60°-90° triangle

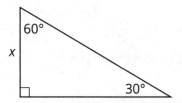

2. Given a 45°-45°-90° triangle, explain how to determine each unknown length.

   a. The length of a leg given the length of the hypotenuse

   b. The length of the hypotenuse given the length of a leg

3. **Emily is building a square bookshelf. She wants to add a diagonal support beam to the back to strengthen it. The diagonal divides the bookshelf into two 45°-45°-90° triangles. if each side of the bookshelf is 4 feet long, what must the length of the support beam be?**

A cable stayed bridge has one or more towers erected above piers in the middle of the span. From these towers, cables stretch down diagonally (usually to both sides).

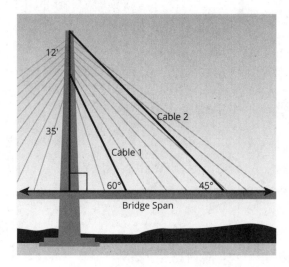

One cable forms a 60° angle with the bridge deck and is connected to the tower 35 feet above the bridge deck. A second cable forms a 45° angle with the bridge deck and is connected to the tower 12 feet above the point at which the first cable connects to the tower.

4. **Calculate the length of both cables and the length of the bridge span from each cable to the tower.**

Assignment

Write

Provide an example to illustrate each term.
1. Isosceles Triangle Base Angle Theorem
2. Isosceles Triangle Base Angle Converse Theorem
3. Perpendicular Bisector Theorem
4. 30°-60°-90° Triangle Theorem
5. 45°-45°-90° Triangle Theorem

Remember

The Perpendicular Bisector Theorem states: "The points on a perpendicular bisector of a line segment are equidistant from the segment's endpoints."

The Isosceles Triangle Base Angles Theorem states: "If two sides of a triangle are congruent, then the angles opposite these sides are congruent."

The 30°-60°-90° Triangle Theorem states: "The length of the hypotenuse in a 30°-60°-90° triangle is 2 times the length of the shorter leg, and the length of the longer leg is $\sqrt{3}$ times the length of the shorter leg."

The 45°-45°-90° Triangle Theorem states: "The length of the hypotenuse in a 45°-45°-90° triangle is $\sqrt{2}$ times the length of a leg."

Practice

1. Solve for the unknown side lengths.

a
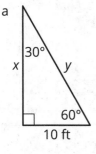

b
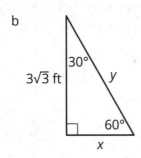

c
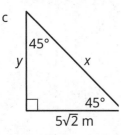

d
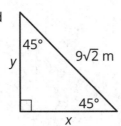

2. Samantha is hiking through the forest and she comes upon a canyon. She wants to know how wide the canyon is. She measures the distance between points A and B as 35 feet. Then, she measures the distance between points B and C as 35 feet. Finally, she measures the distance between points C and D as 80 feet. How wide is the canyon? Explain your reasoning.

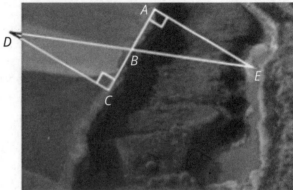

3. Explain why m∠NMO = 20°.

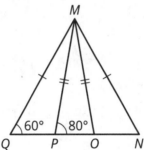

4. Jill is building a livestock pen in the shape of a triangle. She is using one side of a barn for one of the sides of her pen and has already placed posts in the ground at points A, B, and C, as shown in the diagram. If she places fence posts every 10 feet, how many more posts does she need? Note: There will be no other posts placed along the barn wall.

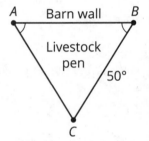

5. A mathematical society in India designed this stamp. The pyramidal design is an equilateral triangle. Suppose the height of the pyramidal design on the stamp is 42 millimeters. Determine the area of the pyramidal design on the stamp.

Stretch

Explain why m∠XAC = 60°.

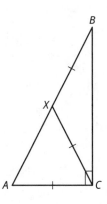

Review

1. Determine the measure of an interior angle of a regular 18-gon.
2. If a regular polygon has 15 sides, what is the measure of each exterior angle? Explain your reasoning.
3. Write a conjecture about the exterior angles of triangles at a vertex. Then, write the converse of the conjecture.
4. Use a compass and straightedge to construct the centroid of △QRS.

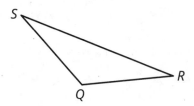

5. Given that *l* ∥ *m* and each angle measure, determine the measures of the remaining unknown angles.

   a. m∠1 = 105°
   b. m∠7 = 22°

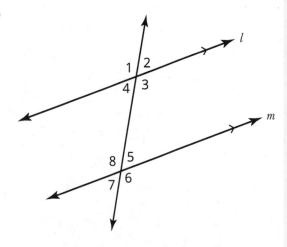

Corners in a Round Room

Angle Relationships Inside and Outside Circles

Warm Up

Determine the value of *x*.

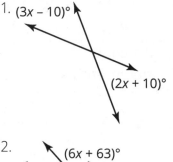

1. (3x – 10)°

   (2x + 10)°

2. (6x + 63)°

   (13x)°

Learning Goals

- Determine the measures of arcs, central angles, and inscribed angles.
- Prove the Inscribed Angle Theorem.
- Prove the Inscribed Right Triangle–Diameter Theorem.
- Prove the Inscribed Quadrilateral–Opposite Angles Theorem.
- Determine the measures of angles formed by two chords, two secants, a tangent and a secant, or two tangents.
- Prove the Interior Angles of a Circle Theorem.
- Prove the Exterior Angles of a Circle Theorem.
- Construct a tangent line to a circle from a point outside the circle.
- Know the Tangent to a Circle Theorem.

Key Terms

- degree measure of an arc
- adjacent arcs
- Arc Addition Postulate
- Inscribed Angle Theorem
- Inscribed Right Triangle–Diameter Theorem
- Inscribed Quadrilateral–Opposite Angles Theorem
- Interior Angles of a Circle Theorem
- Exterior Angles of a Circle Theorem
- Tangent to a Circle Theorem

You have reasoned about and proved a number of angle relationships for lines and polygons. How can these angle relationships help you reason about and prove theorems involving the angle and arc measures of circles?

Look at the Time

Recall that the degree measure of a circle is 360°.

Each minor arc of a circle is associated with and determined by a specific central angle. The **degree measure of an arc** is the same as the degree measure of its central angle. For example, if ∠PRQ is a central angle and m∠PRQ = 30°, then m$\widehat{PQ}$ = 30°.

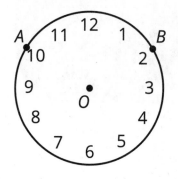

1. **Imagine the face of a clock. Consider that it is a circle with center O. Point A on the circle corresponds with the number 10 on the clock and point B corresponds with the number 2.**

    a. **Draw a central angle using the given points. Identify the central angle you drew and its corresponding minor arc.**

    b. **Without using a protractor, determine the central angle measure and the measure of the minor arc. Explain your reasoning.**

Remember:

Adjacent arcs are two arcs of the same circle sharing a common endpoint.

c. **Plot and label point C such that $\widehat{BC}$ = $\widehat{AB}$. Explain your reasoning.**

The **Arc Addition Postulate** states: "The measure of an arc formed by two adjacent arcs is the sum of the measures of the two arcs."

2. Consider circle *O* in Question 1.

    a. Plot and label point *D* on the circle such that it corresponds to the number 7 on the clock. Use the Arc Addition Postulate to determine the measure of $\overset{\frown}{BD}$.

    b. At which numbers on the clock could you plot point *E* such that $\overset{\frown}{BD} \cong \overset{\frown}{AE}$? Explain your reasoning.

3. If the measures of two central angles of the same circle (or congruent circles) are equal, are their corresponding minor arcs congruent? Explain your reasoning.

4. If the measures of two minor arcs of the same circle (or congruent circles) are equal, are their corresponding central angles congruent? Explain your reasoning.

5. Alicia explains to her classmate that $\overset{\frown}{SC}$ is congruent to $\overset{\frown}{TX}$. How did Alicia arrive at this conclusion? Is Alicia correct? Explain your reasoning.

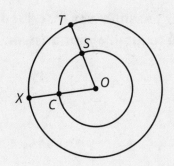

The Inscribed Angle Theorem

Recall the conjecture you made in a previous topic about the measure of an inscribed angle related to the measure of its intercepted arc. You reasoned through recorded observations that the measure of the inscribed angle is half the measure of the intercepted arc.

Inscribed angles formed by two chords can be drawn three different ways with respect to the center of the circle.

Remember:

An inscribed angle is an angle whose vertex is on a circle and whose sides contain chords of the circle. An intercepted arc is a portion of the circumference of the circle located on the interior of the angle whose endpoints lie on the sides of an angle.

Case 1	Case 2	Case 3
∠MPT is inscribed in such a way that the center point lies on one side of the inscribed angle.	∠MPT is inscribed in such a way that the center point lies on the interior of the inscribed angle.	∠MPT is inscribed in such a way that the center point lies on the exterior of the inscribed angle.

1. **What do the intercepted arcs in each case have in common?**

2. **Is there another possible way inscribed angles can be drawn? Use an example to justify your answer.**

To prove your conjecture that the measure of an inscribed angle is half the measure of the intercepted arc, you must prove each case. Let's consider Case 1.

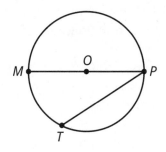

Given: ∠MPT is inscribed in circle O.
　　　Point O lies on diameter $\overline{PM}$.
Prove: $m\angle MPT = \frac{1}{2} m\widehat{MT}$

You can use construction and algebraic reasoning to create a proof plan.

Worked Example

Let's consider how to prove that
$m\angle MPT = \frac{1}{2} m\widehat{MT}$ for Case 1.
Connect points O and T to form radius $\overline{OT}$.

Label ∠MPT as x.
∠OTP = x because △OTP is isosceles.
Then, ∠MOT = $2x$ and $m\widehat{MT} = 2x$.
Therefore, $m\widehat{MT} = 2(m\angle MPT)$ or
　　　　$\angle MPT = \frac{1}{2} m\widehat{MT}$.

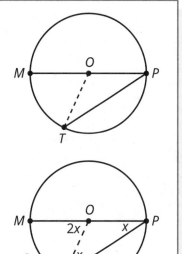

3. **Complete a formal proof for Case 1.**

Statements	Reasons
1. ∠MPT is inscribed in circle O.　　$m\angle MPT = x$　　Point O lies on diameter $\overline{PM}$.	1. Given
2. Connect points O and T to form radius $\overline{OT}$.	2. Construction

You have used the Addition and Subtraction Properties of Equality as reasons in proofs. You can also use the Multiplication and Division Properties of Equality as reasons in proofs.

4. **Use algebraic reasoning to demonstrate your conjecture for the other two cases.**

a. **Case 2**

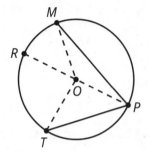

b. **Case 3**

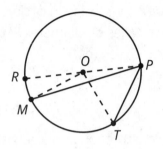

Because you have proved your conjecture is true, you can now refer to it as a theorem. The **Inscribed Angle Theorem** states: "The measure of an inscribed angle is half the measure of its intercepted arc."

5. **State the converse of the Inscribed Angle Theorem. Do you think the converse is true?**

There is a special case of the Inscribed Angle Theorem that applies to a specific type of inscribed polygon.

Consider △ABC that is inscribed in circle P.

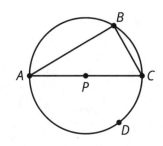

Remember:

An inscribed polygon is a polygon drawn inside a circle such that each vertex of the polygon touches the circle.

1. **What kind of triangle is △ABC? How do you know?**

2. **Write a conjecture about the type of triangle inscribed in a circle when one side of the triangle is a diameter.**

3. **Write the converse of the conjecture you wrote in Question 2. Do you think this statement is also true?**

It would appear that △ABC is a right triangle and that ∠B is a right angle. In general, it appears that if a triangle is inscribed in a circle such that one side of the triangle is a diameter of the circle, then the triangle is a right triangle.

4. **Create a proof of this conjecture.**

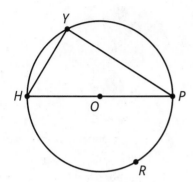

   Given: △HYP is inscribed in circle O such that $\overline{HP}$ is the diameter of the circle.
   Prove: △HYP is a right triangle.

Because you have proved that the relationship is true, you can now refer to it as a theorem. The **Inscribed Right Triangle–Diameter Theorem** states: "If a triangle is inscribed in a circle such that one side of the triangle is a diameter of the circle, then the triangle is a right triangle."

In a previous topic, you made a conjecture that the opposite angles of cyclic quadrilaterals, or inscribed quadrilaterals, are supplementary. This observation can be stated as a conjecture and then proved using the Inscribed Angle Theorem.

5. **Create a proof of this conjecture.**

   Given: Quadrilateral *QUAD* is inscribed in circle *O*.
   Prove: ∠*Q* and ∠*A* are supplementary angles.
   ∠*U* and ∠*D* are supplementary angles.

Because you have proved that this conjecture is true, you can now refer to it as a theorem. The **Inscribed Quadrilateral–Opposite Angles Theorem** states: "If a quadrilateral is inscribed in a circle, then the opposite angles are supplementary."

Interior Angles of a Circle Theorem

The vertex of an angle can be located inside of a circle, outside of a circle, or on a circle. In this activity, you will explore angles with a vertex located inside of a circle.

1. **Circle *O* with chords $\overline{AD}$ and $\overline{BC}$ is shown.**

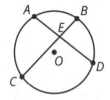

$m\overset{\frown}{BD} = 70°$

$m\overset{\frown}{AC} = 110°$

a. **Consider ∠*BED*. How is this angle different from the angles that you have investigated so far? How is this angle the same?**

b. **Can you determine the measure of ∠*BED* with the information you have so far? If so, how? Explain your reasoning.**

c. **Draw chord *CD*. Use the information given in the figure to name the measures of any angles that you do know. Explain your reasoning.**

d. **How does ∠*BED* relate to ∠*CED*?**

e. **Write a statement to show the relationship between m∠*BED*, m∠*EDC*, and m∠*ECD*.**

f. **What is the measure of ∠*BED*?**

g. **Describe the measure of ∠*BED* in terms of the measure of the arc intercepted by ∠*BED* and the arc intercepted by the vertical angle of ∠*BED*.**

2. **Draw a circle with two chords that intersect inside it. Use measuring tools to determine the measure of an angle formed by the intersecting chords and the measures of the arcs that are intercepted by the angle and its vertical angle.**

3. **Consider the different measures you determined in the circles from Questions 1 and 2. Look for patterns and make a conjecture about the measure of an interior angle of a circle and the measures of the arcs that are intercepted by the angle and its vertical angle.**

Let's first explore your conjecture for a circle where the vertex of the interior angle is at the center of the circle.

4. **Consider circle O with diameters BD and PF. If ∠BOP and ∠FOD form vertical angles, then m∠BOP = $\frac{1}{2}$ (m$\widehat{BP}$ + m$\widehat{FD}$). Use reasoning to demonstrate why this is true.**

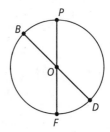

You've shown that the conjecture is true for two chords intersecting at the center of the circle. Now let's explore whether the conjecture holds true for any two chords that intersect in a circle.

Draw and Deduce

An auxiliary chord is drawn from point *E* to point *H*. How does this chord help you reason about the measure of ∠*KFH*?

5. **Use algebraic reasoning to prove the conjecture.**

   Given: Chords *EK* and *GH* intersect at point *F* in circle *O*.

   Prove: m∠*KFH* = $\frac{1}{2}$ (m$\widehat{HK}$ + m$\widehat{EG}$)

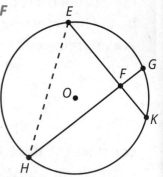

Because you have proved that this conjecture is true, you can now refer to it as a theorem. The **Interior Angles of a Circle Theorem** states: "If an angle is formed by two intersecting chords or secants of a circle such that the vertex of the angle is in the interior of the circle, then the measure of the angle is half of the sum of the measures of the arcs intercepted by the angle and its vertical angle."

Exterior Angles of a Circle Theorem

In this activity, you will explore angles with a vertex located outside of a circle. Before you can prove the conjectures you will make about these types of angles, you should be able to construct a tangent line to a circle through a point outside the circle.

1. **Construct tangent lines to a circle through a point outside of the circle.**

   Step 1: Draw a circle with center point _C_ and locate point _P_ outside of the circle.

   Step 2: Draw $\overline{PC}$.

   Step 3: Construct the perpendicular bisector of $\overline{PC}$.

   Step 4: Label the midpoint of the perpendicular bisector of $\overline{PC}$ point _M_.

   Step 5: Adjust the radius of your compass to the distance from point _M_ to point _C_.

   Step 6: Place the compass point on point _M_, and cut two arcs that intersect circle _C_.

   Step 7: Label the two points at which the arcs cut through circle _C_ point _A_ and point _B_.

   Step 8: Connect point _P_ and _A_ to form tangent line _PA_ and connect point _P_ and _B_ to form tangent line _PB_.

   Line _PA_ and line _PB_ are tangent to circle _C_.

Let's explore how the measure of an angle outside a circle, such as ∠APB that you constructed, relates to the measures of the arcs its intercepts.

2. **Circle *T* with points *K*, *L*, *M*, and *N* is shown.**

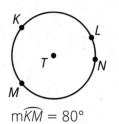

$m\widehat{KM} = 80°$
$m\widehat{LN} = 30°$

   a. **Draw secants $\overleftrightarrow{KL}$ and $\overleftrightarrow{MN}$. Where do the secants intersect? Label this point as point *P* on the figure.**

   b. **Draw chord $\overline{KN}$. Can you determine the measure of ∠KPM with the information you have so far? If so, how? Explain your reasoning.**

   c. **Use the information given in the figure to name the measures of any angles that you do know. Explain how you determined your answers.**

   d. **How does ∠KPN relate to △KPN?**

   e. **Write a statement to show the relationship between m∠KPN, m∠NKP, and m∠KNM.**

   f. **What is the measure of ∠KPN?**

   g. **Describe the measure of ∠KPM in terms of the measures of both arcs intercepted by ∠KPM.**

An angle with a vertex located in the exterior of a circle can be formed by a secant and a tangent, two secants, or two tangents.

3. **For each case, draw and label the exterior angle described. Then, determine the measure of the exterior angle and the measures of the arcs that are intercepted by the angle.**

   a. **Case 1: exterior angle formed by a secant and a tangent**

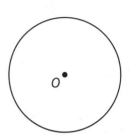

   b. **Case 2: exterior angle formed by two secants**

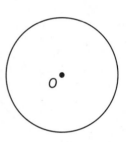

   c. **Case 3: exterior angle formed by two tangents**

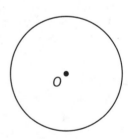

4. **Consider the different measures you determined in the circles from Questions 2 and 3. Look for patterns and make a conjecture about the measure of an exterior angle of a circle and the measure of the arcs that are intercepted by the angle.**

It appears that if an angle is formed by two intersecting chords or secants of a circle such that the vertex of the angle is in the exterior of the circle, then the measure of the angle is half of the difference of the measures of the arcs intercepted by the angle.

To prove this conjecture, you must prove each of the three cases. Analyze the proof of Case 1 in the worked example.

Worked Example

Case 1

Given: Secant EX and tangent TJ intersect at point J.

Prove: $m\angle EJT = \frac{1}{2}(m\widehat{ET} - m\widehat{RT})$

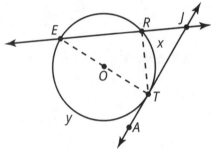

Label the measure of $\widehat{RT}$ as x and the measure of $\widehat{ET}$ as y.

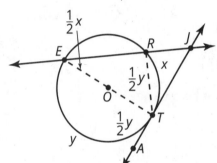

This means $m\angle TER = \frac{1}{2}x$ and $m\angle ETA = \frac{1}{2}y$ since each is an inscribed angle of the intercepted arc.

Angle ETA is an exterior angle of $\triangle TEJ$, so $m\angle ETA = m\angle EJT + m\angle TER$.

Using substitution, $\qquad \frac{1}{2}y = m\angle EJT + \frac{1}{2}x$.

Therefore, $\qquad m\angle EJT = \frac{1}{2}y - \frac{1}{2}x$,

or $\qquad m\angle EJT = \frac{1}{2}(y - x)$.

5. **Reason algebraically to prove the remaining cases of the Exterior Angles of a Circle Theorem.**

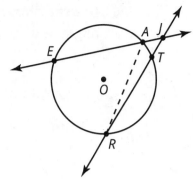

a. **Case 2**

Given: Secants *EJ* and *RJ* intersect at point *J*.

Prove: m∠EJR = $\frac{1}{2}$(m$\widehat{ER}$ − m$\widehat{AT}$)

b. **Case 3**

Given: Tangents *EJ* and *AJ* intersect at point *J*.

Prove: m∠EJT = $\frac{1}{2}$(m$\widehat{ERT}$ − m$\widehat{ET}$)

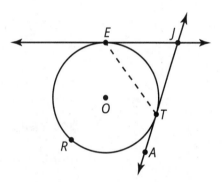

6. **Use the diagram shown to determine the measure of each angle or arc.**

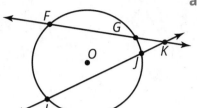

   a. **Determine m$\widehat{FI}$.**

   $m\angle K = 20°$

   $m\widehat{GJ} = 80°$

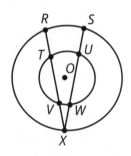

   b. **Determine m$\angle X$.**

   $m\widehat{VW} = 40°$

   $m\widehat{TU} = 85°$

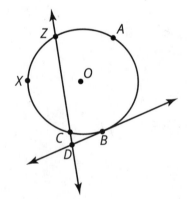

   c. **Determine m$\angle D$.**

   $m\widehat{ZXC} = 120°$

   $m\widehat{CB} = 30°$

Because you have proved this relationship is true, you can now refer to it as a theorem. The **Exterior Angles of a Circle Theorem** states: "If an angle is formed by two intersecting chords or secants of a circle such that the vertex of the angle is in the exterior of the circle, then the measure of the angle is half of the difference of the measures of the arcs intercepted by the angle."

Think back on the first case of exterior angles you drew in the previous activity involving a secant and a tangent. There is a special case when the secant contains the diameter of the circle.

1. **Consider ∠UTV with vertex located on circle C. Line VW is drawn tangent to circle C at point T.**

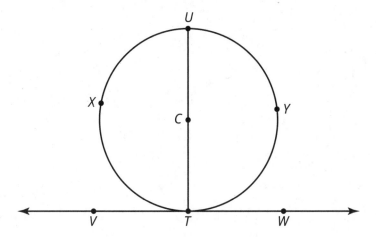

Remember:

An inscribed angle is an angle whose measure is half the measure of its intercepted arc.

a. **Determine m$\widehat{UXT}$ and m$\widehat{UYT}$. Explain your reasoning.**

b. **Determine m∠UTV and m∠UTW. Explain your reasoning.**

It appears that when a line is drawn tangent to a circle, the angles formed at the point of tangency are right angles, and therefore the radius drawn to the point of tangency is perpendicular to the tangent line.

This relationship can be proved and then stated as a theorem.

The proof of this relationship is completed by contradiction. A proof by contradiction begins with an assumption that is the opposite of what you would like to prove. Using the assumption and its implications, you arrive at a contradiction. When this happens, the proof is complete.

Worked Example

Line segment *CA* is a radius of circle *C*. Point *A* is the point at which the radius intersects the tangent line.

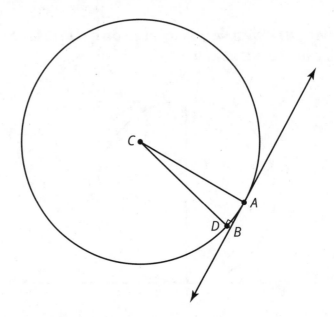

Step 1: Assumption: The tangent line is not perpendicular to the radius ($\overline{CA}$) of the circle.

Step 2: Point *B*, another point on the tangent line, is the point at which $\overline{CB}$ is perpendicular to the tangent line.

Step 3: Consider right triangle *CBA* with hypotenuse *CA* and leg *CB*, so $CA > CB$.

Step 4: Impossible!! $CB > CA$ because CB = length of radius (CD) + DB.

The assumption is incorrect; therefore, the tangent line is perpendicular to the radius ($\overline{CA}$) of the circle.

This completes the proof of the Tangent to a Circle Theorem.

Because you have proved that this relationship is true, you can now refer to it as a theorem. The **Tangent to a Circle Theorem** states: "A line drawn tangent to a circle is perpendicular to a radius of the circle drawn to the point of tangency."

You can use the Tangent to a Circle Theorem to solve problems.

2. **When you are able to see past buildings and hills or mountains—when you can look all the way to the horizon, how far is that? You can use the Pythagorean Theorem to help you tell.**

   Imagine you are standing on the surface of the Earth and you have a height of h. The distance to the horizon is given by d in the diagram shown, and R is the radius of Earth.

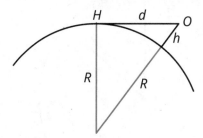

   Using your height, create a formula you can use to determine how far away the horizon is.

3. **Molly is standing at the top of Mount Everest, which has an elevation of 29,029 feet. Her eyes are 5 feet above ground level. The radius of Earth is approximately 3960 miles. How far can Molly see on the horizon?**

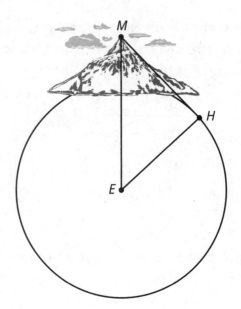

You can apply the theorems you know involving circles to solve problems.

1. **Aubrey wants to take a family picture. Her camera has a 70°
   field of view, but to include the entire family in the picture,
   she needs to cover a 140° arc. Explain what Aubrey needs to do
   to fit the entire family in the picture. Use the diagram to draw
   the solution.**

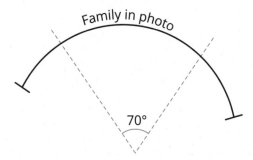

2. **Yesterday, Ms. Angle taught her students how to determine the
   measure of an inscribed angle. Mitchell told his classmate that
   he finally understood why a circle is always 360°. Use △PAW
   drawn in the diagram to explain what Mitchell was thinking.**

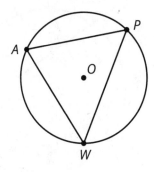

3. Safiye says that using only the given information in the diagram, she can determine all the unknown measures of the circle. Is she correct? Justify your reasoning.

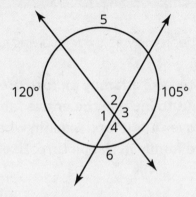

4. **Apply the theorems you know to determine each measure.**

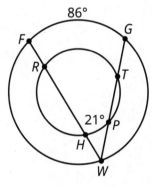

   a. **Determine m$\widehat{RT}$.**
      m$\widehat{FG}$ = 86°
      m$\widehat{HP}$ = 21°

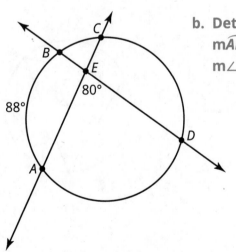

   b. **Determine m$\widehat{CD}$.**
      m$\widehat{AB}$ = 88°
      m∠AED = 80°

c. **Determine m∠TCX.**

   m∠*TSX* = 17°

   m∠*STW* = 50°

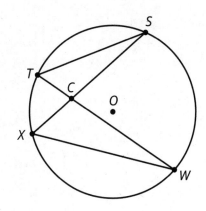

d. **Determine m∠EXT.**

   m∠*RET* = 40°

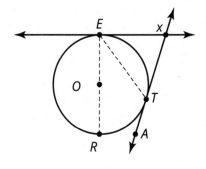

TALK the TALK

Circular Reasoning

1. **What additional information can you conclude about the measures of the arcs and angles in each diagram? Explain your reasoning.**

a.

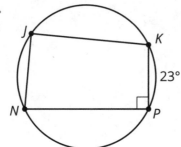

b.

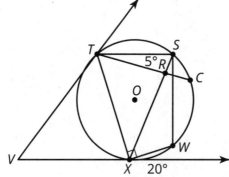

2. Karl raises his hand and informs Ms. Rhombi that he has discovered another property related to the angles of an inscribed quadrilateral. Karl shows his teacher the diagram shown.

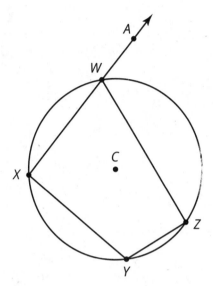

He claims that the measure of any exterior angle of the quadrilateral is equal to the measure of the opposite interior angle in the quadrilateral. In other words, m∠AWZ = m∠Y.

Explain Karl's reasoning.

Assignment

Write

Define each theorem in your own words.

1. Inscribed Angle Theorem
2. Inscribed Right Triangle-Diameter Theorem
3. Inscribed Quadrilateral-Opposite Angles Theorem
4. Interior Angles of a Circle Theorem
5. Exterior Angles of a Circle Theorem
6. Tangent to a Circle Theorem

Remember

- The measure of an inscribed angle is half the measure of the arc it intercepts.
- The measure of an interior angle of a circle is half the sum of the measures of its intercepted arc and its vertical angle's intercepted arc.
- The measure of an exterior angle of a circle is half the difference of the measures of its intercepted arcs.
- A radius drawn to the point of tangency is perpendicular to the tangent line.

Practice

1. Consider circle O with diameter GB. Line AD is tangent to circle O at point A and $\overleftrightarrow{DB}$ is tangent to circle O at point B. The measure of $\angle GBA$ is 38°. Chord GC bisects $\angle G$. Determine each measure.

   a. m$\angle A$
   b. m$\angle G$
   c. m$\widehat{AG}$
   d. m$\widehat{AB}$
   e. m$\angle ADB$
   f. m$\widehat{AC}$

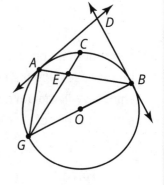

2. In the figure shown, quadrilateral $LMNP$ is inscribed in circle R, m$\angle P = 57°$, and m$\angle L$ = m$\angle N$. What are m$\angle M$, m$\angle L$, and m$\angle N$? Explain your reasoning.

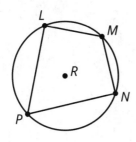

3. Explain how knowing m$\angle ERT$ can help you determine m$\angle EXT$.

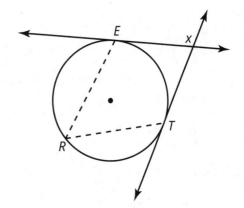

4. Construct a circle and label the center Z.

   a. Construct a tangent line to circle Z through a point X. Label the point of tangency as point Y.
   b. What is the measure of $\angle ZYX$? Explain your reasoning.

Stretch

Ruben says that, in a right triangle, if you draw a line segment from the right angle's vertex to the center of the hypotenuse, the segment that you draw is always half the length of the hypotenuse. How can you show that Ruben's conjecture is correct?

Review

1. A hazard sign is placed near a steep stairwell. The sign design is an equilateral triangle. Suppose the height of the sign is 15 inches. Determine the area of the sign.

2. The roof of a house is in the shape of an triangle. If the builder uses 4 foot shingles in rows on the roof, how many shingles will the builder need for the first row on both sides of the roof? Explain your reasoning.

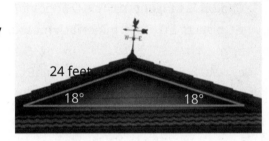

24 feet

18°   18°

3. Use a compass and straightedge to construct the incenter of △ABC.

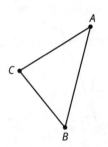

4. Which type(s) of quadrilateral have two congruent diagonals?

5. Solve for x and y.

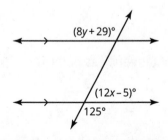

$(8y+29)°$

$(12x-5)°$

125°

Justifying Line and Angle Relationships Summary

KEY TERMS

- Addition Property of Equality
- Subtraction Property of Equality
- Reflexive Property
- Substitution Property
- Transitive Property
- flow chart proof
- two-column proof
- Right Angle Congruence Postulate
- Congruent Supplement Theorem
- Vertical Angle Theorem
- paragraph proof
- Corresponding Angles Theorem
- Corresponding Angles Converse Theorem
- Same-Side Interior Angles Theorem
- Alternate Interior Angles Theorem

- Alternate Exterior Angles Theorem
- Same-Side Exterior Angles Theorem
- Alternate Interior Angles Converse Theorem
- Same-Side Interior Angles Converse Theorem
- Alternate Exterior Angles Converse Theorem
- Same-Side Exterior Angles Converse Theorem
- Perpendicular/Parallel Line Theorem
- Triangle Sum Theorem
- Exterior Angle Theorem
- Perpendicular Bisector Converse Theorem
- Isosceles Triangle Base Angles Theorem
- Isosceles Triangle Base Angles Converse Theorem

- 30°-60°-90° Triangle Theorem
- 45°-45°-90° Triangle Theorem
- extract the roots
- rationalize the denominator
- Hypotenuse-Angle (HA) Congruence Theorem
- Angle-Angle-Side (AAS) Congruence Theorem
- degree measure of an arc
- adjacent arcs
- Arc Addition Postulate
- Inscribed Angle Theorem
- Inscribed Right Triangle–Diameter Theorem
- Inscribed Quadrilateral–Opposite Angles Theorem
- Interior Angles of a Circle Theorem
- Exterior Angles of a Circle Theorem
- Tangent to a Circle Theorem

Proof Positive

Many properties of real numbers can be applied in geometry. These properties are important when making conjectures and proving new theorems.

Property	Statements
Addition Property of Equality	If a, b, and c are real numbers and $a = b$, then $a + c = b + c$.
Subtraction Property of Equality	If a, b, and c are real numbers and $a = b$, then $a - c = b - c$.
Reflexive Property	If a is a real number, then $a = a$.
Substitution Property	If a and b are real numbers and $a = b$, then a can be substituted for b.
Transitive Property	If a, b, and c are real numbers, $a = b$, and $b = c$, then $a = c$.

Angle measures:
If $m\angle 1 = m\angle 3$, then $m\angle 1 + m\angle 2 = m\angle 3 + m\angle 2$.

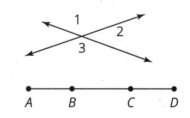

Segment measures:
If $m\overline{AB} = m\overline{CD}$, then $m\overline{AB} + m\overline{BC} = m\overline{CD} + m\overline{BC}$.

Distances:
If $AB = CD$, then $AB + BC = CD + BC$.

Consider the diagram which shows four collinear points A, B, C, and D such that point B lies between points A and C, point C lies between points B and D, and $\overline{AB} \cong \overline{CD}$.

Consider the conditional statement: If $\overline{AB} \cong \overline{CD}$, then $\overline{AC} \cong \overline{BD}$. When you begin the proof process, you take the parts of a conditional statement and organize them into "Given" and "Prove" statements.

Given: $\overline{AB} \cong \overline{CD}$
Prove: $\overline{AC} \cong \overline{BD}$

You can also use the postulates and properties you have learned so far to create different forms of proofs.

A **flow chart proof** is a proof in which the steps and reasons for each step are written in boxes. Arrows connect the boxes and indicate how each step and reason is generated from one or more other steps and reasons.

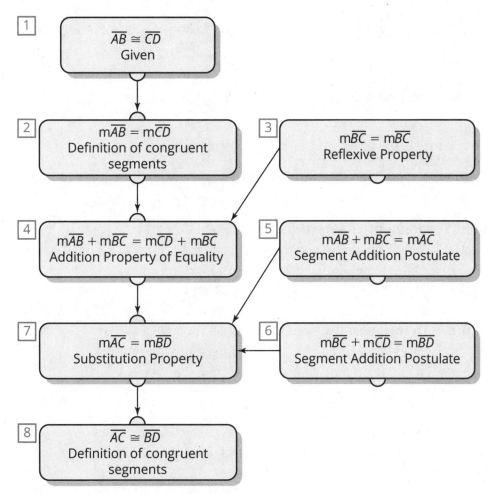

1. $\overline{AB} \cong \overline{CD}$
Given

2. $m\overline{AB} = m\overline{CD}$
Definition of congruent segments

3. $m\overline{BC} = m\overline{BC}$
Reflexive Property

4. $m\overline{AB} + m\overline{BC} = m\overline{CD} + m\overline{BC}$
Addition Property of Equality

5. $m\overline{AB} + m\overline{BC} = m\overline{AC}$
Segment Addition Postulate

7. $m\overline{AC} = m\overline{BD}$
Substitution Property

6. $m\overline{BC} + m\overline{CD} = m\overline{BD}$
Segment Addition Postulate

8. $\overline{AC} \cong \overline{BD}$
Definition of congruent segments

A **two-column proof** is a proof in which the steps are written in the left column and the corresponding reasons are written in the right column. Each step and corresponding reason are numbered.

Statements	Reasons
1. $\overline{AB} \cong \overline{CD}$	1. Given
2. $m\overline{AB} = m\overline{CD}$	2. Definition of congruent segments
3. $m\overline{BC} = m\overline{BC}$	3. Reflexive Property
4. $m\overline{AB} + m\overline{BC} = m\overline{CD} + m\overline{BC}$	4. Addition Property of Equality
5. $m\overline{AB} + m\overline{BC} = m\overline{AC}$	5. Segment Addition Postulate
6. $m\overline{BC} + m\overline{CD} = m\overline{BD}$	6. Segment Addition Postulate
7. $m\overline{AC} = m\overline{BD}$	7. Substitution Property
8. $\overline{AC} \cong m\overline{BD}$	8. Definition of congruent segments

The **Right Angle Congruence Postulate** states: "All right angles are congruent."

For example, consider $\overrightarrow{CD}$ that is perpendicular to $\overline{AB}$. Both $\angle ACD$ and $\angle DCB$ are right angles. Therefore, $\angle ACD \cong \angle DCB$.

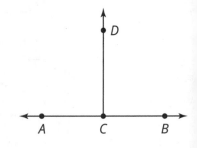

The **Congruent Supplement Theorem** states: "If two angles are supplements of the same angle or of congruent angles, then the angles are congruent." For example, if $\angle 1$ is supplementary to $\angle 2$, $\angle 3$ is supplementary to $\angle 4$, and $\angle 2 \cong \angle 4$, then $\angle 1 \cong \angle 3$.

The **Vertical Angle Theorem** states: "Vertical angles are congruent." For example, if $\angle 1$ and $\angle 2$ are a linear pair, $\angle 2$ and $\angle 3$ are a linear pair, $\angle 3$ and $\angle 4$ are a linear pair, and $\angle 4$ and $\angle 1$ are a linear pair, then $\angle 1 \cong \angle 3$ and $\angle 2 \cong \angle 4$.

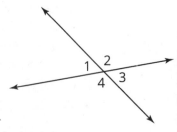

Once you have proved a theorem, you know that it is true in all instances. You can apply these theorems when determining unknown geometric measures.

For example, given $\overleftrightarrow{AB}$ intersects $\overleftrightarrow{CD}$ at point E, you can determine m$\angle AED$.

$x + 94 = 4x + 25$

$94 = 3x + 25$

$69 = 3x$

$x = 23$

m$\angle AEC = 117°$

m$\angle AED = 180° - 117° = 63°$

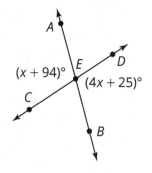

LESSON

2

A Parallel Universe

The **Corresponding Angles Theorem** states: "If two parallel lines are intersected by a transversal, then corresponding angles are congruent." For example, $\angle 1 \cong \angle 5$, $\angle 2 \cong \angle 6$, $\angle 3 \cong \angle 7$, and $\angle 4 \cong \angle 8$.

The **Corresponding Angles Converse Theorem** states: "If two lines intersected by a transversal form congruent corresponding angles, then the lines are parallel."

The **Same-Side Interior Angles Theorem** states: "If two parallel lines are intersected by a transversal, then the interior angles on the same side of the transversal are supplementary." For example, m$\angle 3$ + m$\angle 5$ = $180°$ and m$\angle 4$ + m$\angle 6$ = $180°$.

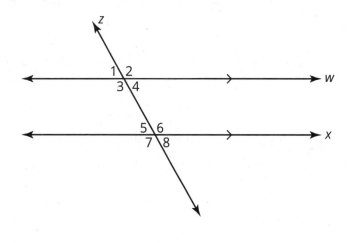

The **Alternate Interior Angles Theorem** states: "If two parallel lines are intersected by a transversal, then the alternate interior angles are congruent." For example, $\angle 3 \cong \angle 6$ and $\angle 4 \cong \angle 5$.

The **Alternate Exterior Angles Theorem** states: "If two parallel lines are intersected by a transversal, then the alternate exterior angles are congruent." For example, $\angle 1 \cong \angle 8$ and $\angle 2 \cong \angle 7$.

The **Same-Side Exterior Angles Theorem** states: "If two parallel lines are cut by a transversal, then the same-side exterior angles are supplementary." For example, m$\angle 1$ + m$\angle 7$ = $180°$ and m$\angle 2$ + m$\angle 8$ = $180°$.

The **Alternate Interior Angles Converse Theorem** states: "If two lines intersected by a transversal form congruent alternate interior angles, then the lines are parallel." The **Same-Side Interior Angles Converse Theorem** states: "If two lines intersected by a transversal from supplementary same-side interior angles, then the lines are parallel." The **Alternate Exterior Angles Converse Theorem** states: "If two lines intersected by a transversal form congruent alternate exterior angles, then the lines are parallel." The **Same-Side Exterior Angles Converse Theorem** states: "If two lines intersected by a transversal from supplementary same-side exterior angles, then the lines are parallel."

The **Perpendicular/Parallel Line Theorem** states: "If two lines are perpendicular to the same line, then the two lines are parallel to each other."

LESSON 3 — Ins and Outs

The **Triangle Sum Theorem** states that the sum of the interior angles of a triangle is equal to 180°.

The **Exterior Angle Theorem** states: "The measure of an exterior angle of a triangle is equal to the sum of the measures of the two remote interior angles." For example, $m\angle d = m\angle b + m\angle c$, $m\angle e = m\angle a + m\angle c$, and $m\angle f = m\angle a + m\angle b$.

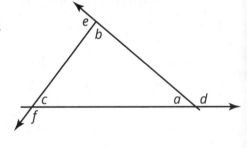

The formula for the sum of the measures of the interior angles of a polygon $= 180(n - 2)°$, where n is the number of sides of the polygon.

In a regular polygon we can also use this formula to determine the measure of each angle given the sum of the interior angles. The interior angle measure of a regular polygon $= \frac{180(n - 2)°}{n}$.

For any simple polygon we can say that the sum of the measures of the exterior angles is 360°, or one full revolution of a shape.

In a regular polygon we can also calculate the measure of each individual exterior angle. The exterior angle measure of a regular polygon $= \frac{360°}{n}$, where n is the number of sides.

The **Perpendicular Bisector Converse Theorem** states: "If a point is equidistant from the endpoints of a line segment, then the point lies on the perpendicular bisector of the segment." For example, if $AC = BC$, then point C lies on the perpendicular bisector, $\overleftrightarrow{CD}$.

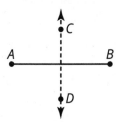

The **Isosceles Triangle Base Angles Theorem** states: "If two sides of a triangle are congruent, then the angles opposite these sides are congruent." For example, in $\triangle ABC$, if side a is congruent to side c, then $\angle A \cong \angle C$.

The **Isosceles Triangle Base Angles Converse Theorem** states: "If two angles of a triangle are congruent, then the sides opposite these angles are congruent." For example, if $\angle A \cong \angle C$, then side a is congruent to side c.

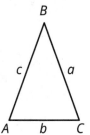

There are geometric theorems specifically related to right triangles. For example, the **30°-60°-90° Triangle Theorem** states: "The length of the hypotenuse in a 30°-60°-90° triangle is 2 times the length of the shorter leg, and the length of the longer leg is $\sqrt{3}$ times the length of the shorter leg." The **45°-45°-90° Triangle Theorem** states: "The length of the hypotenuse in a 45°-45°-90° triangle is $\sqrt{2}$ times the length of a leg."

A standard procedure involving radicals is to **extract the roots**, which is the process of removing all perfect square numbers from under the radical symbol.

$$\sqrt{18} = \sqrt{9} \cdot 2$$
$$= \sqrt{3^2} \cdot 2$$
$$= 3\sqrt{2}$$

A standard math convention is to **rationalize the denominator**, which is a process of rewriting a fraction with no irrational numbers in the denominator.

$$\frac{11}{\sqrt{2}} \cdot \frac{\sqrt{2}}{\sqrt{2}} = 11\frac{\sqrt{2}}{2}$$

The **Hypotenuse-Angle (HA) Congruence Theorem** states: "If the hypotenuse and an acute angle of one right triangle are congruent to the hypotenuse and an acute angle of another right triangle, then the two triangles are congruent." For example, in right triangle ABC, $\overline{AC}$ is the hypotenuse and in right triangle EDC, $\overline{EC}$ is the hypotenuse. Since $\overline{AC} \cong \overline{EC}$ and $\angle ACB \cong \angle ECD$ by the Vertical Angle Theorem, then $\triangle ABC \cong \triangle EDC$.

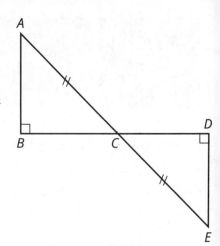

The **Angle-Angle-Side Congruence Theorem** states: "If two angles and the non-included side of one triangle are congruent to two angles and the non-included side of another triangle, then the two triangles are congruent." For example, $\overline{BC} \cong \overline{EF}$, $\angle A \cong \angle D$, and $\angle C \cong \angle F$. Therefore, $\triangle ABC \cong \triangle DEF$ by AAS.

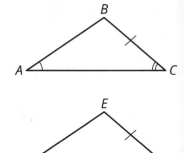

LESSON

5

Corners in a Round Room

Each minor arc of a circle is associated with, and determined by, a specific central angle. The **degree measure of an arc** is the same as the degree measure of its central angle. For example, if $\angle PRQ$ is a central angle and $m\angle PRQ = 30°$, then $m\overset{\frown}{PQ} = 30°$.

The **Arc Addition Postulate** states: "The measure of an arc formed by two adjacent arcs is the sum of the measures of the two arcs." **Adjacent arcs** are two arcs of the same circle sharing a common endpoint. For example, $\overset{\frown}{BC}$ is adjacent to $\overset{\frown}{CD}$ and $m\overset{\frown}{BC} + m\overset{\frown}{CD} = m\overset{\frown}{BD}$.

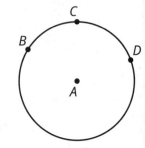

The **Inscribed Angle Theorem** states: "The measure of an inscribed angle is half the measure of its intercepted arc." For example, $m\angle CBD = \frac{1}{2}m\widehat{CD}$.

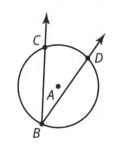

The **Inscribed Right Triangle-Diameter Theorem** states: "If a triangle is inscribed in a circle such that one side of the triangle is a diameter of the circle, then the triangle is a right triangle." For example, $\triangle BCD$ is inscribed in circle A and side $\overline{BD}$ is also a diameter of circle A. Therefore, $\triangle BCD$ is a right triangle.

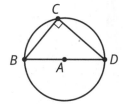

The **Inscribed Quadrilateral-Opposite Angles Theorem** states: "If a quadrilateral is inscribed in a circle, then the opposite angles are supplementary." For example, quadrilateral $BCDE$ is inscribed in circle A. Therefore, $m\angle B + m\angle D = 180°$ and $m\angle C + m\angle E = 180°$.

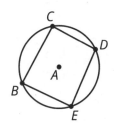

The vertex of an angle can be located inside of a circle, outside of a circle, or on a circle.

The **Interior Angles of a Circle Theorem** states: "If an angle is formed by two intersecting chords or secants of a circle such that the vertex of the angle is in the interior of the circle, then the measure of the angle is half of the sum of the measures of the arcs intercepted by the angle and its vertical angle."

For example, $m\angle AED = \frac{1}{2}(m\widehat{AD} + m\widehat{BC})$.

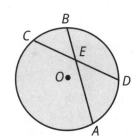

The **Exterior Angles of a Circle Theorem** states: "If an angle is formed by two intersecting chords or secants of a circle such that the vertex of the angle is in the exterior of the circle, then the measure of the angle is half of the difference of the measures of the arcs intercepted by the angle."

For example, $m\angle ABC = \frac{1}{2}(m\widehat{ADC} - m\widehat{AC})$.

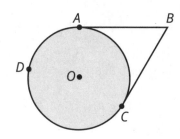

The **Tangent to a Circle Theorem** states: "A line drawn tangent to a circle is perpendicular to a radius of the circle drawn to the point of tangency." For example, $\overleftrightarrow{BD}$ is tangent to circle A at point C. Therefore, $\overleftrightarrow{BD}$ is perpendicular to $\overline{AC}$.

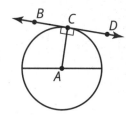

Using Congruence Theorems

Congruence theorems are all about analyzing triangles in terms of component sides and angles – especially right triangles.

Lesson 1
SSS, SAS, AAS, . . . S.O.S!
Using Triangle Congruence to Determine Relationships Between Segments . . . M2-185

Lesson 2
Props To You
Properties of Quadrilaterals M2-197

Lesson 3
Three-Chord Song
Relationships Between Chords M2-225

Module 2: Establishing Congruence

TOPIC 3: USING CONGRUENCE THEOREMS

As students prove more theorems, they have a larger repertoire of reasons that they can use in new proofs. In this topic, students use the theorems that they have proved to prove new theorems about triangles, quadrilaterals, and angles formed in circles. Students use triangle congruence theorems to verify properties of parallelograms, and they use the congruence theorems they have proved to prove theorems related to the chords of circles. The final lesson opens with a real-world scenario that students can think broadly about solving.

Where have we been?

Students build from the fundamentals of proof that they learned in the previous topic. Previously, students explained how the criteria for the SSS, SAS, and ASA congruence theorems follow from the definition of congruence in terms of rigid motion. And, students proved the AAS Congruence Theorem and the HA Congruence Theorem for right triangles. They now use these theorems to prove three additional congruence theorems for right triangles.

Where are we going?

Students will use logical reasoning not just in geometry but as they progress through advanced mathematics. Mathematics is about understanding and providing valid reasons why numeric, algebraic, and geometric relationships exist and whether or not they exist in all cases.

Venn Diagram of Quadrilaterals

There have been different definitions of *trapezoid* over time. In this course, *trapezoid* is defined as "a quadrilateral with <u>at least one pair</u> of parallel sides."

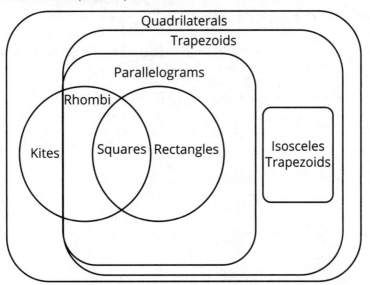

Don't Make a Mueller-Lyer Out of Me

Which of the blue lines shown is longer? Most people will answer that the line on the right appears to be longer.

But in fact, both blue lines are the exact same length! This famous optical illusion is known as the Mueller-Lyer illusion. You can measure the lines to see for yourself. You can also draw some of your own to see how it almost always works! Appearances can be deceiving, which is why congruence in mathematics is defined precisely.

Talking Points

It can be helpful to know about geometric congruence for college admissions tests.

Here is an example of a sample question:

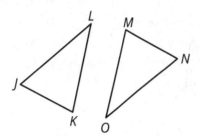

In the diagram above, $\overline{LJ} \cong \overline{ON}$ and $\overline{LK} \cong \overline{OM}$. List a congruence relationship that would be sufficient to prove that the two triangles are congruent.

To solve this problem, you need to know the Side-Side-Side Congruence Theorem or the Side-Angle-Side Congruence Theorem.

To prove the two triangles are congruent by SSS, you can show that $\overline{JK} \cong \overline{NM}$. To prove the triangles are congruent by SAS, you can show that $\angle L \cong \angle O$.

Key Terms

tangent segment
A tangent segment is a line segment formed by connecting a point outside of the circle to a point of tangency.

Trapezoid Midsegment Theorem
The Trapezoid Midsegment Theorem states: "The midsegment of a trapezoid is parallel to each of the bases and its length is one half the sum of the lengths of the bases."

Diameter-Chord Theorem
The Diameter-Chord Theorem states that the perpendicular bisector of a chord bisects the chord's intercepted arc.

Equidistant Chord Theorem
The Equidistant Chord Theorem states: "If two chords of the same circle or congruent circles are congruent, then they are equidistant from the center of the circle."

SSS, SAS, AAS, . . . S.O.S!

Using Triangle Congruence to Determine Relationships Between Segments

Warm Up

Determine all the angle measures and side lengths of each right triangle.

1.

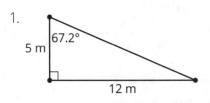

2.

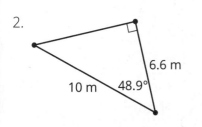

3.

Learning Goals

- Prove the Hypotenuse-Leg Congruence Theorem.
- Use SSS, SAS, ASA, and/or AAS triangle congruence to justify the Leg-Leg Congruence Theorem and the Leg-Angle Congruence Theorem.
- Analyze a proof of the Tangent Segment Theorem.
- Apply right triangle congruence theorems to solve problems.

Key Terms

- Hypotenuse-Leg (HL) Congruence Theorem
- Leg-Leg (LL) Congruence Theorem
- Leg-Angle (LA) Congruence Theorem
- tangent segment
- Tangent Segment Theorem
- tangent circles

You know about triangle congruence theorems, such as Side-Side-Side and Side-Angle-Side. What congruence theorems apply to right triangles?

Pulling Your Leg

Let's investigate a conjecture about right triangles.

1. Consider right triangle **ABC** with right angle **C**.

   a. **Construct a right triangle using $\overline{CA}$ as a leg and $\overline{AB}$ as the hypotenuse. Then, write the steps you performed to construct the triangle.**

   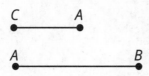

   b. **How does the length of side $\overline{CB}$ compare to the lengths of your classmates' sides $\overline{CB}$?**

   c. **Use a protractor to measure $\angle A$ and $\angle B$ in $\triangle ABC$. How do the measures of these angles compare to the measures of your classmates' $\angle A$ and $\angle B$?**

   d. **Is your triangle congruent to your classmates' triangles? Why or why not?**

Hypotenuse-Leg Congruence Theorem

Many congruence theorems apply to all triangles. There are also theorems that apply only to right triangles. You have already proved the Hypotenuse-Angle Congruence Theorem. Methods for proving that two right triangles are congruent are somewhat shorter. You can prove that two right triangles are congruent using only two measurements.

1. **Explain why only two pairs of corresponding parts are needed to prove that two right triangles are congruent.**

2. **Are all right angles congruent? Explain your reasoning.**

Through an example, you have used construction and measurements to demonstrate that all right triangles with a given leg length and hypotenuse length are congruent. Now, lets prove this conjecture is true in all cases.

3. Complete the two-column proof of this conjecture.

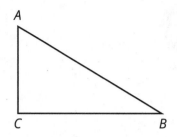

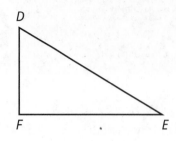

Given:
Right triangle *ABC* with right angle *C*.
Right triangle *DEF* with right angle *F*.
$$\overline{AC} \cong \overline{DF}$$
$$\overline{AB} \cong \overline{DE}$$
Prove: $\triangle ABC \cong \triangle DEF$

Draw and Deduce
Mark the diagram with the given information to visualize what you know.

Statements	Reasons
a. Right triangle *ABC* with right angle *C*. Right triangle *DEF* with right angle *F*.	
b. $\angle C \cong \angle F$	
c. $\overline{AC} \cong \overline{DF}$ and $\overline{AB} \cong \overline{DE}$	
d. $AC = DF$ and $AB = DE$	
e. $(AC)^2 = (DF)^2$ and $(AB)^2 = (DE)^2$	
f. $(AC)^2 + (CB)^2 = (AB)^2$ and $(DF)^2 + (FE)^2 = (DE)^2$	
g. $(AC)^2 + (CB)^2 = (DF)^2 + (FE)^2$	
h. $(CB)^2 = (FE)^2$	
i. $CB = FE$	
j. $\overline{CB} \cong \overline{FE}$	
k. $\triangle ABC \cong \triangle DEF$	

4. Sam used algebra to reason about the conjecture. Explain why Sam's reasoning is correct. Show your work.

Sam
So, $a^2 + x^2 = y^2$, and $b^2 + x^2 = y^2$. So $a = b$, and the triangles are congruent by SSS or SAS.

The **Hypotenuse-Leg (HL) Congruence Theorem** states: "If the hypotenuse and leg of one right triangle are congruent to the hypotenuse and leg of another right triangle, then the triangles are congruent."

Applying Triangle Congruence Theorems

You have learned about the Hypotenuse-Angle Congruence Theorem and the Hypotenuse-Leg Congruence Theorem. There are two other right angle theorems that can be proved with similar reasoning. The **Leg-Leg (LL) Congruence Theorem** states: "If the two corresponding shorter legs of two right triangles are congruent, then the two triangles are congruent." The **Leg-Angle (LA) Congruence Theorem** states: "If the leg and an acute angle of one right triangle are congruent to the corresponding leg and acute angle of another right triangle, then the triangles are congruent."

1. **Explain how the LL Congruence Theorem and the LA Congruence Theorem are each equivalent to another triangle congruence theorem that you know.**

Determine whether there is enough information to prove that the two triangles are congruent. If so, name the congruence theorem used.

2. **If $\overline{CS} \perp \overline{SD}$, $\overline{WD} \perp \overline{SD}$, and P is the midpoint of $\overline{CW}$, is $\triangle CSP \cong \triangle WDP$?**

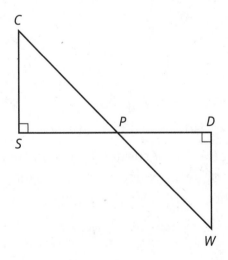

3. **Pat always trips on the third step and she thinks that step may be a different size. The contractor told her that all the treads and risers are perpendicular to each other. Is that enough information to state that the steps are the same size? In other words, if $\overline{WN} \perp \overline{NZ}$ and $\overline{ZH} \perp \overline{HK}$, is $\triangle WNZ \cong \triangle ZHK$?**

4. **If $\overline{JA} \perp \overline{MY}$ and $\overline{JY} \cong \overline{AY}$, is $\triangle JYM \cong \triangle AYM$?**

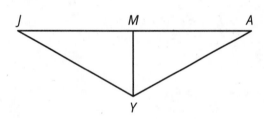

5. **If $\overline{ST} \perp \overline{SR}$, $\overline{AT} \perp \overline{AR}$, and $\angle STR \cong \angle ATR$, is $\triangle STR \cong \triangle ATR$?**

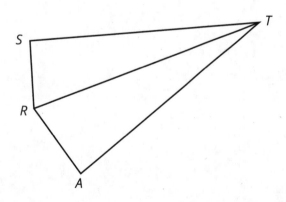

Consider point *P* located outside of circles *M*, *E*, and *S*. Lines *AF* and *BG* are drawn tangent to the circles as shown.

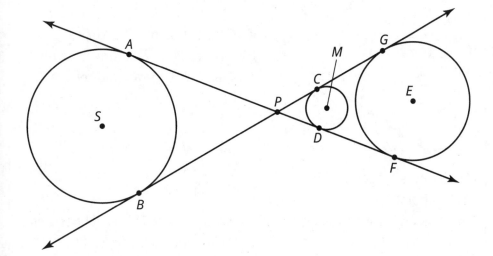

A **tangent segment** is a line segment formed by connecting a point outside of the circle to a point of tangency.

1. **Identify the two tangent segments drawn from point *P* associated with each circle. Then, compare the lengths of the two segments.**

    a. **circle *S***

    b. **circle *M***

    c. **circle *E***

Think about:

Which tools can you use to compare lengths?

It appears that tangent segments drawn from the same point on the exterior of a circle are congruent.

Worked Example

Consider this proof plan of the Tangent Segment Theorem.

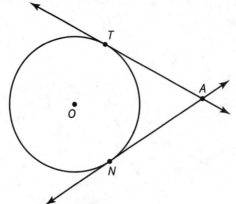

Given: $\overleftrightarrow{AT}$ is tangent to circle O at point T.
$\overleftrightarrow{AN}$ is tangent to circle O at point N.
Prove: $\overline{AT} \cong \overline{AN}$

$\overleftrightarrow{AT}$ is tangent to circle O at point T.
$\overleftrightarrow{AN}$ is tangent to circle O at point N.

Connect points O and T to form radius $\overline{OT}$. Connect points O and N to form radius $\overline{ON}$. Connect points O and A to form $\overline{OA}$.

$\overline{OT} \cong \overline{ON}$
$\overline{ON} \perp \overleftrightarrow{AN}$
$\overline{OT} \perp \overleftrightarrow{AT}$

$\angle ONA$ and $\angle OTA$ are right angles.
$\triangle ONA$ and $\triangle OTA$ are right triangles.

$\overline{OA} \cong \overline{OA}$
$\triangle ONA \cong \triangle OTA$
$\overline{AT} \cong \overline{AN}$

2. **How do you know that $OT = ON$?**

3. **How do you know that $\triangle ONA \cong \triangle OTA$?**

The **Tangent Segment Theorem** states: "If two tangent segments are drawn from the same point on the exterior of a circle, then the tangent segments are congruent."

4. In the figure, $\overleftrightarrow{KP}$ and $\overleftrightarrow{KS}$ are tangent to circle W and m∠PKS = 46°.
   Calculate m∠KPS. Explain your reasoning.

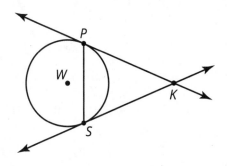

5. In the figure, $\overleftrightarrow{PS}$ is tangent to circle M and m∠SMO = 119°.
   Calculate m∠MPS. Explain your reasoning.

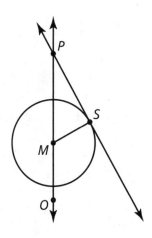

6. In the figure,
   • Circle B and circle O are tangent circles.
   • The length of radius BR is 4.
   • The length of radius OT is 7.
   • Segment RT is a common tangent.

   Calculate the length of segment RT.

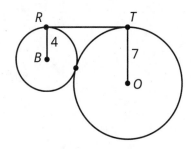

> **Tangent circles**
> are circles that lie in
> the same plane and
> intersect at exactly
> one point.

TALK the TALK

Congruence Theorems to the Rescue

You have many different theorems you can use to prove that two triangles are congruent depending on what you know. Let's consider how the right triangle congruence theorems are related to the triangle congruence theorems associated with all triangles.

1. **List the four triangle congruence theorems associated with right triangles.**

2. **List the four triangle congruence theorems associated with all triangles.**

3. **Associate each theorem in Question 1 with one or more related theorems in Question 2. Draw examples to justify your answers.**

Write

Describe how each right triangle congruence theorem compares to one or more triangle congruence theorems in your own words.

1. Hypotenuse-Leg (HL) Congruence Theorem
2. Leg-Leg (LL) Congruence Theorem
3. Leg-Angle (LA) Congruence Theorem

Remember

The Hypotenuse-Leg Congruence Theorem states that if the hypotenuse and leg of one right triangle are congruent to the hypotenuse and leg of another right triangle, then the triangles are congruent.

The Tangent Segment Theorem states that if two tangent segments are drawn from the same point on the exterior of a circle, then the tangent segments are congruent.

Practice

1. Determine the information that is needed to use the indicated theorem to show that the triangles are congruent.

a. △RQW ≅ △RPW by HL

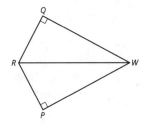

b. △JNZ ≅ △HNC by LA

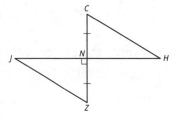

2. Calculate the measure of each angle. Explain your reasoning.

a. If $\overline{RS}$ is a tangent segment and $\overline{OS}$ is a radius, what is the measure of ∠ROS?

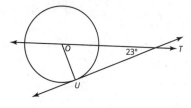

b. If $\overline{UT}$ is a tangent segment and $\overline{OU}$ is a radius, what is the measure of ∠TOU?

c. If $\overline{VW}$ is a tangent segment and $\overline{OV}$ is a radius, what is the measure of ∠VWO?

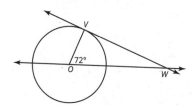

Stretch

In the figure shown, $\overline{EF}$ is tangent to the circle at F, and $\overline{EG}$ is tangent to the circle at G. Line segments HF, PG, HJ, and PJ are also tangent segments. If $m\overline{EF} = 10$ units, what is the perimeter of $\triangle EHP$? Explain your reasoning.

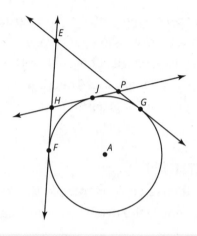

Review

1. In the figure shown, quadrilateral $ABCD$ is inscribed in circle P, $m\widehat{BC} = 55°$, $m\widehat{CD} = 109°$, and $m\widehat{DA} = 91°$. What are $m\angle A$, $m\angle B$, $m\angle C$, and $m\angle D$? Explain your reasoning.

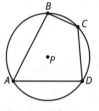

2. Consider circle O. The measure of $\angle EOD$ is 155°. The measure of $\angle A$ is 40°. Determine $m\widehat{BC}$.

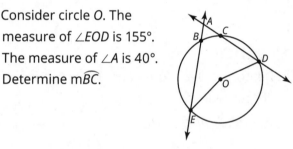

3. Identify the property that justifies the statement: If $\angle A \cong \angle B$ and $\angle B \cong \angle C$, then $\angle A \cong \angle C$.

4. Consider the figure. What theorem tells you that $\angle KXL \cong \angle MXN$?

5. Consider circle R with diameter $\overline{KN}$. Line JP is tangent to circle R at point P. The measure of $\angle J$ is 42°, the measure of $\angle LRM$ is 45°, and the measure of $\angle PRO$ is 80°. Determine the measure of $\widehat{KL}$.

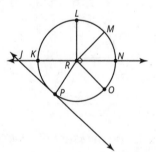

6. In the figure shown, quadrilateral $QRST$ is inscribed in circle B, $m\angle R = 98°$, and $m\angle Q$ is 14° more than $m\angle R$. What are $m\angle Q$, $m\angle S$, and $m\angle T$? Explain your reasoning.

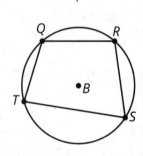

Props To You

Properties of Quadrilaterals

Warm Up

Draw a quadrilateral with the given property. Do not draw the same quadrilateral twice.

1. congruent angles

2. congruent diagonals

3. congruent sides

Learning Goals

- Prove the properties of a parallelogram, a rhombus, a rectangle, a square, a trapezoid, and a kite.
- Solve problems using the properties of a parallelogram, a rhombus, a rectangle, a square, a trapezoid, and a kite.

Key Terms

- Parallelogram/Congruent-Parallel Side Theorem
- base angles of a trapezoid
- Trapezoid Midsegment Theorem

You previously made conjectures about the properties of quadrilaterals using recorded observations. How can you use the theorems you have learned thus far to prove that quadrilaterals have the properties you reasoned about?

Making Connections

Recall the different properties of quadrilaterals you investigated in an earlier topic. In this activity you will consider how different properties are associated with one or more quadrilaterals.

1. **Locate the Organization of Quadrilaterals Flow Chart at the end of this lesson. Write the name of each quadrilateral inside its figure. Use markers to identify congruent sides and parallel sides so that the given label applies.**

2. **Locate and cut out the Properties of Quadrilaterals at the end of this lesson. Glue each property next to the figure to which it applies. If the property applies to more than one quadrilateral, glue it next to the most inclusive shape to which it applies.**

3. **How did you determine which property to glue within each shape category?**

On the Organization of Quadrilaterals Flow Chart, how do the arrows represent associations between the shapes?

4. **Is there a property associated with each category? If not, explain why.**

A parallelogram is defined as a quadrilateral with both pairs of opposite sides parallel. Through investigation you learned that opposite sides of a parallelogram are congruent. How can you prove this is true for all parallelograms?

1. **Consider parallelogram** *PARG* **with diagonals** $\overline{PR}$ **and** $\overline{AG}$ **intersecting at point** *M*.

   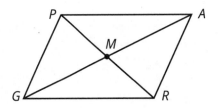

   a. **To prove both pairs of opposites sides of a parallelogram are congruent, which two triangles could you prove congruent? Explain your reasoning.**

   b. **How can you use the definition of a parallelogram to determine congruent angles in the triangles?**

   c. **What do the triangles share in common?**

2. **Use parallelogram** *PARG* **to prove that opposite sides of a parallelogram are congruent.**

   Given: Parallelogram *PARG* **with diagonals** $\overline{PR}$ **and** $\overline{AG}$ **intersecting at point** *M*
   Prove: $\overline{PG} \cong \overline{AR}$ **and** $\overline{GR} \cong \overline{PA}$

Now that you have proved that opposite sides of a parallelogram are congruent, you can use this property as a valid reason in future proofs.

Now let's consider how to prove that pairs of opposite angles of a parallelogram are congruent. There is not enough information from your previous proof to conclude that both pairs of opposite angles are congruent.

3. **What additional angles would you need to show congruent to prove that opposite angles of a parallelogram are congruent?**

Draw and Deduce
Which relationships have you proved that can be used in this proof?

4. **Use parallelogram *PARG* to prove that opposite angles of a parallelogram are congruent.**

   Given: Parallelogram *PARG* with diagonals $\overline{PR}$ and $\overline{AG}$ intersecting at point *M*
   Prove: ∠*GPA* ≅ ∠*ARG*

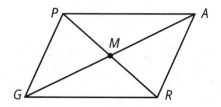

5. Prove that the diagonals of a parallelogram bisect each other using what you have already proved about the angles and sides of the parallelogram in Question 1.

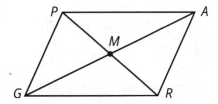

Draw and Deduce
Which segments in parallelogram *PARG* need to be proved congruent? Which triangles can help you prove their congruency?

6. Ray told his math teacher that he thinks a quadrilateral is a parallelogram if only one pair of opposite sides is known to be both congruent and parallel.

   Is Ray correct? Use the diagram from Question 1 to either prove or disprove his conjecture.

Ask yourself:

How can you prove that a pair of lines are parallel?

Draw and Deduce	The **Parallelogram/Congruent–Parallel Side Theorem** states: "If one pair of opposite sides of a quadrilateral is both congruent and parallel, then the quadrilateral is a parallelogram."

Draw and Deduce
What triangle congruence theorem can you use in your reasoning?

The **Parallelogram/Congruent–Parallel Side Theorem** states: "If one pair of opposite sides of a quadrilateral is both congruent and parallel, then the quadrilateral is a parallelogram."

A rhombus is a parallelogram with all sides congruent. Can this classification be proved?

7. **Prove that rhombus *RHOM* is a parallelogram.**

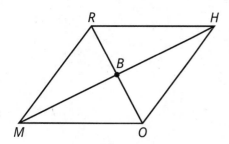

8. **Since a rhombus is a parallelogram, what properties hold true for all rhombi?**

9. **Prove that the diagonals of a rhombus are perpendicular. Use the rhombus in *RHOM*.**

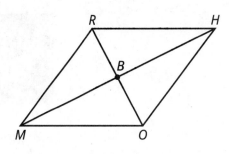

10. **Prove that the diagonals of a rhombus bisect the vertex angles. Use the rhombus *RHOM*.**

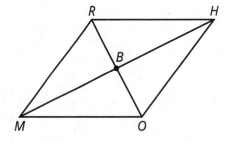

A rectangle is a parallelogram with all angles congruent. Can you prove that this is true for all rectangles?

1. Consider rectangle *ABCD*.

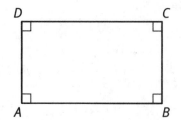

   a. What is the measure of each angle? Explain your reasoning.

   b. What do the angle measures tell you about the relationships between adjacent sides?

   c. What theorem can you use to prove $\overline{DA} \parallel \overline{CB}$ and $\overline{DC} \parallel \overline{AB}$? Is this enough information to conclude rectangle *ABCD* is a parallelogram? Explain your reasoning.

   d. Based on your reasoning, what properties hold true for all rectangles?

2. **Prove that the diagonals of a rectangle are congruent.**

   Given: Rectangle *RECT* with diagonals $\overline{RC}$ and $\overline{ET}$
   intersecting at point *A*

   Prove: $\overline{RC} \cong \overline{TE}$

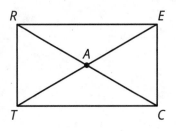

A square is a parallelogram with all angles and all sides congruent.

3. **Margot says you have to prove that the diagonals of a square are perpendicular and congruent, and they bisect the vertex angles. Vanessa says you don't have to prove these properties of a square. Who is correct? Explain your reasoning.**

A trapezoid is a quadrilateral with at least one pair of parallel sides. When
a trapezoid has exactly one pair of parallel sides, the parallel sides are
called the bases and its non-parallel sides are called the legs. The **base
angles of a trapezoid** are either pair of angles that share a base as
a common side.

Recall that an isosceles trapezoid is a trapezoid with congruent non-parallel
sides. You conjectured that the base angles of an isosceles trapezoid
are congruent.

Worked Example

You can prove that the base angles of an
isosceles trapezoid are congruent.

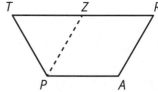

Given: Isosceles Trapezoid $TRAP$ with $\overline{TR} \parallel \overline{PA}$,
$\overline{TP} \cong \overline{RA}$
Prove: $\angle T \cong \angle R$

Statements	Reasons
1. Isosceles Trapezoid $TRAP$ with $\overline{TR} \parallel \overline{PA}$, $\overline{TP} \cong \overline{RA}$	1. Given
2. $\overline{ZP} \parallel \overline{RA}$	2. Construction
3. Quadrilateral $ZRAP$ is a parallelogram.	3. Definition of parallelogram
4. $\overline{ZP} \cong \overline{RA}$	4. Opposite sides of a parallelogram are congruent
5. $\overline{TP} \cong \overline{ZP}$	5. Transitive Property
6. $\triangle TPZ$ is an isosceles triangle.	6. Definition of isosceles triangle
7. $\angle T \cong \angle TZP$	7. Isosceles Triangle Theorem
8. $\angle TZP \cong \angle R$	8. Corresponding Angle Theorem
9. $\angle T \cong \angle R$	9. Transitive Property

1. Analyze the worked example.

   a. How does constructing $\overline{ZP}$ parallel to $\overline{RA}$ help lead to the conclusion?

   b. Why is Step 8 important?

2. You must also prove $\angle A \cong \angle TPA$. Show $\angle A \cong \angle TPA$.

3. Kala insists that if a trapezoid with one pair of parallel sides has one pair of congruent base angles, then the trapezoid must be isosceles. She thinks proving two pairs of base angles are congruent is not necessary. Is Kala correct? Use reasoning and the trapezoid from the worked example to justify your answer.

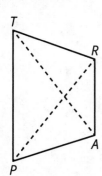

4. **Prove that the diagonals of an isosceles trapezoid are congruent.**

Given: Isosceles trapezoid *TRAP* with $\overline{TP} \parallel \overline{RA}$,
$\overline{TR} \cong \overline{PA}$, and diagonals $\overline{TA}$ and $\overline{PR}$

Prove: $\overline{TA} \cong \overline{PR}$

You also conjectured that the length of the midsegment connecting the legs of a trapezoid is half the sum of its base lengths, and that the midsegment is parallel to each base.

To prove this conjecture regarding the midsegment of a trapezoid, it is necessary to connect points *M* and *E* of trapezoid *MDSG* to form $\overline{ME}$, and then extend $\overline{ME}$ until it intersects the extension of $\overline{DS}$ at point *T*.

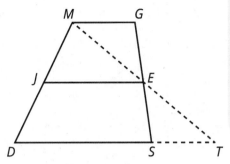

5. Complete the Prove statement and answer each question to plan to prove the Trapezoid Midsegment Theorem.

   a. Given: *MDSG* is a trapezoid with bases $\overline{MG}$ and $\overline{DS}$.
      J is the midpoint of $\overline{MD}$.
      E is the midpoint of $\overline{GS}$.

      Prove:

   b. Is ∠*MGE* is congruent to ∠*TSE*? Explain your reasoning.

   c. Is △*MGE* congruent to △*TSE*? Explain your reasoning.

   d. How does $\overline{JE}$ relate to △*MDT*? Explain your reasoning.

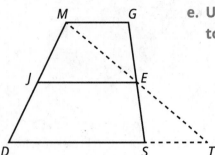

e. Use the Midsegment of a Triangle Theorem and reasoning to prove that $\overline{JE} \parallel \overline{MG}$ and $\overline{JE} \parallel \overline{DS}$.

f. Use the Midsegment of a Triangle Theorem and reasoning to prove that $JE = \frac{1}{2}(MG + DS)$.

The **Trapezoid Midsegment Theorem** states: "The midsegment that connects the legs of a trapezoid is parallel to each of the bases and its length is one half the sum of the lengths of the bases."

Recall the conjectures you have made about kites. A kite is a quadrilateral with two pairs of congruent adjacent sides. When a kite is not a parallelogram, it has its own properties.

Consider kite *KITE* with diagonals $\overline{KT}$ and $\overline{IE}$.

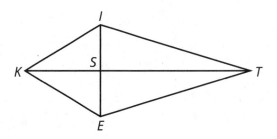

- Only one pair of opposite angles are congruent. It is the pair of angles formed by the non-congruent sides. So, $\angle KIT \cong \angle KET$.
- Only one diagonal bisects the other. The diagonal that is bisected connects the vertices of the congruent angles. So, $\overline{IS} \cong \overline{ES}$.
- The other diagonal bisects the opposite vertex angles it connects. So, $\angle IKS \cong \angle EKS$ and $\angle ITS \cong \angle ETS$.

1. **To prove that two opposite angles of a kite are congruent, which triangles in kite *KITE* would you prove congruent? Explain your reasoning.**

2. **Prove that the two opposite angles of a kite are congruent.**

   Given: Kite *KITE* with diagonals $\overline{KT}$ and $\overline{IE}$ intersecting at point *S*.
   Prove: $\angle KIT \cong \angle KET$

3. Do you have enough information to conclude $\overline{KT}$ bisects $\angle IKE$ and $\angle ITE$? Explain your reasoning.

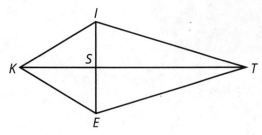

4. What two triangles could you use to prove $\overline{IS} \cong \overline{ES}$?

5. If $\overline{IS} \cong \overline{ES}$, is that enough information to determine that one diagonal of a kite bisects the other diagonal? Explain your reasoning.

6. Prove that the diagonals of a kite are perpendicular to each other.

7. What does your proof tell you about the classification of a rhombus?

Use what you know about the properties of quadrilaterals to solve
each problem.

1. **Ofelia is making a square mat for a picture frame. How can she make sure the mat is a square using only a ruler?**

2. **Gretchen is putting together a bookcase. It came with diagonal support bars that are to be screwed into the top and bottom on the back of the bookcase. Unfortunately, the instructions were lost and Gretchen does not have the directions or a measuring tool. She has a screwdriver, a marker, and a piece of string. How can Gretchen attach the supports to make certain the bookcase will be a rectangle and the shelves are parallel to the ground?**

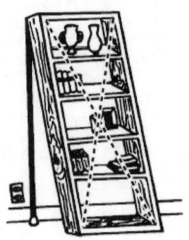

3. **Ms. Baker told her geometry students that anyone bringing in a picture of a flag with a parallelogram would get extra credit.**

a. **Albert brought in a picture of the United States flag. The teacher handed Albert a ruler and told him to prove the quadrilateral that contains the stars is a parallelogram. What are two ways Albert could prove the specified quadrilateral is a parallelogram?**

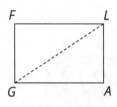

b. **Ms. Baker told Albert he needed to prove that if a quadrilateral has opposite sides congruent, then the quadrilateral is a parallelogram. Use the diagram to help Albert prove the statement.**

Given: Quadrilateral *FLAG* with diagonal $\overline{GL}$, $\overline{FL} \cong \overline{GA}$, $\overline{LA} \cong \overline{GF}$

Prove: Quadrilateral *FLAG* is a parallelogram.

4. Ms. Baker held up two different lengths of rope shown and a piece of chalk. She asked her students if they could use this rope and chalk to construct a rhombus on the blackboard. Rena raised her hand and said she could construct a rhombus with the materials. Ms. Baker handed Rena the chalk and rope. What did Rena do?

5. Could quadrilaterals 1, 2, and 3 on the kite shown be squares if the kite is not a parallelogram? Explain your reasoning.

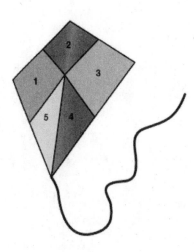

TALK the TALK

Name That Shape

1. Mr. King said he was thinking of a quadrilateral and
   wanted his students to name the quadrilateral. He said he
   would answer a few yes-no questions to give them a hint.
   What questions would you ask Mr. King?

2. What is the fewest number of questions you could
   ask Mr. King to be sure you know the correct answer?
   Explain your reasoning.

Organization of Quadrilaterals Flow Chart

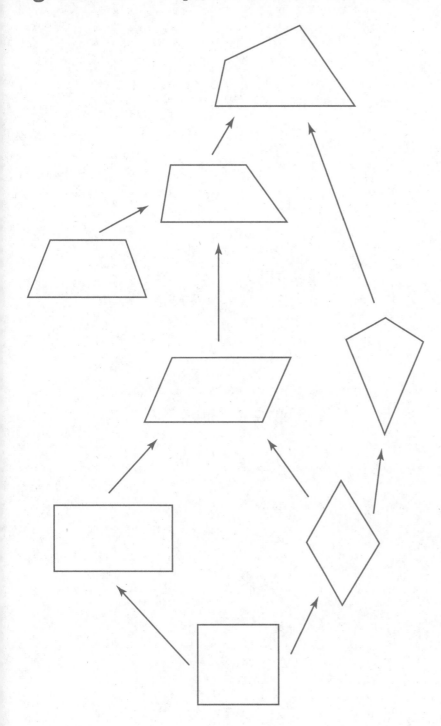

Properties of Quadrilaterals

two diagonals	two pairs of adjacent congruent sides	opposite angles are congruent
four sides	diagonals bisect each other	all sides are congruent
diagonals are congruent	all angles are congruent	opposite sides are congruent
diagonals are perpendicular	at least one pair of parallel sides	diagonals are congruent

Write

Define each term in your own words.

1. Parallelogram/Congruent-Parallel Side Theorem
2. base angles of a trapezoid
3. Trapezoid Midsegment Theorem

Remember

- Properties of a parallelogram: opposite sides are parallel and congruent; opposite angles are congruent; diagonals bisect each other
- Properties of a rhombus: all sides are congruent; diagonals are perpendicular and bisect the vertex angles
- Properties of a rectangle: angles and diagonals are congruent
- Properties of isosceles trapezoids: base angles are congruent; diagonals are congruent
- Properties of a kite: two pairs of adjacent, congruent sides; one pair of opposite angles congruent; one diagonal bisects the other and the vertex angles; diagonals are perpendicular

Practice

1. The neighbors in a rural community get together for a barn-raising. The first step is to build the rectangular base of the barn. One neighbor explains to everyone how diagonals can be used to verify the base is rectangular. What could the neighbor have said?
2. Jim tells you he is thinking of a quadrilateral that is either a square or a rhombus, but not both. He wants you to guess which quadrilateral he is thinking of and allows you to ask one question about the quadrilateral. Which question should you ask?
3. Consider the Ace of Diamonds playing card shown. The large diamond in the center of the playing card is a quadrilateral. Classify the quadrilateral based only on each piece of given information.

   a. The diagonals of the quadrilateral bisect each other.
   b. The four sides of the quadrilateral are congruent.
   c. The four angles and the four sides of the quadrilateral are congruent.
   d. The diagonals of the quadrilateral bisect the vertex angles.
   e. The four angles of the quadrilateral are congruent.
   f. The opposite sides of the quadrilateral are both congruent and parallel.
   g. The opposite angles of the quadrilateral are congruent.

Stretch

1. Consider the circle shown. Diameter *MI* is perpendicular to chord *DA*.

   Write a conjecture about the relationship between a diameter and a chord when they are perpendicular. Prove that your conjecture is true in all cases.

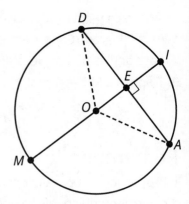

Review

1. Determine the information that is needed to show that △*ABC* ≅ △*QRS* by the HL Congruence Theorem.

 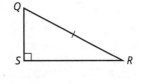

2. If $\overline{MP}$ is a tangent segment and $\overline{OP}$ is a radius, what is the measure of ∠*MOP*? Explain your reasoning.

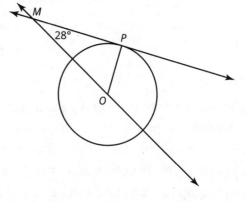

3. An inflatable slide is modeled from a triangle as shown. The length of the shorter leg of the triangle is 12 feet. Use the 30°-60°-90° Triangle Theorem to determine the length of the hypotenuse and the longer leg of the triangle.

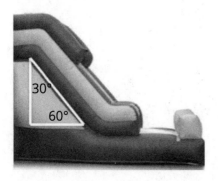

4. Shen and Marco both live the same distance from the school. Shen's house is 51.3° northwest of the school, and Marco's house is 51.3° northeast of the school. If the distance from the school to the stop sign is 0.5 mile, how far is it from the school to the traffic light? Explain your reasoning.

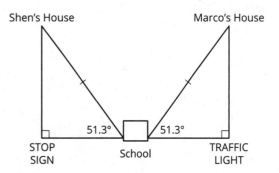

5. Determine the measure of the unknown angle in each figure.

a.

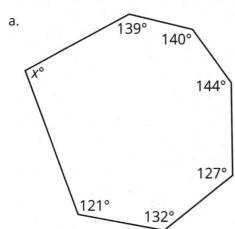

b.

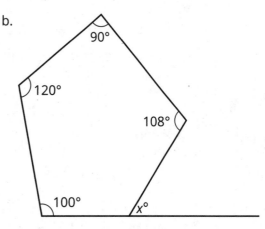

Three-Chord Song

Relationships Between Chords

Warm Up

1. Identify the geometric objects and then write everything you know about this diagram.

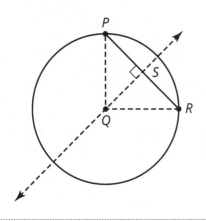

Learning Goals

- Prove the Diameter-Chord Theorem.
- Prove the Equidistant Chord Theorem and its converse.
- Prove the Congruent Chord–Congruent Arc Theorem and its converse.

Key Terms

- Diameter-Chord Theorem
- Equidistant Chord Theorem
- Equidistant Chord Converse Theorem
- Congruent Chord–Congruent Arc Theorem
- Congruent Chord–Congruent Arc Converse Theorem

You have analyzed relationships among angles and chords. What relationships exist between chord lengths and other parts of a circle?

That Darn Kitty!

A neighbor gave you a plate of cookies as a housewarming present. Before you could eat a single cookie, the cat jumped onto the kitchen counter and knocked the cookie plate onto the floor, shattering it into many pieces. The cookie plate will need to be replaced and returned to the neighbor. Unfortunately, cookie plates come in various sizes and you need to know the exact diameter of the broken plate. It would be impossible to reassemble all of the broken pieces, but one large chunk has remained intact.

You think that there has to be an easy way to determine the diameter of the broken plate. As you sit staring at the large piece of the broken plate, your sister Sarah comes home from school. You update her on the latest crisis, and she begins to smile. Sarah tells you not to worry because she learned how to solve for the diameter of the plate in geometry class today. She gets a piece of paper, a compass, a straightedge, a ruler, and a marker out of her backpack and says, "Watch this!"

1. **What do you think Sarah did?**

Chords and their perpendicular bisectors lead to several interesting conclusions. In this lesson, you will make conjectures about the relationships among some special segments of circles and prove theorems about these geometric relationships.

1. **Consider circle *C* with points *B*, *Y*, and *R*.**

   a. **Draw chords $\overline{YR}$, $\overline{BR}$, and $\overline{BY}$ and construct the perpendicular bisector of each chord.**

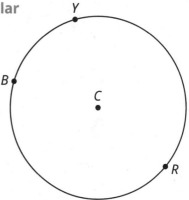

   b. **What do you notice about the relationship between the perpendicular bisectors of a chord and the center point of the circle?**

Think
about:

Which point of concurrency is associated with the perpendicular bisectors of a triangle?

The perpendicular bisector of a chord appears to also bisect the chord's intercepted arc. This observation can be proved and stated as a theorem.

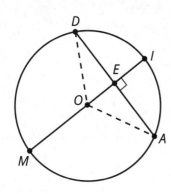

2. **Prove this relationship between the perpendicular bisector of a chord and the chord's intercepted arc.**

   Given: $\overline{MI}$ is a diameter of circle O.
   $\overline{MI} \perp \overline{DA}$

   Prove: $\overline{MI}$ bisects $\overline{DA}$.
   $\overline{MI}$ bisects $\overarc{DA}$.

Statements	Reasons
1. $\overline{MI}$ is a diameter of circle O. $\overline{MI} \perp \overline{DA}$	1. Given
2. Connect points O and D to form radius $\overline{OD}$. Connect points O and A to form radius $\overline{OA}$.	2. Construction

The **Diameter-Chord Theorem** states: "If a circle's diameter is perpendicular to a chord, then the diameter bisects the chord and bisects the arc determined by the chord."

3. Use circle *T* to draw two congruent chords that are not parallel to each other and do not pass through the center point of the circle.

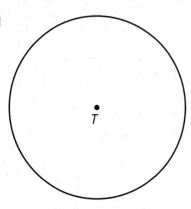

a. Construct the perpendicular bisector of each chord.

b. Choose a construction tool and compare the distance each chord is from the center point of the circle.

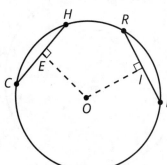

Congruent chords appear to be equidistant from the center point of the circle. This observation can be proved and stated as a theorem.

4. Prove this relationship regarding chords.

Given: $\overline{CH} \cong \overline{DR}$

$\overline{OE} \perp \overline{CH}$

$\overline{OI} \perp \overline{DR}$

Prove: $\overline{CH}$ and $\overline{DR}$ are equidistant from center O.

Here's a hint. You need to show $OE = OI$.

Statements	Reasons
1. $\overline{CH} \cong \overline{DR}$ $\overline{OE} \perp \overline{CH}$ $\overline{OI} \perp \overline{DR}$	1. Given
2. Connect points O and H, O and C, O and D, and O and R to form radii $\overline{OH}$, $\overline{OC}$, $\overline{OD}$, and $\overline{OR}$, respectively.	2. Construction

The **Equidistant Chord Theorem** states: "If two chords of the same circle or congruent circles are congruent, then they are equidistant from the center of the circle."

Let's conjecture that the converse of this theorem is also true. That is, if two chords of the same circle or congruent circles are equidistant from the center of the circle, then the chords are congruent.

5. **Prove this converse statement is true in all cases.**

   Given: *OE* = *OI*

   ($\overline{CH}$ and $\overline{DR}$ are equidistant from the center point.)

   $\overline{OE} \perp \overline{CH}$

   $\overline{OI} \perp \overline{DR}$

   Prove: $\overline{CH} \cong \overline{DR}$

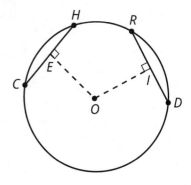

Statements	Reasons
1. *OE* = *OI* $\overline{OE} \perp \overline{CH}$ $\overline{OI} \perp \overline{DR}$	1. Given
2. Connect points *O* and *H*, *O* and *C*, *O* and *D*, and *O* and *R* to form radii $\overline{OH}$, $\overline{OC}$, $\overline{OD}$, and $\overline{OR}$, respectively.	2. Construction

> The **Equidistant Chord Converse Theorem** states: "If two chords of the same circle or congruent circles are equidistant from the center of the circle, then the chords are congruent."

ACTIVITY

3.2 Chords and Arcs

The color wheel is made of three different kinds of colors: primary, secondary, and tertiary. Primary colors (red, blue, and yellow) are the colors you start with. Secondary colors (orange, green, and purple) are created by mixing two primary colors. Tertiary colors (red-orange, yellow-orange, yellow-green, blue-green, blue-purple, red-purple) are created by mixing a primary color with a secondary color.

1. **Consider circle C shown.**

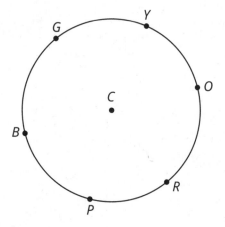

   a. **Draw two congruent chords.**

   b. **Draw four radii by connecting the endpoints of each chord with the center point of the circle.**

Color theory is a set of rules that is used to create color combinations. A color wheel is a visual representation of color theory.

2. **Make a conjecture about the two central angles and the two intercepted minor arcs formed by each pair of radii.**

It appears that if two chords of the same circle or congruent circles are congruent, then their corresponding arcs are congruent. Let's prove this conjecture.

3. **Prove this conjecture relating chords and their corresponding arcs.**

Given: $\overline{CH} \cong \overline{DR}$
Prove: $\overparen{CH} \cong \overparen{DR}$

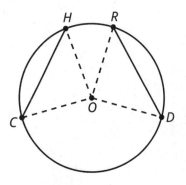

Remember:

Don't forget to write a statement for the construction that was made.

The **Congruent Chord–Congruent Arc Theorem** states: "If two chords of the same circle or congruent circles are congruent, then their corresponding arcs are congruent."

The **Congruent Chord–Congruent Arc Converse Theorem** states: "If arcs of the same circle or congruent circles are congruent, then their corresponding chords are congruent."

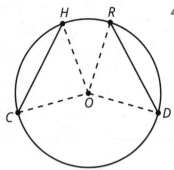

4. **Prove the Congruent Chord–Congruent Arc Converse Theorem.**

Given: $\overset{\frown}{CH} \cong \overset{\frown}{DR}$

Prove: $\overline{CH} \cong \overline{DR}$

Statements	Reasons
1. $\overset{\frown}{CH} \cong \overset{\frown}{DR}$	1. Given
2. Connect points O and H, O and C, O and D, and O and R to form radii OH, OC, OD, and OR, respectively.	2. Construction

TALK the TALK

Broken Plate

1. Write the Equidistant Chord Theorem and its converse as a biconditional statement.

2. Write the Congruent Chord–Congruent Arc Theorem and its converse as a biconditional statement.

Consider the problem from the Getting Started.

3. **Describe how Sarah can determine the diameter of the plate with the broken piece. Then, show your work on the broken plate shown.**

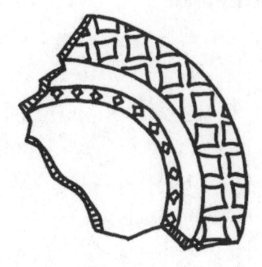

Assignment

Write

Match each definition with its corresponding term.

1. Diameter–Chord Theorem

    a. If two chords of the same circle or congruent circles are congruent, then their corresponding arcs are congruent.

2. Equidistant Chord Theorem

    b. If two chords of the same circle or congruent circles are congruent, then they are equidistant from the center of the circle.

3. Equidistant Chord Converse Theorem

    c. If two arcs of the same circle or congruent Arc Theorem circles are congruent, then their corresponding chords are congruent.

4. Congruent Chord–Congruent Arc Theorem

    d. If two chords of the same circle or congruent circles are equidistant from the center of the circle, then the chords are congruent.

5. Congruent Chord–Congruent Arc Converse Theorem

    e. If a diameter of a circle is perpendicular to a chord, then the diameter bisects the chord and bisects the arc determined by the chord.

Remember

The Diameter–Chord Theorem states: "If a circle's diameter is perpendicular to a chord, then the diameter bisects the chord and bisects the arc determined by the chord."

The Equidistant Chord Theorem states: "If two chords of the same circle or congruent circles are congruent, then they are equidistant from the center of the circle."

The Congruent Chord–Congruent Arc Theorem states: "If two chords of the same circle or congruent circles are congruent, then their corresponding arcs are congruent."

Practice

1. Use circle *T* to complete parts (*a*) through (*g*).

   a. Draw an inscribed right angle in circle *T*. Label each point where the angle intersects the circle. What is the name of the right angle?

   b. Draw the chord determined by the inscribed right angle. What is the name of the chord?

   c. Draw a second inscribed right angle in circle *T*. Label each point where the angle intersects the circle. What is the name of the second right angle?

   d. Draw the chord determined by the second inscribed right angle. What is the name of the chord?

   e. Describe the relationship between the arcs that correspond to the chords you named in parts (b) and (d). Explain your reasoning.

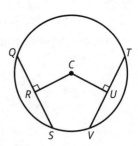

2. The figure shows a section of a circle. Draw two chords and construct their perpendicular bisectors to locate the center of the circle. Explain your work.

3. In circle *G* shown below, *MG* = 1.84 centimeters, *GL* = 1.98 centimeters, m∠*GLH* = 90°, and m∠*GMK* = 90°. Determine which chord is longer, $\overline{IH}$ or $\overline{JK}$. Explain your reasoning.

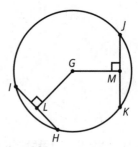

Stretch

1. The circle shown has a diameter of 40 centimeters. The length of *RC* is 12 centimeters, and the length of *UV* is 16 centimeters.

   a. Determine the length of *CU*. Explain your reasoning.

   b. Determine the length of *QS*. Explain your reasoning.

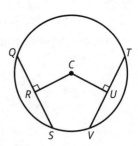

Review

1. Paloma tells you she is thinking of a quadrilateral that is either a rectangle or a square, but not both. She wants you to guess which quadrilateral she is thinking of and allows you to ask one question about the quadrilateral. What question should you ask?

2. Consider the kite shown. The kite without the tail is a quadrilateral. Classify the quadrilateral based only on each piece of given information.

   a. The diagonals of the quadrilateral are perpendicular to each other and bisect each other.

   b. The four angles and the four sides of the quadrilateral are congruent.

3. Given: ∠3 is supplementary to ∠6, ∠1 ≅ ∠12, and m∠12 = 52°. Using the diagram in conjunction with postulates and theorems, determine the measures of the unknown angles.

4. If ∠1 ≅ ∠5, which theorem leads to the conclusion that $Q \parallel S$?

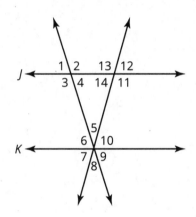

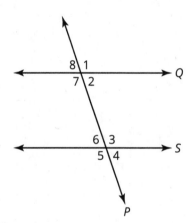

5. The degree measure of each exterior angle of a regular decagon is represented by the expression $5x + 1$. Solve for x.

Using Congruence Theorems Summary

KEY TERMS

- Hypotenuse-Leg (HL) Congruence Theorem
- Leg-Leg (LL) Congruence Theorem
- Leg-Angle (LA) Congruence Theorem
- tangent segment
- Tangent Segment Theorem

- tangent circles
- Parallelogram/Congruent–Parallel Side Theorem
- base angles of a trapezoid
- Trapezoid Midsegment Theorem
- Diameter–Chord Theorem
- Equidistant Chord Theorem

- Equidistant Chord Converse Theorem
- Congruent Chord–Congruent Arc Theorem
- Congruent Chord–Congruent Arc Converse Theorem

LESSON 1 SSS, SAS, AAS, ... S.O.S!

Many congruence theorems apply to all triangles. There are also theorems that only apply to right triangles. Methods for proving that two right triangles are congruent are somewhat shorter. You can prove that two right triangles are congruent using only two measurements.

The **Hypotenuse-Leg (HL) Congruence Theorem** states: "If the hypotenuse and leg of one right triangle are congruent to the hypotenuse and leg of another right triangle, then the triangles are congruent." For example, given $\overline{AC} \cong \overline{DF}$ and $\overline{AB} \cong \overline{DE}$, then $\triangle ABC \cong \triangle DEF$.

The **Leg-Leg (LL) Congruence Theorem** states: "If the two corresponding shorter legs of two right triangles are congruent, then the two triangles are congruent." For example, given $\overline{AC} \cong \overline{DF}$ and $\overline{BC} \cong \overline{EF}$, then $\triangle ABC \cong \triangle DEF$.

The **Leg-Angle (LA) Congruence Theorem** states: "If the leg and an acute angle of one right triangle are congruent to the corresponding leg and acute angle of another right triangle, then the triangles are congruent." For example, given $\overline{AC} \cong \overline{DF}$ and $\angle A \cong \angle D$, then $\triangle ABC \cong \triangle DEF$.

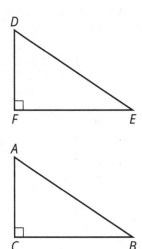

A **tangent segment** is a line segment formed by connecting a point outside of the circle to a point of tangency. The **Tangent Segment Theorem** states that if two tangent segments are drawn from the same point on the exterior of a circle, then the tangent segments are congruent. For example, $\overline{CB}$ is tangent to circle A at point B and $\overline{CD}$ is tangent to circle A at point D. Therefore, $\overline{CB} \cong \overline{CD}$.

Tangent circles are circles that lie in the same plane and intersect at exactly one point. For example, circle A and circle E are tangent circles.

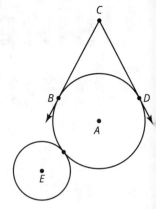

Props to You

A parallelogram is a quadrilateral with both pairs of opposite sides parallel. The **Parallelogram/Congruent–Parallel Side Theorem** states: "If one pair of opposite sides of a quadrilateral is both congruent and parallel, then the quadrilateral is a parallelogram." For example, given quadrilateral $RHOM$, $\overline{RM} \cong \overline{OH}$, and $\overline{RM} \parallel \overline{OH}$, then quadrilateral $RHOM$ is a parallelogram.

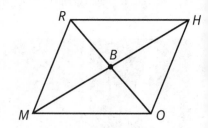

A rectangle is a quadrilateral with opposite sides congruent and all angles congruent. A rectangle is a parallelogram. A square is a quadrilateral with all angles and all sides congruent. A square is a rectangle.

A trapezoid is a quadrilateral with at least one pair of parallel sides. When a trapezoid has exactly one pair of parallel sides, the bases of the trapezoid are its parallel sides and the legs of the trapezoid are its non-parallel sides. The **base angles of a trapezoid** are either pair of angles that share a base as a common side. An isosceles trapezoid is a trapezoid with congruent non-parallel sides. The base angles of an isosceles trapezoid are congruent. For example, quadrilateral $TRAP$ is an isosceles trapezoid with bases $\overline{TR}$ and $\overline{PA}$. Therefore, $\angle T \cong \angle R$ and $\angle A \cong \angle P$.

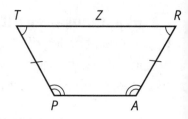

The length of the midsegment connecting the legs of a trapezoid is half the sum of its base lengths. The **Trapezoid Midsegment Theorem** states: "The midsegment that connects the legs of a trapezoid is parallel to each of the bases and its length is one half the sum of the lengths of the bases." For example, in trapezoid $MGSD$, $\overline{JE}$ is a midsegment connecting the legs of the trapezoid. Therefore, it is parallel to each of the bases and $JE = \frac{1}{2}(MG + DS)$.

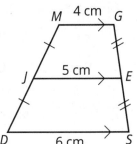

A kite is a quadrilateral with two pairs of congruent adjacent sides. When a kite is not a parallelogram, it has its own properties.

Consider kite $KITE$ with diagonals $\overline{KT}$ and $\overline{IE}$.

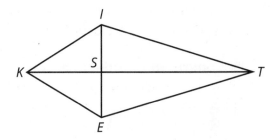

- Only one pair of opposite angles are congruent. It is the pair of angles formed by the non-congruent sides. So, $\angle KIT \cong \angle KET$.

- Only one diagonal bisects the other. The diagonal that is bisected connects the vertices of the congruent angles. So, $\overline{IS} \cong \overline{ES}$.

- The other diagonal bisects the opposite vertex angles it connects. So, $\angle IKS \cong \angle EKS$ and $\angle ITS \cong \angle ETS$.

LESSON

3

Three-Chord Song

The **Diameter–Chord Theorem** states: "If a circle's diameter is perpendicular to a chord, then the diameter bisects the chord and bisects the arc determined by the chord." For example, in circle O, diameter $\overline{IM} \perp$ chord $\overline{DA}$. Therefore, $\overline{DE} \cong \overline{AE}$ and $\overparen{DI} \cong \overparen{AI}$.

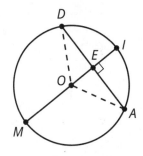

The **Equidistant Chord Theorem** states: "If two chords of the same circle or congruent circles are congruent, then they are equidistant from the center of the circle." For example, in circle A, chord $\overline{BC} \cong$ chord $\overline{DE}$. Therefore, $AF = AG$.

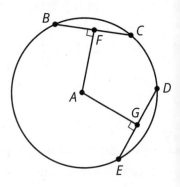

The **Equidistant Chord Converse Theorem** states: "If two chords of the same circle or congruent circles are equidistant from the center of the circle, then the chords are congruent."

The **Congruent Chord–Congruent Arc Theorem** states: "If two chords of the same circle or congruent circles are congruent, then their corresponding arcs are congruent." For example, in circle A, $\overset{\frown}{BC} \cong \overset{\frown}{DE}$.

The **Congruent Chord–Congruent Arc Converse Theorem** states: "If two arcs of the same circle or congruent circles are congruent, then their corresponding chords are congruent."

Glossary

A

Addition Property of Equality

The addition property of equality states: "If $a = b$, then $a + c = b + c$."

Example

If $x = 2$, then $x + 5 = 2 + 5$, or $x + 5 = 7$ is an example of the Addition Property of Equality.

Addition Rule for Probability

The Addition Rule for Probability states: "The probability that Event A occurs or Event B occurs is the probability that Event A occurs plus the probability that Event B occurs minus the probability that both A and B occur."

$$P(A \text{ or } B) = P(A) + P(B) = P(A \text{ and } B)$$

Example

You flip a coin two times. Calculate the probability of flipping a heads on the first flip or flipping a heads on the second flip.

Let A represent the event of flipping a heads on the first flip. Let B represent the event of flipping a heads on the second flip.

$P(A \text{ or } B) = P(A) + P(B) - P(A \text{ and } B)$

$P(A \text{ or } B) = \frac{1}{2} + \frac{1}{2} - \frac{1}{4}$

$P(A \text{ or } B) = \frac{3}{4}$

So, the probability of flipping a heads on the first flip or flipping a heads on the second flip is $\frac{3}{4}$.

adjacent arcs

Adjacent arcs are two arcs of the same circle sharing a common endpoint.

Example

Arcs ZA and AB are adjacent arcs.

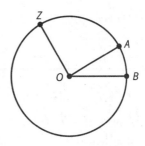

adjacent side

The adjacent side of a triangle is the side adjacent to the reference angle that is not the hypotenuse.

Example

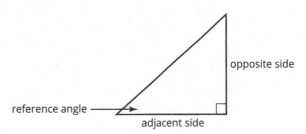

altitude

An altitude is a line segment drawn from a vertex of a triangle perpendicular to the line containing the opposite side.

Example

Segment *EG* is an altitude of △*FED*.

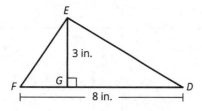

angle

An angle is formed by two rays that share a common endpoint.

angle bisector

An angle bisector is a ray drawn through the vertex of an angle that divides the angle into two angles of equal measure, or two congruent angles.

Example

Ray *BY* is an angle bisector.

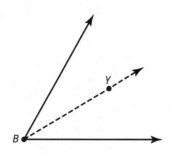

angle of incidence

The angle of incidence is the angle formed by the incidence ray and a line perpendicular to the surface of a mirror.

Example

The angle of incidence measures 40°.

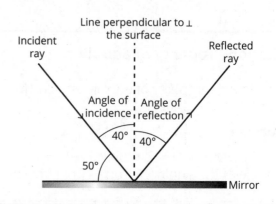

angle of reflection

The angle of reflection is the angle formed by the reflected ray and a line perpendicular to the surface of a mirror.

Example

The angle of reflection measures 40°.

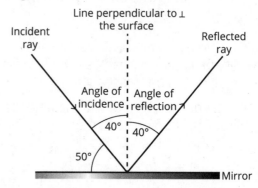

angular velocity

Angular velocity is a type of circular velocity described as an amount of angle movement in radians over a specified amount of time. Angular velocity can be expressed as $\omega = \frac{\theta}{t}$, where ω = angular velocity, θ = angular measurement in radians, and t = time.

arc

An arc is a part of a circle that is the curve between two points on the circle. An arc is named using its two endpoints.

Example

Arc CD is an arc of circle O. The symbol used to describe arc CD is $\overset{\frown}{CD}$.

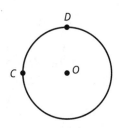

arc length

An arc length is a portion of the circumference of a circle. The length of an arc of a circle can be calculated by multiplying the circumference of the circle by the ratio of the measure of the arc to 360°.

$$\text{arc length} = 2\pi r \cdot \frac{x°}{360°}$$

Example

In circle A, the radius $\overline{AB}$ is 3 centimeters and the measure of $\overset{\frown}{BC}$ is 83 degrees.

$$(2\pi r)\left(\frac{\text{m}\overset{\frown}{BC}}{360°}\right) = 2\pi(3)\left(\frac{83}{360°}\right)$$
$$\approx 4.35$$

So, the length of $\overset{\frown}{BC}$ is approximately 4.35 centimeters.

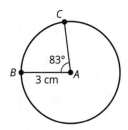

auxiliary line

An auxiliary line is a line that is drawn to help complete a geometric proof.

Example

An auxiliary line is drawn parallel to $\overleftrightarrow{AB}$ through point C.

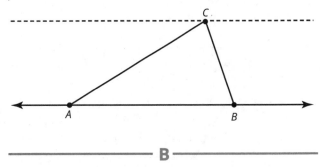

B

base angles of an isosceles triangle

The base angles of an isosceles triangle are the angles between the base and the congruent sides of the triangle.

Example

Angles A and C are the base angles of isosceles triangle ABC.

base angles of a trapezoid

The base angles of a trapezoid are either pair of angles that share a base as a common side.

Example

Angle *T* and angle *R* are one pair of base angles of trapezoid *PART*. Angle *P* and angle *A* are another pair of base angles.

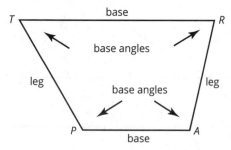

biconditional statement

A biconditional statement is a statement written in the form "if and only if *p*, then *q*." It is a combination of both a conditional statement and the converse of that conditional statement. A biconditional statement is true only when the conditional statement and the converse of the statement are both true.

Example

Consider the property of an isosceles trapezoid: "The diagonals of an isosceles trapezoid are congruent." The property states that if a trapezoid is isosceles, then the diagonals are congruent. The converse of this statement is true: "If the diagonals of a trapezoid are congruent, then the trapezoid is an isosceles trapezoid." So, this property can be written as a biconditional statement: "A trapezoid is isosceles if and only if its diagonals are congruent."

C

categorical data (qualitative data)

Categorical data are data that each fit into exactly one of several different groups, or categories. Categorical data are also called "qualitative data."

Example

Animals: lions, tigers, bears, etc.
U.S. Cities: Los Angeles, Atlanta, New York City, Dodge City, etc.

The set of animals and the set of U.S. cities are two examples of categorical data sets.

Cavalieri's Principle

Cavalieri's Principle states that if all one-dimensional slices of two-dimensional figures have the same lengths, then the two-dimensional figures have the same area. The principle also states that given two solid figures included between parallel planes, if every plane cross section parallel to the given planes has the same area in both solids, then the volumes of the solids are equal.

center

The center of a circle is a fixed point in the plane that is at an equal distance from every point on the circle.

Example

Point *H* is the center of the circle.

central angle

A central angle of a circle is an angle whose sides are radii. The measure of a central angle is equal to the measure of its intercepted arc.

Example

In circle O, $\angle AOC$ is a central angle and $\overset{\frown}{AC}$ is its intercepted arc. If m$\angle AOC = 45°$, then m$\overset{\frown}{AC} = 45°$.

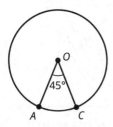

centroid

The centroid of a triangle is the point at which the medians of the triangle intersect.

Example

Point X is the centroid of triangle $\triangle ABC$.

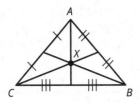

chord

A chord is a line segment whose endpoints are points on a circle. A chord is formed by the intersection of the circle and a secant line.

Example

Segment CD is a chord of circle O.

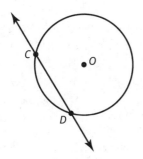

circular permutation

A circular permutation is a permutation in which there is no starting point and no ending point. The circular permutation of n objects is $(n - 1)!$.

Example

A club consists of four officers: a president (P), a vicepresident (VP), a secretary (S), and a treasurer (T). There are $(4 - 1)!$, or 6 ways for the officers to sit around a round table.

circumcenter

The circumcenter of a triangle is the point at which the perpendicular bisectors intersect.

Example

Point X is the circumcenter of $\triangle ABC$.

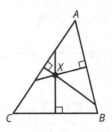

circumscribed angle

A circumscribed angle has its two sides tangent to a circle.

Example

Angle ABC is circumscribed in circle O.

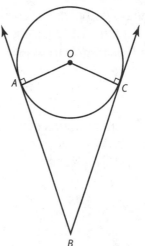

circumscribed circle

A circumscribed circle is a circle that passes through all the vertices of a polygon.

Example

Circle Q is circumscribed around $\triangle ABC$.

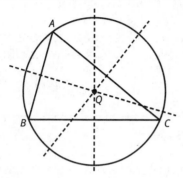

coincident

Two line segments are coincident if they lie exactly on top of each other.

collinear points

Collinear points are points that are located on the same line.

Example

Points A, B, and C are collinear.

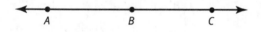

combination

A combination is an unordered collection of items. One notation for the combinations of r elements taken from a collection of n elements is:

$$_nC_r = C(n, r) = C^n_r$$

Example

The two-letter combinations of the letters A, B, and C are: AB, AC, BC.

compass

A compass is a tool used to create arcs and circles.

Example

Compass

complement of an event

The complement of an event is an event that contains all the outcomes in the sample space that are not outcomes in the event. In mathematical notation, if E is an event, then the complement of E is often denoted as $\bar{E}$ or E^c.

Example

A number cube contains the numbers 1 though 6. Let E represent the event of rolling an even number. The complement of Event E is rolling an odd number.

composite figure

A composite figure is a figure that is formed by combining different shapes.

compound event

A compound event combines two or more events, using the word "and" or the word "or."

Example

You roll a number cube twice. Rolling a six on the first roll and rolling an odd number on the second roll are compound events.

concavity

The concavity of a parabola describes the orientation of the curvature of the parabola.

Example

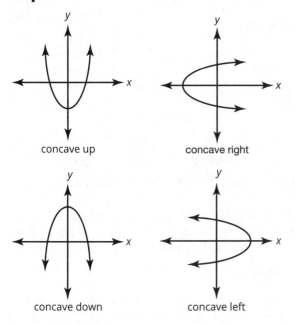

concave up

concave right

concave down

concave left

concentric circles

Concentric circles are circles in the same plane that have a common center.

Example

The circles shown are concentric because they are in the same plane and have a common center H.

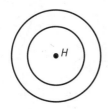

conclusion

A conclusion is the "then" part of an "if-then" statement.

Example

In the statement "If two positive numbers are added, then the sum is positive," the conclusion is "the sum is positive."

concurrent

Concurrent lines, rays, or line segments are three or more lines, rays, or line segments intersecting at a single point.

Example

Lines ℓ, m, and n are concurrent lines.

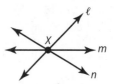

conditional statement

A conditional statement is a statement that can be written in the form "If p, then q."

conditional probability

A conditional probability is the probability of event B, given that event A has already occurred. The notation for conditional probability is $P(B|A)$, which reads, "the probability of event B, given event A."

Example

The probability of rolling a 4 or less on the second roll of a number cube, given that a 5 is rolled first, is an example of a conditional probability.

conic section

A conic section is a curve obtained as the intersection of the surface of a double-napped cone with a plane.

Example

A parabola is a conic section that results from the intersection of a plane with one nappe of the double-napped cone, parallel to the edge of the cone.

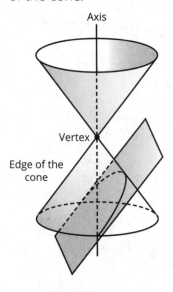

conjecture

A conjecture is a hypothesis that something is true. The hypothesis can later be proved or disproved.

conjugate axis

The conjugate axis is the line through the center of a hyperbola and perpendicular to the transverse axis

construct

When you construct geometric figures, you create exact figures without measurements, using paper folding or a compass and a straightedge—and geometric reasoning.

converse

To state the converse of a conditional statement, interchange the hypothesis and the conclusion.
    Conditional Statement: If p, then q.
    Converse: If q, then p.

Example

Conditional Statement: If $a = 0$ or $b = 0$, then $ab = 0$.
Converse: If $ab = 0$, then $a = 0$ or $b = 0$.

corresponding parts of congruent triangles are congruent (CPCTC)

CPCTC states that if two triangles are congruent, then each part of one triangle is congruent to the corresponding part of the other triangle.

Example

In the triangles shown, $\triangle XYZ \cong \triangle LMN$. Because corresponding parts of congruent triangles are congruent (CPCTC), the following corresponding parts are congruent.

- $\angle X \cong \angle L$
- $\angle Y \cong \angle M$
- $\angle Z \cong \angle N$
- $\overline{XY} \cong \overline{LM}$
- $\overline{YZ} \cong \overline{MN}$
- $\overline{XZ} \cong \overline{LN}$

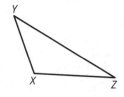 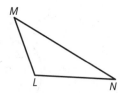

cosecant (csc)

The cosecant (csc) of an acute angle in a right triangle is the ratio of the length of the hypotenuse to the length of the side opposite the angle.

Example

In $\triangle ABC$, the cosecant of $\angle A$ is:

$$\csc A = \frac{\text{length of hypotenuse}}{\text{length of side opposite } \angle A} = \frac{AB}{BC}$$

The expression "csc A" means "the cosecant of angle A."

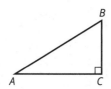

cosine (cos)

The cosine (cos) of an acute angle in a right triangle is the ratio of the length of the side adjacent to the angle to the length of the hypotenuse.

Example

In $\triangle ABC$, the cosine of $\angle A$ is:

$$\cos A = \frac{\text{length of side adjacent to } \angle A}{\text{length of hypotenuse}} = \frac{AC}{AB}$$

The expression "cos A" means "the cosine of angle A."

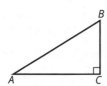

cotangent (cot)

The cotangent (cot) of an acute angle in a right triangle is the ratio of the length of the side adjacent to the angle to the length of the side opposite the angle.

Example

In $\triangle ABC$, the cotangent of $\angle A$ is:

$$\cot A = \frac{\text{length of side adjacent to } \angle A}{\text{length of side opposite } \angle A} = \frac{AC}{BC}$$

The expression "cot A" means "the cotangent of angle A."

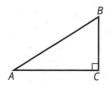

counterexample

A counterexample is a single example that shows that a statement is not true.

Example

Your friend claims that you add fractions by adding the numerators and then adding the denominators. A counterexample is $\frac{1}{2} + \frac{1}{2}$. The sum of these two fractions is 1. Your friend's method results in $\frac{1+1}{2+2}$, or $\frac{1}{2}$. Your friend's method is incorrect.

Counting Principle

The Counting Principle states that if action A can occur in m ways and for each of these m ways action B can occur in n ways, then actions A and B can occur in $m \cdot n$ ways.

Example

In the school cafeteria, there are 3 different main entrées and 4 different sides. So, there are $3 \cdot 4$, or 12 different lunches that can be created.

co-vertices

The endpoints of the minor axis of an ellipse are the co-vertices.

cyclic quadrilateral

A cyclic quadrilateral is a quadrilateral whose vertices all lie on a single circle.

Example

Quadrilateral *MATH* is a cyclic quadrilateral whose vertices all lie on circle *O*.

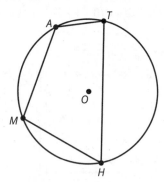

——————————— D ———————————

degenerate conics

The intersections of a plane and a double-napped cone that form a point, a line, or intersecting lines are degenerate conics.

degree measure of an arc

The degree measure of a minor arc is equal to the degree measure of its central angle. The degree measure of a major arc is determined by subtracting the degree measure of the minor arc from 360°.

Example

The measure of minor arc *AB* is 30°. The measure of major arc *BZA* is 360° − 30° = 330°.

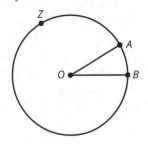

dependent events

Dependent events are events for which the occurrence of one event has an impact on the occurrence of subsequent events.

Example

A jar contains 1 blue marble, 1 green marble, and 2 yellow marbles. You randomly choose a yellow marble without replacing the marble in the jar, and then randomly choose a yellow marble again. The events of randomly choosing a yellow marble first and randomly choosing a yellow marble second are dependent events because the 1st yellow marble was not replaced in the jar.

diagonal

A diagonal is a line segment joining two vertices of a polygon but is not a side of the polygon.

diameter

The diameter of a circle is a line segment with each endpoint on the circle that passes through the center of the circle.

Example

In circle *O*, $\overline{AB}$ is a diameter.

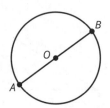

diameter of a sphere

The diameter of a sphere is a line segment with each endpoint on the sphere that passes through the center of the sphere.

Example

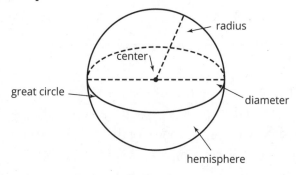

dilation

A dilation is a transformation of the figure in which the figure stretches or shrinks with respect to a fixed point, or center of dilation.

Example

Triangle *DEF* is a dilation of △*ABC*. The center of dilation is point *Y*.

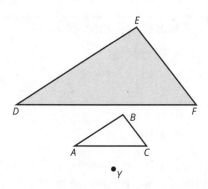

directed line segment

A directed line segment is assigned a direction from one endpoint to the other.

Example

Directed line segment *AB* is mathematically different from directed line segment *BA*.

directrix

The directrix of a parabola is a line such that all points on the parabola are equidistant from the focus and the directrix.

Example

The focus of the parabola shown is the point (0, 2). The directrix of the parabola shown is the line $y = -2$. All points on the parabola are equidistant from the focus and the directrix.

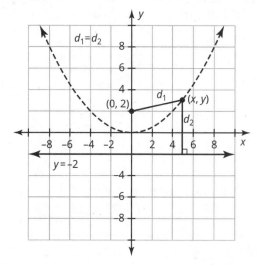

disc

A disc is the set of all points on a circle and in the interior of a circle

Distance Formula

The Distance Formula states that if (x_1, y_1) and (x_2, y_2) are two points on the coordinate plane, then the distance d between (x_1, y_1) and (x_2, y_2) is given by $d = \sqrt{(x_2 - x_1)^2 + (y_2 - y_1)^2}$.

Example

To find the distance between the points $(-1, 4)$ and $(2, -5)$, substitute the coordinates into the Distance Formula.

$$d = \sqrt{(x_2 - x_1)^2 + (y_2 - y_1)^2}$$
$$d = \sqrt{(2 + 1)^2 + (-5 - 4)^2}$$
$$d = \sqrt{3^2 + (-9)^2}$$
$$d = \sqrt{9 + 81}$$
$$d = \sqrt{90}$$
$$d \approx 9.49$$

So, the distance between the points $(-1, 4)$ and $(2, -5)$ is approximately 9.49 units.

disjoint sets

Two or more sets are disjoint sets if they do not have any common elements.

Example

Let N represent the set of 9th grade students. Let T represent the set of 10th grade students. The sets N and T are disjoint sets because the two sets do not have any common elements. Any student can be in one grade only.

draw

To draw is to create a geometric figure using tools such as a ruler, straightedge, compass, or protractor. A drawing is more accurate than a sketch.

— E —

eccentricity

Eccentricity, e, is a parameter associated with every conic section. It is a measure of how much the conic section deviates from being a circle. When $e = 0$, the conic section is a circle.

element

A member of a set is called an element of that set.

Example

Set B contains the elements a, b, and c.

$B = \{a, b, c\}$

ellipse

When a plane intersects a single nappe not perpendicular to the axis, but at an angle that is less than the central angle of the nappe, the curve that results is an ellipse. An ellipse is the locus of all points in a plane for which the sum of whose distances from two given points is a constant.

Example

The sum of the distances from each focus to any point, P, on the curve of the ellipse is constant.

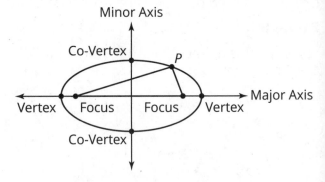

Euclidean geometry

Euclidean geometry is a geometry of straight lines and flat planes based on postulates developed by the ancient Greek mathematician Euclid. There are other types of geometry, such as spherical geometry and hyperbolic geometry, which are used to study curved space.

event

An event is an outcome or a set of outcomes in a sample space.

Example

A number cube contains the numbers 1 through 6. Rolling a 6 is one event. Rolling an even number is another event.

expected value

The expected value is the average value when the number of trials in a probability experiment is large.

exterior angle of a polygon

An exterior angle of a polygon is an angle that is adjacent to an interior angle of a polygon.

Example

Angle *JHI* is an exterior angle of quadrilateral *FGHI*. Angle *EDA* is an exterior angle of quadrilateral *ABCD*.

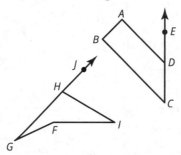

extract the roots

To extract a root is the process of removing all perfect square numbers from under the radical symbol.

Example

To extract the root for $\sqrt{18}$, remove all perfect square numbers that are factors of 18.

$$\sqrt{18} = \sqrt{9} \cdot 2$$
$$= \sqrt{3^2} \cdot 2$$
$$= 3\sqrt{2}$$

F

factorial

The factorial of *n*, written as *n*!, is the product of all non-negative integers less than or equal to *n*.

Example

$3! = 3 \times 2 \times 1 = 6$

flow chart proof

A flow chart proof is a proof in which the steps and corresponding reasons are written in boxes. Arrows connect the boxes and indicate how each step and reason is generated from one or more other steps and reasons.

Example

A flow chart proof is shown for the conditional statement: If $\overline{AB} \cong \overline{CD}$, then $\overline{AC} \cong \overline{BD}$.

Given: $\overline{AB} \cong \overline{CD}$

Prove: $\overline{AC} \cong \overline{BD}$

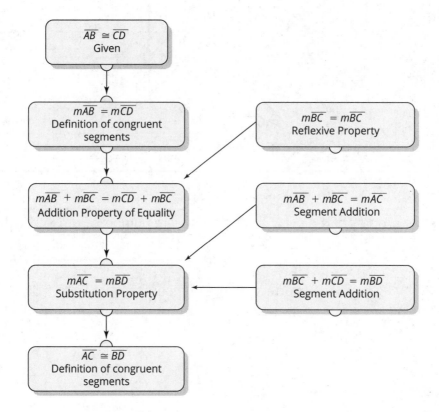

focus

The focus of a parabola is a point such that all points on the parabola are equidistant from the focus and the directrix.

Example

The focus of the parabola shown is the point (0, 2). The directrix of the parabola shown is the line $y = -2$. All points on the parabola are equidistant from the focus and the directrix.

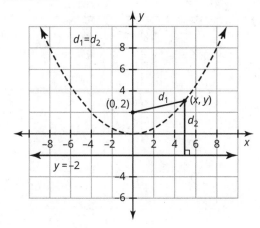

foci (focus)

For two given points, the foci, an ellipse is the locus of points such that the sum of the distance to each focus is constant, and a hyperbola is the locus of points such that the difference of the distances from each focus is constant.

frequency table

A frequency table shows the frequency of an item, number, or event appearing in a sample space.

Example

The frequency table shows the number of times a sum of two number cubes occurred.

Sum of Two Number Cubes	Frequency
2	1
3	2
4	3
5	4
6	5
7	6
8	5
9	4
10	3
11	2
12	1

general form of a parabola

The general form of a parabola centered at the origin is an equation of the form $Ax^2 + Dy = 0$ or $By^2 + Cx = 0$.

Example

The equation for the parabola shown can be written in general form as $x^2 - 2y = 0$.

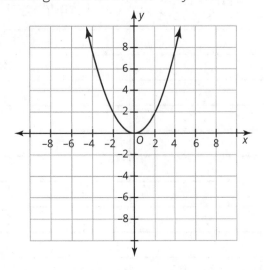

geometric mean

The geometric mean of two positive numbers a and b is the positive number x such that $\frac{a}{x} = \frac{x}{b}$.

Example

The geometric mean of 3 and 12 is 6.

$$\frac{3}{x} = \frac{x}{12}$$

$$x^2 = 36$$

$$x = 6$$

geometric probability

Geometric probability is probability that involves a geometric measure, such as length, area, volume, and so on.

Example

A dartboard has the size and shape shown. The gray shaded area represents a scoring section of the dartboard. Calculate the probability that a dart that lands on a random part of the target will land in a gray scoring section.

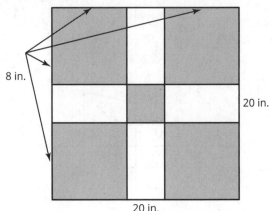

Calculate the area of the dartboard: $20(20) = 400$ in.^{2}

There are 4 gray scoring squares with 8-in. sides and a gray scoring square with $20 - 8 - 8 = 4$-in. sides. Calculate the area of the gray scoring sections: $4(8)(8) + 4(4) = 272$ in.^{2}

Calculate the probability that a dart will hit a gray scoring section: $\frac{272}{400} = 0.68 = 68\%$.

great circle of a sphere

The great circle of a sphere is a cross section of a sphere when a plane passes through the center of the sphere.

Example

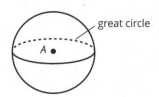

great circle

hemisphere

A hemisphere is half of a sphere bounded by a great circle.

Example

A hemisphere is shown.

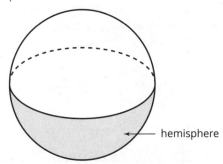

←— hemisphere

hyperbola

When a plane parallel to the axis of the cone intersects both nappes of the cone, the curve that results is a hyperbola. A hyperbola is the locus of all points in a plane for which the difference of whose distances from two given points is a constant.

Example

The difference of the distances from each focus to any point, *P*, on the curves of a hyperbola is constant.

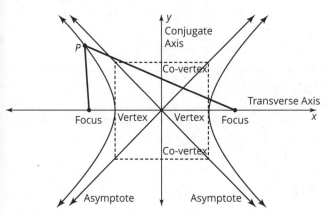

hypothesis

A hypothesis is the "if" part of an "if-then" statement.

Example

In the statement, "If the last digit of a number is a 5, then the number is divisible by 5," the hypothesis is "If the last digit of a number is a 5."

incenter

The incenter of a triangle is the point at which the angle bisectors of the triangle intersect.

Example

Point *X* is the incenter of △*ABC*.

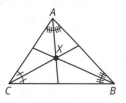

included angle

An included angle is an angle formed by two consecutive sides of a figure.

Example

In △*ABC*, ∠*A* is the included angle formed by consecutive sides $\overline{AB}$ and $\overline{AC}$.

included side

An included side is a line segment between two consecutive angles of a figure.

Example

In △*ABC*, $\overline{AB}$ is the included side formed by consecutive angles *A* and *B*.

independent events

Independent events are events for which the occurrence of one event has no impact on the occurrence of the other event.

Example

You randomly choose a yellow marble, replace the marble in the jar, and then randomly choose a yellow marble again. The events of randomly choosing a yellow marble first and randomly choosing a yellow marble second are independent events because the 1st yellow marble was replaced in the jar.

indirect measurement

Indirect measurement is a technique that uses proportions to determine a measurement when direct measurement is not possible.

Example

You can use a proportion to solve for the height x of the flagpole.

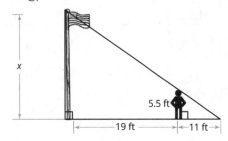

$$\frac{x}{5.5} = \frac{19 + 11}{11}$$
$$\frac{x}{5.5} = \frac{30}{11}$$
$$11x = 165$$
$$x = 15$$

The flagpole is 15 feet tall.

inscribed angle

An inscribed angle is an angle whose vertex is on a circle and whose sides contain chords of the circle.

Example

Angle BAC is an inscribed angle. The vertex of angle BAC is on the circle and the sides of angle BAC contain the chords $\overline{AB}$ and $\overline{AC}$.

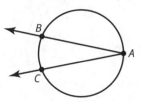

inscribed polygon

An inscribed polygon is a polygon drawn inside another polygon or circle in which all the vertices of the interior polygon lie on the outer figure.

Example

Quadrilateral $KLMN$ is inscribed in circle J.

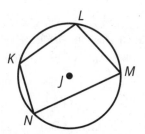

intercepted arc

An intercepted arc is formed by the intersections of the sides of an inscribed angle with a circle.

Example

$\overparen{PR}$ is an intercepted arc of inscribed angle PSR.

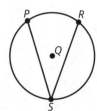

interior angle of a polygon

An interior angle of a polygon is an angle which is formed by consecutive sides of the polygon or shape.

Example

The interior angles of $\triangle ABC$ are $\angle ABC$, $\angle BCA$, and $\angle CAB$.

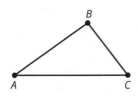

intersecting sets

Two or more sets are intersecting sets if they have common elements.

Example

Let V represent the set of students who are on the girls' volleyball team. Let M represent the set of students who are in the math club. Julia is on the volleyball team and belongs to the math club. The sets V and M are intersecting sets because the two sets have at least one common element, Julia.

inverse cosine

The inverse cosine, or arccosine, of x is the measure of an acute angle whose cosine is x.

Example

In right triangle ABC, if $\cos A = x$, then $\cos^{-1} x = m\angle A$.

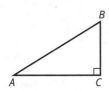

inverse sine

The inverse sine, or arcsine, of x is the measure of an acute angle whose sine is x.

Example

In right triangle ABC, if $\sin A = x$, then $\sin^{-1} x = m\angle A$.

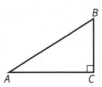

inverse tangent

The inverse tangent (or arctangent) of x is the measure of an acute angle whose tangent is x.

Example

In right triangle ABC, if $\tan A = x$, then $\tan^{-1} x = m\angle A$.

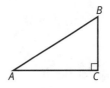

isometric paper

Isometric paper is often used by artists and engineers to create three-dimensional views of objects in two dimensions.

Example

The rectangular prism is shown on isometric paper.

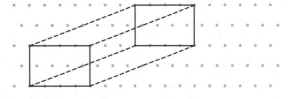

isometry

An isometry is a rigid motion transformation that preserves size and shape.

isosceles trapezoid

An isosceles trapezoid is a trapezoid whose nonparallel sides are congruent.

Example

In trapezoid *JKLM*, side $\overline{KL}$ is parallel to side $\overline{JM}$, and the length of side $\overline{JK}$ is equal to the length of side $\overline{LM}$, so trapezoid *JKLM* is an isosceles trapezoid.

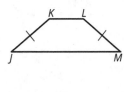

--- **K** ---

kite

A kite is a quadrilateral with two pairs of equal adjacent sides. If the diagonals of a quadrilateral are perpendicular, non-congruent, and only one bisects the other, it can only be classified as a kite.

Example

Quadrilateral *ABCD* is a kite.

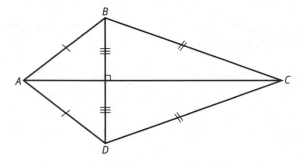

--- **L** ---

Law of Cosines

Law of Cosines, or

$$a^2 = c^2 + b^2 - 2bc \cdot \cos A$$
$$b^2 = a^2 + c^2 - 2ac \cdot \cos B$$
$$c^2 = a^2 + b^2 - 2ab \cdot \cos C$$

can be used to determine the unknown lengths of sides or the unknown measures of angles in *any* triangle.

Example

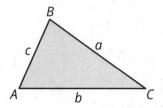

In $\triangle ABC$, the measure of $\angle A$ is 65°, the length of side *b* is 4.4301 feet, and the length of side *c* is 7.6063 feet. Use the Law of Cosines to calculate the length of side *a*.

$$a^2 = 4.4301^2 + 7.6063^2 - 2(4.4301)(7.6063) \cos 65°$$

The length of side *a* is 7 feet.

Law of Reflection

The Law of Reflection states that the measure of the angle of incidence equals the measure of the angle of reflection.

Law of Sines

The Law of Sines, or $\frac{\sin A}{a} = \frac{\sin B}{b} = \frac{\sin C}{c}$, can be used to determine the unknown side length or the unknown angle measures in any triangle.

Example

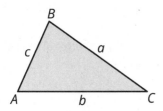

In △ABC, the measure of ∠A is 65°, the measure of angle B is 80°, and the length of side a is 7 feet. Use the Law of Sines to calculate the length of side b.

$$\frac{7}{\sin 65°} = \frac{b}{\sin 80°}$$

The length of side b is 7.6063 feet.

lateral face

A lateral face of a three-dimensional object is a face that is not a base.

Example

Each lateral face of a right triangular prism is a rectangle.

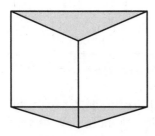

lateral surface area

The lateral surface area of a three-dimensional figure is the sum of the areas of its lateral faces.

Example

The lateral surface area of the right triangular prism is 108 square centimeters.

Lateral surface area = (5 × 6) + (5 × 6) + (8 × 6)

= 30 + 30 + 48

= 108

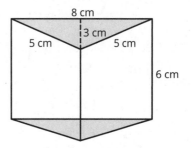

line

A line is made up of an infinite number of points that extend infinitely in two opposite directions. A line is straight and has only one dimension.

Example

The line below can be called line k or line AB.

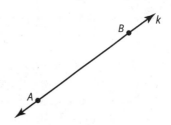

line segment

A line segment is a portion of a line that includes two points and all of the collinear points between the two points.

Example

The line segment shown is named $\overline{AB}$ or $\overline{BA}$.

linear velocity

Linear velocity is a type of circular velocity described as an amount of distance over a specified amount of time. Linear velocity can be expressed as $v = \frac{s}{t}$, where v = velocity, s = arc length, and t = time.

locus of points

A locus of points is a set of points that satisfy one or more conditions.

Example

A circle is defined as a locus of points that are a fixed distance, called the radius, from a given point, called the center.

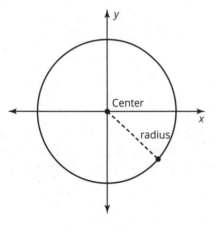

M

---

major arc

Two points on a circle determine a major arc and a minor arc. The arc with the greater measure is the major arc. The other arc is the minor arc.

Example

Circle Q is divided by points A and B into two arcs, arc ACB and arc AB. Arc ACB has the greater measure, so it is the major arc. Arc AB has the lesser measure, so it is the minor arc.

major axis

The major axis is the longest line segment that runs through the center of an ellipse and both foci.

median

The median of a triangle is a line segment drawn from a vertex to the midpoint of the opposite side.

Example

The 3 medians are drawn on the triangle shown.

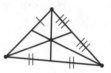

midpoint

A midpoint is a point that is exactly halfway between two given points.

Example

Because point B is the midpoint of segment AC, segment AB is congruent to segment BC.

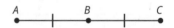

Midpoint Formula

The Midpoint Formula states that if (x_1, y_1) and (x_2, y_2) are two points on the coordinate plane, then the midpoint of the line segment that joins these two points is given by $\left(\frac{x_1 + x_2}{2}, \frac{y_1 + y_2}{2}\right)$.

Example

To find the midpoint between the points $(-1, 4)$ and $(2, -5)$, substitute the coordinates into the Midpoint Formula.

$$\left(\frac{x_1 + x_2}{2}, \frac{y_1 + y_2}{2}\right) = \left(\frac{-1 + 2}{2}, \frac{4 - 5}{2}\right)$$

$$= \left(\frac{1}{2}, \frac{-1}{2}\right)$$

So, the midpoint between the points $(-1, 4)$ and $(2, -5)$ is $\left(\frac{1}{2}, -\frac{1}{2}\right)$.

midsegment

A midsegment of a polygon is any line segment that connects two midpoints of the sides of the polygon.

Example

Segment *XY* is a midsegment of trapezoid *ABCD*.

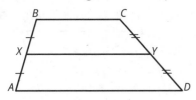

midsegment of a triangle

A midsegment of a triangle is a line segment formed by connecting the midpoints of two sides of a triangle.

Example

Segment *AB* is a midsegment.

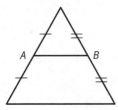

minor arc

Two points on a circle determine a minor arc and a major arc. The arc with the lesser measure is the minor arc. The other arc is the major arc.

Example

Circle *Q* is divided by points *A* and *B* into two arcs, arc *ACB* and arc *AB*. Arc *AB* has the lesser measure, so it is the minor arc. Arc *ACB* has the greater measure, so it is the major arc.

minor axis

The minor axis is the shortest line segment that runs through the center of an ellipse.

nappes

Nappes are two congruent cones that touch at the vertex with an axis of symmetry that passes through the center of each base.

Example

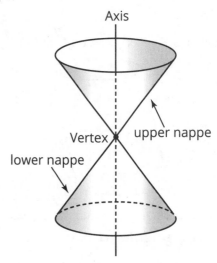

non-uniform probability model

When all probabilities in a probability model are not equivalent to each other, it is called a non-uniform probability model.

Example

Spinning the spinner shown represents a non-uniform probability model because the probability of landing on a shaded space is not equal to the probability of landing on a non-shaded space.

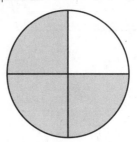

oblique cylinder

When a circle is translated through space in a direction that is not perpendicular to the plane containing the circle, the solid formed is an oblique cylinder.

Example

The prism shown is an oblique cylinder.

oblique rectangular prism

When a rectangle is translated through space in a direction that is not perpendicular to the plane containing the rectangle, the solid formed is an oblique rectangular prism.

Example

The prism shown is an oblique rectangular prism.

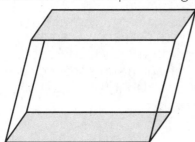

oblique triangular prism

When a triangle is translated through space in a direction that is not perpendicular to the plane containing the triangle, the solid formed is an oblique triangular prism.

Example

The prism shown is an oblique triangular prism.

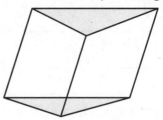

opposite side

The opposite side of a triangle is the side opposite the reference angle.

Example

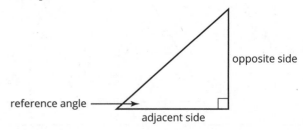

organized list

An organized list is a visual model for determining the sample space of events.

Example

The sample space for flipping a coin 3 times can be represented as an organized list.

HHH	THH
HHT	THT
HTH	TTH
HTT	TTT

orthocenter

The orthocenter of a triangle is the point at which the altitudes of the triangle intersect.

Example

Point X is the orthocenter of △ABC.

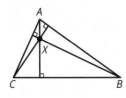

outcome

An outcome is the result of a single trial of an experiment.

Example

Flipping a coin has two outcomes: heads or tails.

— P —

parabola (conic section)

When a plane intersects one nappe of the double-napped cone parallel to the edge of the cone, the curve that results is a parabola. A parabola is the set of all points in a plane that are equidistant from a fixed point called the focus and a fixed line called the directrix.

Example

The focus of the parabola shown is the point $(0, 2)$. The directrix of the parabola shown is the line $y = -2$. All points on the parabola are equidistant from the focus and the directrix.

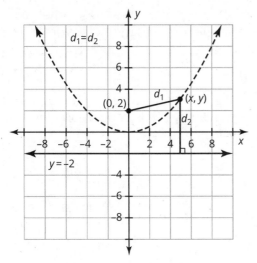

paragraph proof

A paragraph proof is a proof that is written in paragraph form. Each sentence includes mathematical statements that are organized in logical steps with reasons.

Example

The proof shown is a paragraph proof that vertical angles 1 and 3 are congruent.

Angle 1 and angle 3 are vertical angles. By the definition of linear pair, angle 1 and angle 2 form a linear pair. Angle 2 and angle 3 also form a linear pair. By the Linear Pair Postulate, angle 1 and angle 2 are supplementary. Angle 2 and angle 3 are also supplementary. Angle 1 is congruent to angle 3 by the Congruent Supplement Theorem.

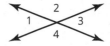

perpendicular bisector

A perpendicular bisector is a line, line segment, or ray that intersects the midpoint of a line segment at a 90° angle.

Example

Line k is the perpendicular bisector of $\overline{AB}$. It is perpendicular to $\overline{AB}$, and intersects $\overline{AB}$ at midpoint M so that $AM = MB$.

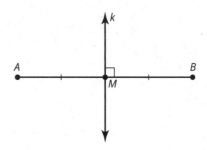

permutation

A permutation is an ordered arrangement of items without repetition.

Example

The permutations of the letters *A*, *B*, and *C* are:

ABC	*ACB*
BAC	*BCA*
CAB	*CBA*

point

A point has no dimension, but can be visualized as a specific position in space, and is usually represented by a small dot.

Example

Point *A* is shown.

point of concurrency

A point of concurrency is the point at which three or more lines intersect.

Example

Point *X* is the point of concurrency for lines *ℓ*, *m*, and *n*.

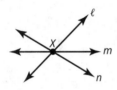

postulate

A postulate is a statement that is accepted to be true without proof.

Example

The following statement is a postulate: A straight line may be drawn between any two points.

probability

The probability of an event is the ratio of the number of desired outcomes to the total number of possible outcomes,
$$P(A) = \frac{\text{desired outcomes}}{\text{possible outcomes}}.$$

Example

When flipping a coin, there are 2 possible outcomes: heads or tails. The probability of flipping a heads is $\frac{1}{2}$.

probability model

A probability model lists the possible outcomes and the probability for each outcome. In a probability model, the sum of the probabilities must equal 1.

Example

The table shows a probability model for flipping a fair coin once.

Outcomes	Head (H)	Tails (H)
Probability	$\frac{1}{2}$	$\frac{1}{2}$

proof

A proof is a series of statements and corresponding reasons forming a valid argument that starts with a hypothesis and arrives at a conclusion.

Pythagorean identity

A Pythagorean identity is a trigonometric identity that expresses the Pythagorean Theorem in terms of trigonometric ratios.

Example

The basic relationship between the sine and cosine is given by the Pythagorean identity $(\sin \theta)^2 + (\cos \theta)^2 = (1)^2$.

radian

One radian is defined as the measure of a central angle whose arc length is the same as the radius of the circle.

radius

The radius of a circle is a line segment with one endpoint on the circle and one endpoint at the center.

Example

In circle O, $\overline{OA}$ is a radius.

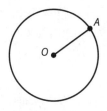

radius of a sphere

The radius of a sphere is a line segment with one endpoint on the sphere and one endpoint at the center.

Example

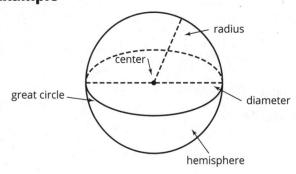

rationalize the denominator

To rationalize the denominator is the process of eliminating a radical from the denominator of an expression. To rationalize the denominator, multiply by a form of one so that the radicand of the radical in the denominator is a perfect square.

Example

Rationalize the denominator of the expression $\frac{5}{\sqrt{3}}$.

$$\frac{5}{\sqrt{3}} = \frac{5}{\sqrt{3}} \cdot \frac{\sqrt{3}}{\sqrt{3}}$$
$$= \frac{5\sqrt{3}}{\sqrt{9}}$$
$$= \frac{5\sqrt{3}}{3}$$

ray

A ray is a portion of a line that begins with a single point and extends infinitely in one direction.

Example

The ray shown is ray AB.

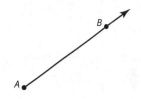

reference angle

A reference angle is the angle of the right triangle being considered. The opposite side and adjacent side are named based on the reference angle.

Example

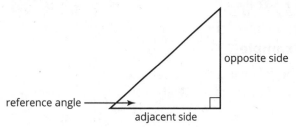

reflection

A reflection is a rigid motion that "flips" a figure across a line. A reflection as a function, R_ℓ, takes as its input, P, the location of a point with respect to some line of reflection ℓ and outputs $R_\ell (P)$, or the opposite of the location of P with respect to the line of reflection.

Example

$R_m (STUV) = S'T'U'V'$

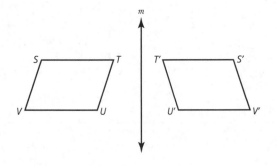

reflectional symmetry

A plane figure has reflectional symmetry if you can draw a line so that the figure to one side of the line is a reflection of the figure on the other side of the line.

Example

The figure shown has reflectional symmetry.

Reflexive Property

The reflexive property states that $a = a$.

Example

The statement $2 = 2$ is an example of the Reflexive Property.

relative frequency

A relative frequency is the ratio or percent of occurrences within a category to the total of the category.

Example

John surveys 100 students in his school about their favorite school subject. Of the 100 students, 37 chose math as their favorite subject. The relative frequency of students show selected math as their favorite subject is $\frac{37}{100}$, or 37%.

remote interior angles of a triangle

The remote interior angles of a triangle are the two angles that are not adjacent to the specified exterior angle.

Example

The remote interior angles with respect to exterior angle 4 are angles 1 and 2.

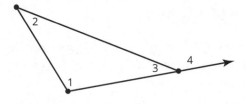

right cylinder

A disc translated through space in a direction perpendicular to the plane containing the disc forms a right cylinder.

Example

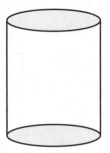

right rectangular prism

A rectangle translated through space in a direction perpendicular to the plane containing the rectangle forms a right rectangular prism.

Example

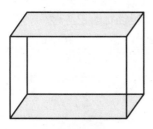

right triangular prism

A triangle translated through space in a direction perpendicular to the plane containing the triangle forms a right triangular prism.

Example

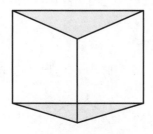

rotation

A rotation is a rigid motion that "spins" a figure about a point. A rotation as a function maps its input, a point P, to another location, $f(P)$. This movement to a new location is defined by a center of rotation, E, and a rotation angle, t. For this reason, a rotation function is written as $R_{E,t}(P)$.

Example

$R_{A,\,40}(\overline{JN}) = \overline{J'N'}$

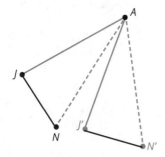

rotation angle

A rotation angle is a directed angle based on a circle. Positive rotation angles turn counterclockwise, and negative rotation angles turn clockwise.

Example

The rotation angle shown rotates point A 45° counterclockwise.

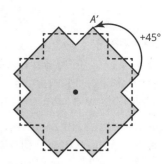

rotational symmetry

A plane figure can also have rotational symmetry if you can rotate the figure more than 0° but less than 360° and the resulting figure is the same as the original figure in the original position.

Example

The figure shown has rotational symmetry.

rigid motion

A rigid motion is a transformation of points in space. Translations, reflections, and rotations are examples of rigid motion.

Rule of Compound Probability involving *and*

The Rule of Compound Probability involving *and* states: "If Event *A* and Event *B* are independent, then the probability that Event *A* happens and Event *B* happens is the product of the probability that Event *A* happens and the probability that Event *B* happens, given that Event *A* has happened."

$$P(A \text{ and } B) = P(A) \cdot P(B)$$

Example

You flip a coin two times. Calculate the probability of flipping a heads on the first flip and flipping a heads on the second flip.

Let *A* represent the event of flipping a heads on the first flip. Let *B* represent the event of flipping a heads on the second flip.

$P(A \text{ and } B) = P(A) \cdot P(B)$

$P(A \text{ and } B) = \frac{1}{2} \cdot \frac{1}{2}$

$P(A \text{ or } B) = \frac{1}{4}$

So, the probability of flipping a heads on the first flip and flipping a heads on the second flip is $\frac{1}{4}$.

S

---

sample space

A list of all possible outcomes of an experiment is called a sample space.

Example

Flipping a coin two times consists of four outcomes: HH, HT, TH, and TT.

secant (sec)

The secant (sec) of an acute angle in a right triangle is the ratio of the length of the hypotenuse to the length of the side adjacent to the angle.

Example

In $\triangle ABC$, the secant of $\angle A$ is:

$$\sec A = \frac{\text{length of hypotenuse}}{\text{length of side adjacent to } \angle A} = \frac{AB}{AC}$$

The expression "sec *A*" means "the secant of angle *A*."

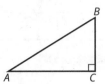

---

secant of a circle

A secant of a circle is a line that intersects the circle at two points.

Example

The line intersecting the circle through points *A* and *B* is a secant.

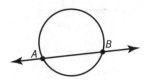

---

sector of a circle

A sector of a circle is a region of the circle bounded by two radii and the included arc.

Example

In circle Y, $\widehat{XZ}$, radius $\overline{XY}$, and radius $\overline{YZ}$ form a sector.

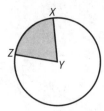

segment bisector

A segment bisector is a line, line segment, or ray that divides a line segment into two line segments of equal measure, or two congruent line segments.

Example

$\overline{AB}$ is a segment bisector of $\overline{CD}$.

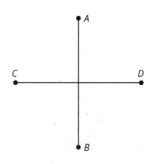

segment of a circle

A segment of a circle is a region bounded by a chord and the included arc.

Example

In circle A, chord $\overline{BC}$ and $\overset{\frown}{BC}$ are the boundaries of a segment of the circle.

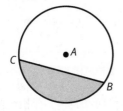

semi-major axis

The semi-major axis of an ellipse is a segment from the center of the ellipse to a vertex and has length a.

semi-minor axis

The semi-minor axis of an ellipse is a segment from the center of the ellipse to a co-vertex and has length b.

set

A set is a collection of items. If x is a member of set B, then x is an element of set B.

Example

Let E represent the set of even whole numbers. $E = \{2, 4, 6, 8, \ldots\}$

similar figures

Similar figures are geometric figures where all pairs of corresponding angles are congruent and the lengths of all corresponding sides are proportional. Dilations produce similar figures.

Example

Figures E and X are similar figures.

similar triangles

Similar triangles are triangles that have all pairs of corresponding angles congruent and all corresponding sides are proportional.

Example

$\triangle ABC \sim \triangle DEF$

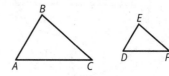

sine (sin)

The sine (sin) of an acute angle in a right triangle is the ratio of the length of the side opposite the angle to the length of the hypotenuse.

Example

In $\triangle ABC$, the sine of $\angle A$ is:

$$\sin A = \frac{\text{length of side opposite } \angle A}{\text{length of hypotenuse}} = \frac{BC}{AB}$$

The expression "sin A" means "the sine of angle A."

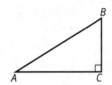

sketch

To sketch is to create a geometric figure without using tools such as a ruler, straightedge, compass, or protractor. A drawing is more accurate than a sketch.

sphere

A sphere is the set of all points in space that are a given distance from a fixed point called the center of the sphere.

Example

A sphere is shown.

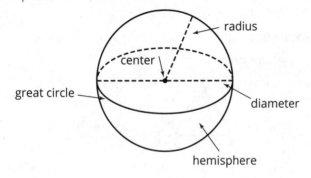

standard form of a parabola

The standard form of a parabola centered at the origin is an equation of the form $x^2 = 4py$ or $y^2 = 4px$, where p represents the distance from the vertex to the focus.

Example

The equation for the parabola shown can be written in standard form as $x^2 = 2y$.

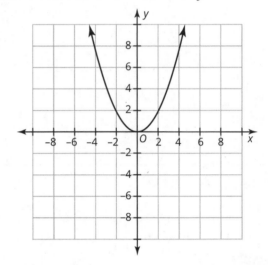

straightedge

A straightedge is a ruler with no numbers.

Substitution Property

The Substitution Property of Equality states: "If a and b are real numbers and $a = b$, then a can be substituted for b."

Example

If $AB = 12$ ft and $CD = 12$ ft, then $AB = CD$.

Subtraction Property of Equality

The Subtraction Property of Equality states: "If $a = b$, then $a - c = b - c$."

Example

If $x + 5 = 7$, then $x + 5 - 5 = 7 - 5$, or $x = 2$ is an example of the Subtraction Property of Equality.

tangent (tan)

The tangent (tan) of an acute angle in a right triangle is the ratio of the length of the side opposite the angle to the length of the side adjacent to the angle.

Example

In △ABC, the tangent of ∠A is:

$$\tan A = \frac{\text{length of side opposite } \angle A}{\text{length of side adjacent to } \angle A} = \frac{BC}{AC}$$

The expression "tan A" means "the tangent of angle A."

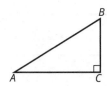

tangent circles

Tangent circles are circles that lie in the same plane and intersect at exactly one point.

Example

Circles O and B are tangent circles.

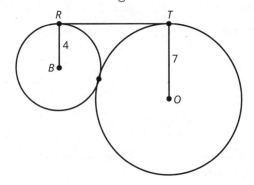

tangent of a circle

A tangent of a circle is a line that intersects the circle at exactly one point, called the point of tangency.

Example

Line RQ is tangent to circle P at point Q.

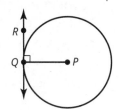

tangent segment

A tangent segment is a line segment formed by connecting a point outside of the circle to a point of tangency.

Example

Line segment AB and line segment AC are tangent segments.

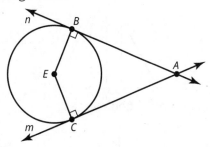

theorem

A theorem is a statement that has been proven to be true.

Example

The Pythagorean Theorem states that if a right triangle has legs of lengths a and b and hypotenuse of length c, then $a^2 + b^2 = c^2$.

total surface area

The total surface area of a three-dimensional figure is the sum of the areas of its bases and lateral faces.

Example

The total surface area of the right triangular prism is 132 square centimeters.

$$\text{Total surface area} = (5 \times 6) + (5 \times 6) + (8 \times 6)$$
$$+ \tfrac{1}{2}(8 \times 3) + \tfrac{1}{2}(8 \times 3)$$
$$= 30 + 30 + 48 + 12 + 12$$
$$= 132$$

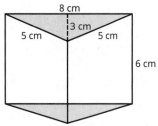

transformation

A transformation is an operation that maps, or moves, a figure, called the preimage, to form a new figure called the image. Three types of transformations are reflections, rotations, and translations.

Example

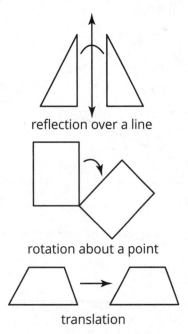

reflection over a line

rotation about a point

translation

Transitive Property

The Transitive Property states: "If $a = b$ and $b = c$, then $a = c$."

Example

If $x = y$ and $y = 2$, then $x = 2$ is an example of the Transitive Property.

translation

A translation is a rigid motion that "slides" a figure up, down, left, or right. A translation as a function, T_{AB}, takes as its input a set of pre-image points and outputs a set of image points. The pre-image points are translated a distance of AB in the direction AB.

Example

$T_{AB}(P) = P'$ and $T_{AC}(P) = P''$

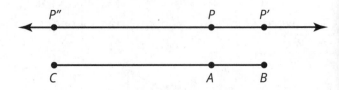

transverse axis

The transvere axis runs through the center of a hyperbola and both foci.

tree diagram

A tree diagram is a diagram that illustrates sequentially the possible outcomes of a given situation.

Example

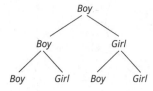

truth table

A truth table is a table that summarizes all possible truth values for a conditional statement $p \rightarrow q$.

truth value

The truth value of a conditional statement is whether the statement is true or false.

two-column proof

A two-column proof is a proof consisting of two columns. In the left column are mathematical statements that are organized in logical steps. In the right column are the reasons for each mathematical statement.

Example

The proof shown is a two-column proof.

Statements	Reasons
1. $\angle 1$ and $\angle 3$ are vertical angles.	**1.** Given
2. $\angle 1$ and $\angle 2$ form a linear pair. $\angle 2$ and $\angle 3$ form a linear pair.	**2.** Definition of linear pair
3. $\angle 1$ and $\angle 2$ are supplementary. $\angle 2$ and $\angle 3$ are supplementary.	**3.** Linear Pair Postulate
4. $\angle 1 \cong \angle 3$	**4.** Congruent Supplement Theorem

two-way frequency table (contingency table)

A two-way frequency table, also called a contingency table, shows the number of data points and their frequencies for two variables. One variable is divided into rows, and the other is divided into columns.

Example

The two-way frequency table shows the hand(s) favored by people who do and do not participate in individual or team sports.

Sports Participation

Favored Hand	Individual	Team	Does Not Play	Total
Left	3	13	8	24
Right	6	23	4	33
Mixed	1	3	2	6
Total	10	39	14	63

two-way relative frequency table

A two-way relative frequency table displays the relative frequencies for two categories of data.

Example

The two-way relative frequency table shows the hand(s) favored by people who do and do not participate in individual or team sports.

	Individual	Team	Does Not Play	Total
Left	$\frac{3}{63} \approx 4.8\%$	$\frac{13}{63} \approx 20.6\%$	$\frac{8}{63} \approx 12.7\%$	$\frac{24}{63} \approx 38.1\%$
Right	$\frac{6}{63} \approx 9.5\%$	$\frac{23}{63} \approx 36.5\%$	$\frac{4}{63} \approx 6.3\%$	$\frac{33}{63} \approx 52.4\%$
Mixed	$\frac{1}{63} \approx 1.6\%$	$\frac{3}{63} \approx 4.8\%$	$\frac{2}{63} \approx 3.2\%$	$\frac{6}{63} \approx 9.5\%$
Total	$\frac{10}{63} \approx 15.9\%$	$\frac{39}{63} \approx 61.9\%$	$\frac{14}{63} \approx 22.2\%$	$\frac{63}{63} = 100\%$

two-way table

A two-way table shows the relationship between two data sets, one data set is organized in rows and the other data set is organized in columns.

Example

The two-way table shows all the possible sums that result from rolling two number cubes once.

2nd Number Cube

1st Number Cube	1	2	3	4	5	6
1	2	3	4	5	6	7
2	3	4	5	6	7	8
3	4	5	6	7	8	9
4	5	6	7	8	9	10
5	6	7	8	9	10	11
6	7	8	9	10	11	12

— U —

uniform probability model

A uniform probability model occurs when all the probabilities in a probability model are equally likely to occur.

Example

Rolling a number cube represents a uniform probability model because the probability of rolling each number is equal.

union of sets

A union of sets is a set formed by combining all the members of the sets. A member may be listed only once.

Example

Let B represent the set of students in the 11th grade band. Let C represent the set of students in the 11th grade chorus. The union of these two sets would be all the students in the 11th grade band or the 11th grade chorus. A student in both would be listed only once.

vertex of a parabola (conic section)

The vertex of a parabola is the point on the axis of symmetry which is exactly midway between the focus and the directrix. It is also the point where the parabola changes direction.

Example

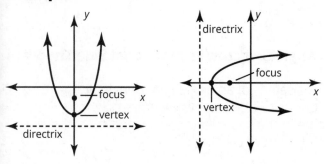

vertices

The endpoints of the major axis of an ellipse are the vertices.

Postulates and Theorems

30°-60°-90° Triangle Theorem

The length of the hypotenuse in a 30°-60°-90° triangle is 2 times the length of the shorter leg, and the length of the longer leg is $\sqrt{3}$ times the length of the shorter leg.

45°-45°-90° Triangle Theorem

The length of the hypotenuse in a 45°-45°-90° triangle is $\sqrt{2}$ times the length of a leg.

Alternate Exterior Angles Theorem

If two parallel lines are intersected by a transversal, then the alternate exterior angles are congruent.

Alternate Exterior Angles Converse Theorem

If two lines intersected by a transversal form congruent alternate exterior angles, then the lines are parallel.

Alternate Interior Angles Theorem

If two parallel lines are intersected by a transversal, then the alternate interior angles are congruent.

Alternate Interior Angles Converse Theorem

If two lines intersected by a transversal form congruent alternate interior angles, then the lines are parallel.

Angle Addition Postulate

If point D lies in the interior of $\angle ABC$, then $m\angle ABD + m\angle DBC = m\angle ABC$.

Angle-Side-Angle Congruence Theorem (ASA)

If two angles and the included side of one triangle are congruent to the corresponding two angles and the included side of another triangle, then the triangles are congruent.

Angle-Angle-Side Congruence Theorem

If two angles and the non-included side of one triangle are congruent to two angles and the non-included side of another triangle, then the two triangles are congruent.

Angle-Angle Similarity Theorem

If two angles of one triangle are congruent to two angles of another triangle, then the triangles are similar.

Angle Bisector/Proportional Side Theorem

A bisector of an angle in a triangle divides the opposite side into two segments whose lengths are in the same ratio as the lengths of the sides adjacent to the angle.

Arc Addition Postulate

The measure of an arc formed by two adjacent arcs is the sum of the measures of the two arcs.

Congruent Chord-Congruent Arc Theorem

If two chords of the same circle or congruent circles are congruent, then their corresponding arcs are congruent.

Congruent Chord-Congruent Converse Arc Theorem

If arcs of the same circle or congruent circles are congruent, then their corresponding chords are congruent.

Congruent Supplement Theorem

If two angles are supplements of the same angle or of congruent angles, then the angles are congruent.

Converse of the Triangle Proportionality Theorem

If a line divides two sides of a triangle proportionally, then it is parallel to the third side.

Corresponding Angles Theorem

If two parallel lines are intersected by a transversal, then corresponding angles are congruent.

Corresponding Angles Converse Theorem

If two lines intersected by a transversal form congruent corresponding angles, then the lines are parallel.

Diameter-Chord Theorem

If a circle's diameter is perpendicular to a chord, then the diameter bisects the chord and bisects the arc determined by the chord.

Equidistant Chord Theorem

If two chords of the same circle or congruent circles are congruent, then they are equidistant from the center of the circle.

Equidistant Chord Converse Theorem

If two chords of the same circle or congruent circles are equidistant from the center of the circle, then the chords are congruent.

Exterior Angle Theorem

The measure of an exterior angle of a triangle is equal to the sum of the measures of the two remote interior angles.

Exterior Angles of a Circle Theorem

If an angle is formed by two intersecting chords or secants of a circle such that the vertex of the angle is in the exterior of the circle, then the measure of the angle is half of the difference of the measures of the arcs intercepted by the angle.

Hypotenuse-Angle (HA) Congruence Theorem

If the hypotenuse and an acute angle of one right triangle are congruent to the hypotenuse and an acute angle of another right triangle, then the two triangles are congruent.

Hypotenuse-Leg (HL) Congruence Theorem

If the hypotenuse and leg of one right triangle are congruent to the hypotenuse and leg of another right triangle, then the triangles are congruent.

Inscribed Angle Theorem

The measure of an inscribed angle is half the measure of its intercepted arc.

Inscribed Right Triangle-Diameter Theorem

If a triangle is inscribed in a circle such that one side of the triangle is a diameter of the circle, then the triangle is a right triangle.

Inscribed Quadrilateral-Opposite Angles Theorem

If a quadrilateral is inscribed in a circle, then the opposite angles are supplementary.

Interior Angles of a Circle Theorem

If an angle is formed by two intersecting chords or secants of a circle such that the vertex of the angle is in the interior of the circle, then the measure of the angle is half of the sum of the measures of the arcs intercepted by the angle and its vertical angle.

Isosceles Triangle Base Angles Theorem

If two sides of a triangle are congruent, then the angles opposite these sides are congruent.

Isosceles Triangle Base Angles Converse Theorem

If two angles of a triangle are congruent, then the sides opposite these angles are congruent.

Leg-Angle (LA) Congruence Theorem

If the leg and an acute angle of one right triangle are congruent to the corresponding leg and acute angle of another right triangle, then the triangles are congruent.

Leg-Leg (LL) Congruence Theorem

If the two corresponding shorter legs of two right triangles are congruent, then the two triangles are congruent.

Linear Pair Postulate

If two angles form a linear pair, then the angles are supplementary.

Parallelogram/Congruent-Parallel Side Theorem

If one pair of opposite sides of a quadrilateral is both congruent and parallel, then the quadrilateral is a parallelogram.

Perpendicular Bisector Theorem

Points on a perpendicular bisector of a line segment are equidistant from the segment's endpoints.

Perpendicular Bisector Converse Theorem

If a point is equidistant from the endpoints of a line segment, then the point lies on the perpendicular bisector of the segment.

Perpendicular/Parallel Line Theorem

If two lines are perpendicular to the same line, then the two lines are parallel to each other.

Proportional Segments Theorem

If three parallel lines intersect two transversals, then they divide the transversals proportionally.

Right Angle Congruence Postulate

All right angles are congruent.

Right Triangle/Altitude Similarity Theorem

If an altitude is drawn to the hypotenuse of a right triangle, then the two triangles formed are similar to the original triangle and to each other.

Right Triangle Altitude/ Hypotenuse Theorem

The measure of the altitude drawn from the vertex of the right angle of a right triangle to its hypotenuse is the geometric mean between the measures of the two segments of the hypotenuse.

Right Triangle Altitude/Leg Theorem

If the altitude is drawn to the hypotenuse of a right triangle, each leg of the right triangle is the geometric mean of the hypotenuse and the segment of the hypotenuse adjacent to the leg.

Same-Side Exterior Angles Theorem

If two parallel lines are intersected by a transversal, then the same-side exterior angles are supplementary.

Same-Side Exterior Angles Converse Theorem

If two lines intersected by a transversal form supplementary same-side exterior angles, then the lines are parallel.

Same-Side Interior Angles Theorem

If two parallel lines are intersected by a transversal, then the interior angles on the same side of the transversal are supplementary.

Same-Side Interior Angles Converse Theorem

If two lines intersected by a transversal form supplementary same-side interior angles, then the lines are parallel.

Segment Addition Postulate

If point B is on $\overline{AC}$ and between points A and C, then $AB + BC = AC$.

Side-Angle-Side Congruence Theorem (SAS)

If two sides and the included angle of one triangle are congruent to the corresponding sides and the included angle of the second triangle, then the triangles are congruent.

Side-Angle-Side Similarity Theorem

If two of the corresponding sides of two triangles are proportional and the included angles are congruent, then the triangles are similar.

Side-Side-Side Congruence Theorem (SSS)

If three sides of one triangle are congruent to the corresponding sides of another triangle, then the triangles are congruent.

Side-Side-Side Similarity Theorem

If all three corresponding sides of two triangles are proportional, then the triangles are similar.

Tangent Segment Theorem

If two tangent segments are drawn from the same point on the exterior of a circle, then the tangent segments are congruent.

Tangent to a Circle Theorem

A line drawn tangent to a circle is perpendicular to a radius of the circle drawn to the point of tangency.

Trapezoid Midsegment Theorem

The midsegment that connects the legs of the trapezoid is parallel to each of the bases and its length is one half the sum of the lengths of the bases.

Triangle Midsegment Theorem

The midsegment of a triangle is parallel to the third side of the triangle and is half the measure of the third side of the triangle.

Triangle Proportionality Theorem

If a line parallel to one side of a triangle intersects the other two sides, then it divides the two sides proportionally.

Triangle Sum Theorem

The sum of the measures of the interior angles of a triangle is equal to 180°.

Vertical Angle Theorem

Vertical angles are congruent.

Index

Symbols
θ symbol, M4-19

A

Acute angle
  cosecant (csc) of, M3-216
  cosine (cos) of, M3-217
  cotangent (cot) of, M3-215
  secant (sec) of, M3-217
  sine (sin) of, M3-216
  tangent (tan) of, M3-214
Addition Rule for Probability,
    M5-46, M5-75
Adjacent arcs, M2-142,
    M2-178. *See also* Arc
Adjacent side, M3-213
  of right triangle, M3-124,
    M3-199
Alternate Exterior Angles
    Converse Theorem,
    M2-93, M2-176
Alternate Exterior Angles
    Theorem, M2-91,
    M2-175
Alternate Interior Angles
    Converse Theorem,
    M2-92, M2-176
Alternate Interior Angles
    Theorem, M2-88–
    M2-91, M2-175
Altitude
  of hypotenuse of right
    triangle, M3-66
  of triangle, M1-186, M1-200
AND
  compound events with,
    M5-30–M5-32
  compound probabilities
    with, M5-33–M5-34
  dependent events with,
    M5-35–M5-37
  or OR, M5-64–M5-66

Angle(s), M1-210
  acute (*See* Acute angle)
  arc relationships and,
    M1-116–M1-117
  base, M1-198
  bisecting, M1-153–M1-154
  central, M1-113, M1-194
  circumscribed, M1-120,
    M1-194
  complementary, M3-190–
    M3-192
  defined, M1-268
  duplicating, M1-147–
    M1-148
  exterior, M1-165–M1-168,
    M1-199
  included, M2-30, M2-54,
    M3-30, M3-111
  inscribed, M1-110, M1-194
  reference, M3-120, M3-124,
    M3-213
  relationships inside and
    outside circles,
    M2-141–M2-165
  remote interior, M1-168,
    M1-199
  rotation, M1-210, M1-268
  using complements,
    M3-191–M3-192
Angle Addition Postulate,
    M2-19, M2-53
Angle-Angle-Side (AAS)
    Congruence Theorem,
    M2-60, M2-131,
    M2-178
Angle-Angle (AA) Similarity
    criterion, M3-25–M3-27
Angle-Angle Similarity
    Theorem, M3-26,
    M3-110
Angle bisector, M1-153,
    M1-197

Angle Bisector/Proportional
    Side Theorem, M3-45,
    M3-111
  applying, M3-46–M3-47
  proving, M3-42–M3-45
Angle of incidence, M3-81,
    M3-114
Angle of inclination, M3-140
Angle of reflection, M3-81,
    M3-114
Angle-side-angle congruence,
    M2-32
Angle-Side-Angle Congruence
    Theorem (ASA), M2-32,
    M2-55
  on the coordinate plane,
    M2-44–M2-46
  using to solve problems,
    M2-41–M2-43
Angular velocity, M4-38,
    M4-92
Applications
  of parabola, M4-182–
    M4-183
  of sector, M4-34–M4-37
Arc
  adjacent, M2-142, M2-178
  and angle relationships,
    M1-116–M1-117
  chords and, M2-232–
    M2-234
  defined, M1-194
  degree measure of,
    M2-142, M2-178
  and inscribed angle,
    M1-118–M1-119
  intercepted, M1-118,
    M1-194
  major, M1-114, M1-194
  minor, M1-114, M1-194
Arc Addition Postulate,
    M2-142, M2-178

Arc length
  defined, M4-13, M4-89
  determining, M4-12–M4-16
  measuring angles and arcs
    using radians, M4-19–
    M4-21
  solving problems with,
    M4-17–M4-18
Area
  composite figure, M1-85–
    M1-86
  doubling and tripling
    circumference and,
    M4-125–M4-129
  of figures on coordinate
    plane, M1-71–M1-79
  formula, deriving another
    version of, M3-201
  heights of triangles,
    M1-80–M1-84
  of a sector, M4-28–M4-30
  solving problems, M1-87–
    M1-92
  See also Perimeter
Auxiliary line, M2-60
  defined, M1-12, M1-97
  drawing, M1-12
Axis
  conjugate, M4-214, M4-237
  major, M4-190, M4-235
  minor, M4-190, M4-235
  transverse, M4-214,
    M4-237

B
Base angles, M1-198
  of trapezoid, M2-206,
    M2-242
Bermuda Triangle, M1-6
Biconditional statement,
    M1-164, M1-198
Bisecting
  an angle, M1-153–M1-154
  line segment, M1-98
Bisectors, and circles parts,
    M1-113–M1-115

C
Categorical data, M5-85,
    M5-166
Cavalieri's Principle,
    M4-57–M-60, M4-94
Center of the circle, M1-194

Central angle, M1-113,
    M1-194
Centroid
  defined, M1-185, M1-200
  and point of concurrency,
    M1-184–M1-185
Chords, M1-114, M1-194
  arcs and, M2-232–M2-234
Circle(s)
  angle relationships inside
    and outside, M2-141–
    M2-165
  circumscribed, M1-180,
    M1-199
  defined, M4-8
  determining arc length,
    M4-12–M4-16
  determining measures
    inside and outside,
    M2-163–M2-165
  determining points on a,
    M4-133–M4-144
  equation, M4-121, M4-129
    doubling and tripling
    circumference and area,
    M4-125–M4-127
  Exterior Angles of a Circle
    Theorem, M2-153–
    M2-158
  Inscribed Angle Theorem,
    M2-144–M2-146
  Interior Angles of a Circle
    Theorem, M2-150–
    M2-152
  parts and bisectors,
    M1-113–M1-115
  problems, M4-141–M4-144
  quadrilaterals formed
    using, M1-132–M1-134
  sectors of a, M4-25–M4-27
  segment of a, M4-25–M4-27
  similar, M4-9–M4-11
  similarity relationships in,
    M4-7–M4-22
  symmtery, reasoning with,
    M4-139–M4-140
  tangent, M2-193, M2-242
  Tangent to a Circle
    Theorem, M2-159–
    M2-162
  theorems of inscribed
    polygons, M2-147–
    M2-149

  using, to make conjecture,
    M1-111–M1-120
  velocities in circular motion,
    M4-38–M4-39
  See also specific circles
Circular motion, velocities in,
    M4-38–M4-39
Circular permutation,
    M5-125–M5-126,
    M5-169
Circumcenter
  defined, M1-110, M1-180,
    M1-199
  and point of concurrency,
    M1-177–M1-180
Circumference
  arc length and, M4-13–
    M4-14
  doubling and tripling area
    and, M4-125–M4-129
Circumscribed angle, M1-120,
    M1-194
Circumscribed circle, M1-180,
    M1-199
Coincident, M1-129, M1-195
Collinear points, M1-208,
    M1-268
Color theory, M2-232
Color wheel, M2-232
Combinations, M5-127–
    M5-130
  calculating probability by
    using, M5-138–M5-143
  defined, M5-127, M5-169
  graphing calculators and,
    M5-130
Compass, M1-18, M1-98
Complementary angles,
    M3-190–M3-192
Complement of an event,
    M5-9, M5-72
Completing the square
  to determine the center,
    M4-122–M4-124
Composite figure
  area and perimeter of,
    M1-85–M1-86,
    M1-106
  defined, M1-106
Compound event, M5-30,
    M5-74
  with AND, M5-30–M5-32
  AND or OR, M5-64–M5-66

more than two, M5-60–
M5-61
with OR, M5-44
without repetition, M5-62–
M5-63
Compound probability
with AND, M5-33–M5-34
calculating, M5-57–M5-68
determining from relative
frequencies, M5-90–
M5-91
with OR, M5-45–M5-47
in two-way table, M5-81–
M5-94
analyzing, M5-85–M5-89
converse of the
multiplication rule,
M5-84
defined, M5-82
determining from relative
frequencies, M5-90–
M5-91
Compound sample spaces,
M5-7–M–25
Concave quadrilaterals,
M1-128, M1-195
Concavity, M4-163, M4-234
Concentric circles, M1-244
defined, M1-204, M1-270
quadrilaterals formed
using, M1-129–M1-131
Conclusion, M1-163, M1-198
Conclusion of a conditional
statement, M2-52
Concurrent lines, M1-176,
M1-199
Conditional probability,
M5-37, M5-75, M5-101–
M5-103
for dependent events,
M5-106–M5-107
formula, M5-104–M5-105
Conditional statement(s),
M1-163
conclusion of, M2-52
defined, M2-10, M2-52
hypothesis of, M2-52
and truth tables, M2-10–
M2-15
truth value of, M2-10,
M2-52
Cone
double-napped, M4-109

formula for volume of,
M4-72–M4-73
nappes, M4-109, M4-162,
M4-230
Congruence
markers, M2-5
solving problems with,
M2-132–M2-134
Congruence theorems
non-examples of, M2-33
Congruent Chord-Congruent
Arc Converse Theorem,
M2-234, M2-244
Congruent Chord-Congruent
Arc Theorem, M2-233,
M2-244
Congruent line segments by
reflection, M2-25–
M2-27
Congruent Supplement
Theorem, M2-73,
M2-174
proofs of, M2-71–M2-73
Conic sections, M4-109–
M4-113, M4-162,
M4-230
Conjecture(s)
about quadrilaterals,
M1-127–M1-141
about triangles, M1-161–
M1-170
constructing diagrams to
make, M1-109
defined, M1-6, M1-10,
M1-97
making, M1-10–M1-11
using circles to make,
M1-111–M1-120
Conjugate axis, M4-214,
M4-237
Constant ρ
graphing a parabola using,
M4-172–M4-176
making sense of, M4-170–
M4-171
Constructing
coordinate plane, M1-17–
M1-30
equilateral triangle,
M1-155–M1-156
geometric figures, M1-18,
M1-98
inscribed hexagon, M1-149

inscribed regular polygon,
M1-145–M1-156
inscribed square, M1-150–
M1-152
parallel lines, M1-36–
M1-39, M1-101–M1-102
perpendicular lines,
M1-19–M1-24, M1-102
segment bisector, M1-99
square(s), M1-25–M1-27
Contingency table, M5-85,
M5-166
Converse, of statement,
M1-163, M1-198
Converse of the Triangle
Proportionality
Theorem, M3-51,
M3-112
Convex quadrilaterals,
M1-128, M1-195
Coordinate plane
area and perimeter,
M1-69–M1-92
of composite figure,
M1-85–M1-86
of figures, M1-71–M1-79
heights of triangles,
M1-80–M1-84
solving problems with,
M1-87–M1-92
ASA on, M2-44–M2-46
calculating distance on,
M1-54–M1-56
classifying shapes on,
M1-51–M1-65
classifying triangles on,
M1-57–M1-59
constructing, M1-17–
M1-30
quadrilateral
classifying, M1-62–M1-63
classifying, formed by
midpoints, M1-64–
M1-65
determining unknown
point of, M1-60–M1-61
SAS on, M2-44–M2-46
SSS on, M2-44–M2-46
using proportionality on,
M3-103–M3-104
Corresponding Angles
Converse Theorem,
M2-86, M2-175

Corresponding Angles Theorem, M2-85–M2-86, M2-175
Corresponding parts of congruent triangles are congruent (CPCTC), M2-29, M2-54, M2-177
Cosecant (csc), M3-157, M3-216
Cosine (cos), M3-120, M3-217
Cosine ratio, M3-174–M3-177, M3-217–M3-218
Cotangent (cot), M3-142, M3-215
Counterexamples, M2-9–M2-10, M2-51
Counting Principle, M5-18–M5-20, M5-74
Co-vertices, M4-190, M4-235
Cross-sections
  point and line segment, M4-104–M4-105
  two-dimensional, M4-106–M4-108
Cyclic quadrilateral, M1-110, M1-141, M1-196
Cylinder
  formula for volume of, M4-55–M4-56
  oblique, M4-56
  right, M4-56, M4-93

D

Data
  categorical, M5-85, M5-166
  qualitative, M5-85, M5-166
Decimal approximation, M4-20
Degenerate conics, M4-110, M4-230
Degree measure of an arc, M2-142, M2-178
Denominator, rationalizing, M2-129, M2-178
Dependent events
  with AND, M5-35–M5-37
  conditional probability for, M5-106–M5-107
  defined, M5-16, M5-17, M5-73, M5-74
  with OR, M5-48–M5-51
Diagonal(s), M1-27, M1-101, M1-195

Diameter, M1-113, M1-194
Diameter-Chord Theorem, M2-184, M2-228, M2-243
Diameter of a sphere, M4-79, M4-95
Dilations
  defined, M3-9, M3-109
  of figures by scale factor, M3-9–M3-12
  of lines, M3-40–M3-41
  similar figures, M3-12
  as transformation, M3-9, M3-109
Directed line segments, M3-115
  defined, M3-100
  partitioning, M3-99–M3-102
Directrix, M4-162, M4-234
Disc, solid, M4-46, M4-92
Disjoint sets, M5-15, M5-73
Distance Formula
  defined, M1-6, M1-55, M1-104
  using, M1-104–M1-105
Doyle, Sir Arthur Conan, M2-60
Drawing
  auxiliary line, M1-12
  geometric figure, M1-9

E

Eccentricity, M4-195, M4-237
Element
  defined, M5-15, M5-73
  permutation with repeated, M5-121–M5-124
The Elements (Euclid), M2-16
Ellipses, M4-113, M4-187–M4-208, M4-230
  defining the, M4-184–M4-193
  graphing the, M4-194–M4-196
    not centered at the origin, M4-199–M4-201
  laws of orbits, M4-202–M4-206
Equation(s)
  for hyperbola, M4-219–M4-221
  of parabola, M4-159–M4-183

perpendicular lines, M1-45
  writing, with given a focus and a directrix, M4-177–M4-181
Equation for a circle, M4-121
  doubling and tripling circumference and area, M4-125–M4-127
Equidistant Chord Converse Theorem, M2-231, M2-244
Equidistant Chord Theorem, M2-184, M2-230, M2-244
Equilateral triangle
  constructing, M1-155–M1-156
  inscribing, M1-155–M1-156
  See also Triangle(s)
Euclid, M2-16
Euclidean geometry, M2-16, M2-52
  conditional statements and truth tables, M2-10–M2-15
  counterexamples, M2-9–M2-10
  formal reasoning in, M2-7–M2-22
  postulates and theorems, M2-16–M2-19
Event(s)
  categorizing scenarios involving, M5-15–M5-17
  complement of an, M5-9, M5-72
  compound
    with AND, M5-30–M5-32
    more than two, M5-60–M5-61
    with OR, M5-44
    without repetition, M5-62–M5-63
  defined, M5-8, M5-71
  dependent, M5-16, M5-17
    with AND, M5-35–M5-37
    conditional probability for, M5-106–M5-107
    with OR, M5-48–M5-51
  independent, M5-16
Expected value
  calculating, M5-157
  defined, M5-156, M5-171

exploring, M5-155–M5-156
using geometric probability to determine, M5-158–M5-160
Exterior angle(s), M1-165–M1-168, M1-199
of polygon, M2-111–M2-113
Exterior Angles of a Circle Theorem, M2-153–M2-158, M2-179
Exterior Angle Theorem, M2-105–M2-106, M2-176
Extract the roots, M2-129, M2-177

F

Factorials, M5-116–M5-117, M5-168
Figure(s)
area and perimeter, M1-71–M1-79
dilating by scale factor, M3-9–M3-12
similar, M3-12
using geometric theorems to demonstrate similarity of, M3-16–M3-17
using similarity transformations to demonstrate similarity of, M3-13–M3-15
Flashlights, M4-222–M4-223
Floodlight, M4-222–M4-223
Flow chart proof, M2-67–M2-68, M2-173. *See also* Proof(s)
Foci, M4-190, M4-235
making sense of, M4-197–M4-198
Focus, M4-162, M4-190, M4-234
Formal reasoning
conditional statements and truth tables, M2-10–M2-15
counterexamples, M2-9–M2-10
in Euclidean geometry, M2-7–M2-22

postulates and theorems, M2-16–M2-19
Forms of proof, M2-65–M2-70
flow chart proof, M2-67–M2-68
two-column proof, M2-69–M2-70
Formula(s)
of area, deriving another version of, M3-201
conditional probability, M5-104–M5-105
for multiple trials, M5-144–M5-145
solving problems using volume and surface area, M4-81–M4-83
surface area, M4-96
volume
of cone, M4-72–M4-73
of cylinder, M4-55–M4-56
of pyramid, M4-68–M4-71
45°-45°-90° Triangle Theorem, M2-128, M2-177
Frequency table, M5-83, M5-166
Function(s)
determining trigonometric, in four quadrants, M4-153
reflections as, M1-229–M1-238
rigid motion as, M1-203
rotations as, M1-243–M1-249, M1-271
translations as, M1-217–M1-225

G

General form, of parabola, M4-166, M4-234
Geometric mean, M3-113
defined, M3-68
Right Triangle Altitude/Hypotenuse Theorem, M3-68
Right Triangle Altitude/Leg Theorem, M3-68
of two positive numbers, M3-68, M3-113

using, M3-70
Geometric probability, M5-151–M5-154
defined, M5-154, M5-171
to determine expected value, M5-158–M5-160
Geometry
Euclidean (*See* Euclidean geometry)
properties of real numbers in, M2-63–M2-64
Graph
ellipses, M4-194–M4-196
not centered at the origin, M4-199–M4-201
parabola using constant ρ, M4-172–M4-176
Great circle of a sphere, M4-79, M4-95

H

Height(s)
determining indirectly, M3-84–M3-85
of triangles, M1-80–M1-84, M1-105–M1-106
Hemisphere, M4-79, M4-95
Horizontal lines, M1-43–M1-44
Hyperbola, M4-113, M4-211–M4-225, M4-230
defining the, M4-213–M4-216
equations for, M4-219–M4-221
Hyperbolic symmetry, M4-224–M4-225
Hypotenuse-Angle Congruence Theorem, M2-60
Hypotenuse-Angle (HA) Congruence Theorem, M2-131, M2-178
Hypotenuse-Leg Congruence Theorem, M2-187–M2-188
Hypotenuse-Leg (HL) Congruence Theorem, M2-188, M2-241
Hypothesis, M1-163, M1-198
Hypothesis of a conditional statement, M2-52

I

Identical lines, M3-40–M3-41

Incenter
  defined, M1-110, M1-183, M1-200
  and point of concurrency, M1-181–M1-183

Included angle, M2-30, M2-54, M3-30, M3-111

Included side, M2-32, M3-30, M3-111

Independent events, M5-16, M5-73, M5-74

Independent trials, M5-135, M5-146
  calculating probability by using combinations, M5-138, M5-143
  using a formula for multiple trials, M5-144–M5-145

Indirect measurement, M3-6, M3-81–M3-83, M3-114

Inscribed angle, M1-194
  and arc, M1-118–M1-119
  defined, M1-110, M1-118

Inscribed Angle Theorem, M2-60, M2-144–M2-146, M2-146, M2-179

Inscribed equilateral triangle, M1-155–M1-156

Inscribed hexagon, constructing, M1-149

Inscribed polygon, M1-197
  constructing, M1-145–M1-156
  defined, M1-149

Inscribed Quadrilateral-Opposite Angles Theorem, M2-149, M2-179

Inscribed Right Triangle-Diameter Theorem, M2-148, M2-179

Inscribed square, constructing, M1-150–M1-152

Intercepted arc, M1-118, M1-194

Interior angle of polygon, M1-129, M1-195, M2-107–M2-110

Interior Angles of a Circle Theorem, M2-150–M2-152, M2-152, M2-179

Intersecting sets, M5-15, M5-73

Inverse cosine (or arccosine), M3-178–M3-180, M3-217

Inverse sine (or arcsine), M3-160–M3-162
  defined, M3-216

Inverse tangent (or arctangent), M3-147–M3-148
  defined, M3-215

Isometric paper, M4-51, M4-93

Isometry/ies, M1-204
  defined, M1-222, M1-268
  sequences, M1-249
    using reflections, M1-237–M1-238
    using translations, M1-237–M1-238

Isosceles trapezoid, M1-134, M1-195

Isosceles Triangle Base Angles Converse Theorem, M2-125, M2-177

Isosceles Triangle Base Angles Theorem, M2-124–M2-125, M2-177

K

Kite, M1-131, M1-195
  properties of, M2-211–M2-212

Kramp, Christian, M5-116

L

Lateral face, M4-51, M4-93

Lateral surface area, M4-75, M4-95

Law of Cosines, M3-206, M3-219
  deriving, M3-205–M3-206

Law of Reflection, M3-81, M3-114

Law of Sines, M3-204, M3-219
  deriving, M3-202–M3-204

Laws of orbits, M4-202–M4-206

Leg-Angle (LA) Congruence Theorem, M2-189, M2-241

Leg-Leg (LL) Congruence Theorem, M2-189, M2-241

Line(s)
  auxiliary, M1-12, M1-97, M2-60
  concurrent, M1-176, M1-199
  defined, M1-19, M1-98, M1-208, M1-268
  dilations of, M3-40–M3-41
  horizontal, M1-43–M1-44
  identical, M3-40–M3-41
  parallel, M3-40–M3-41
  perpendicular (See perpendicular lines)
  vertical, M1-43–M1-44
  See also specific lines

Linear Pair Postulate, M2-17, M2-52

Linear velocity, M4-38, M4-92

Line of reflection, M1-233

Line segments, M1-19, M1-98, M1-268
  directed, M3-115
  partitioning directed, M3-99–M3-102
  trisecting, M3-97–M3-98
  using proportionality on the coordinate plane, M3-103–M3-104

Locus of points, M4-162, M4-234

M

Major arc, M1-114, M1-194. *See also* Arc

Major axis, M4-190, M4-235

Median
  defined, M1-184, M1-200
  of triangle, M1-184, M3-56–M3-57

Method of indivisibles, M4-58

Midpoint, M1-20, M1-98

Midpoint Formula, M1-64, M1-105

Midsegments
  defined, M1-139, M1-196

of quadrilaterals, M1-139–
M1-140
and triangle inequality,
M1-169–M1-170
Minor arc, M1-114, M1-194.
See also Arc
Minor axis, M4-190,
M4-235
Multiple trials, formula for,
M5-144–M5-145
Multiplication
rule, converse of the,
M5-84

N

Nappes, M4-109, M4-162,
M4-230
Non-uniform probability
model, M5-8, M5-72
Numbers
positive, M3-68, M3-113
real, M2-63–M2-64

O

Oblique
cylinder, M4-56, M4-93
rectangular prism, M4-54,
M4-93
triangular prism, M4-52,
M4-93
Opposite side, M3-213
of right triangle, M3-124
OR
AND or, M5-64–M5-66
compound events with,
M5-44
compound probabilities
with, M5-45–M5-47
dependent events with,
M5-48–M5-51
Organized list, M5-12, M5-73
Orthocenter
defined, M1-110, M1-187,
M1-200
and point of concurrency,
M1-186–M1-187
Outcome, M5-8, M5-71
Overwijk, Alexander, M1-112

P

Parabola, M4-113
applications of, M4-182–
M4-183

concavity of, M4-163,
M4-234
defined, M4-162, M4-230
directrix, M4-162
equations of, M4-159–
M4-183
focus, M4-162
general form of, M4-166,
M4-234
locus of points, M4-162
as a locus of points,
M4-162–M4-164
making sense of constant
ρ, M4-170–M4-171
standard form of, M4-166,
M4-234
vertex of, M4-163, M4-234
writing equations with
given a focus and a
directrix, M4-177–
M4-181
Paragraph proof, M2-78. *See
also* Proof(s)
Parallel line converse
theorems, M2-92–
M2-93
Parallel lines, M3-40–M3-41
constructing, M1-36–
M1-39, M1-101–M1-102
Parallel line theorems,
M2-83–M2-94
Alternate Interior Angles
Theorem, M2-88–M2-91
Corresponding Angles
Theorem, M2-85–M2-86
parallel line converse
theorems, M2-92–
M2-93
Perpendicular/Parallel Line
Theorem, M2-94
Same-Side Interior Angles
Theorem, M2-87
Parallelogram(s)
defined, M2-199, M2-242
properties of, M2-199–
M2-203
Parallelogram/Congruent-
Parallel Side Theorem,
M2-202, M2-242
Perimeter, M1-69–M1-92
of composite figure,
M1-85–M1-86
of figures, M1-71–M1-79

heights of triangles, M1-80–
M1-84
solving problems, M1-87–
M1-92
See also Area
Permutation
calculating by using
combinations, M5-138–
M5-143
circular, M5-125–M5-126,
M5-169
defined, M5-118–M5-120
with repeated elements,
M5-121–M5-124
Perpendicular bisector,
M1-21, M1-99
Perpendicular Bisector
Converse Theorem,
M2-123, M2-177
Perpendicular Bisector
Theorem, M1-234–
M1-235, M1-270,
M2-121–M2-123,
M2-177
Perpendicular lines
constructing, M1-19–
M1-24, M1-102
slopes of, M1-40–M1-42
using squares for showing
slopes of, M1-5
writing equations of, M1-45
Perpendicular/Parallel Line
Theorem, M2-94,
M2-176
Point, M1-19, M1-98, M1-268
Point of concurrency,
M1-175–M1-187
defined, M1-176, M1-199–
M1-200
investigating
centroid, M1-184–M1-185
circumcenter, M1-177–
M1-180
incenter, M1-181–M1-183
orthocenter, M1-186–
M1-187
Points on a circle
center is not at the origin,
M4-137–M4-138
circle problems, M4-141–
M4-144
determining, M4-133–
M4-144

identifying, M4-135–
    M4-136
reasoning with circle
    symmetry, M4-139–
    M4-140
Polygon(s), M1-52
    Exterior Angle Theorem,
        M2-105–M2-106
    inscribed, M1-197
    sum of measures of
        exterior angles of,
        M2-111–M2-113
    sum of measures of interior
        angles of, M2-107–
        M2-110
    Triangle Sum Theorem,
        M2-105–M2-106
Postulate, M2-6, M2-52
    defined, M1-121, M1-194,
        M2-16
    and theorems, M2-16–
        M2-19
Prism
    right rectangular, M4-54,
        M4-93
    right triangular, M4-52,
        M4-93
Probability
    addition rule for, M5-46,
        M5-75
    compound
        with AND, M5-33–M5-34
        with OR, M5-45–M5-47
    conditional, M5-37, M5-75
    defined, M5-8, M5-71
    geometric, M5-154, M5-171
Probability model
    defined, M5-8, M5-71
    non-uniform, M5-8, M5-72
    uniform, M5-8, M5-72
Proof(s), M2-6, M2-26,
    M2-172
    analyzing, M2-59
    of the congruent
        supplement theorem,
        M2-71–M2-73
    defined, M1-234, M1-270
    flow chart, M2-67–M2-68,
        M2-173
    forms of, M2-65–M2-70
    paragraph, M2-78
    two-column, M2-69–M2-70,
        M2-173

of the Vertical Angle
    Theorem, M2-74–M2-75
Proportionality
    using on the coordinate
        plane, M3-103–M3-104
Proportional Segments
    Theorem, M3-52,
    M3-112
Pythagorean identity,
    M4-149–M4-155
    defined, M4-151, M4-233
    determining tangent
        funtions in all
        quadrants, M4-154
    determining trignometric
        funtions in four
        quadrants, M4-153
Pythagorean Theorem,
    M3-143, M3-214
    for calculating distance
        between two points on
        coordinate plane,
        M1-55, M1-104
    similar triangles, proving
        with, M3-71–M3-72

Q
Quadrilaterals
    concave, M1-128, M1-195
    conjecture about, M1-127–
        M1-141
    convex, M1-128, M1-195
    coordinate plane
        classifying, M1-62–M1-63
        classifying, formed by
            midpoints, M1-64–
            M1-65
        determining unknown
            point, M1-60–M1-61
    cyclic, M1-110, M1-141,
        M1-196
    formed using a circle,
        M1-132–M1-134
    formed using concentric
        circles, M1-129–M1-131
    kite as, M1-131, M1-195
    midsegments of, M1-139–
        M1-140
    properties of, M2-197–
        M2-215, M2-219
        kites, M2-211–M2-212
        parallelograms, M2-199–
            M2-203

rectangles, M2-204–
    M2-205
    rhombi, M2-199–M2-203
    squares, M2-204–M2-205
    trapezoids with one pair
        of parallel sides,
        M2-206–M2-210
    using to solve problems,
        M2-213–M2-215
    Venn diagram of, M2-183
Qualitative data, M5-85,
    M5-166

R
Radian(s), M3-143, M4-19,
    M4-90
Radius, M1-113, M1-194
    of a sphere, M4-79, M4-95
Rationalize the denominator,
    M2-129, M2-178
Ratios
    in 30°-60°-90° triangles,
        M3-128–M3-130
    constant, in right triangles,
        M3-123–M3-127
    trigonometric (See
        Trigonometric ratios)
Ray, M1-210, M1-268
Real numbers, properties of,
    M2-63–M2-64, M2-172
Reasoning, formal. See
    Formal reasoning
Rectangles
    defined, M2-204, M2-242
    properties of, M2-204–
        M2-205
Rectangular prism
    oblique, M4-54, M4-93
    right, M4-54, M4-93
Reference angle, M3-120,
    M3-124, M3-213
Reflectional symmetry,
    M1-257–M1-263,
    M1-272
Reflections, M1-101
    defined, M1-232, M1-269
    as functions, M1-229–
        M1-238
    line of, M1-233
    sequences of isometries
        using, M1-237–M1-238
Relative frequencies, M5-86,
    M5-167

determining compound probability from, M5-90–M5-91

Remote interior angles, M1-168, M1-199

Repeated elements, permutation with, M5-121–M5-124

Rhombi, properties of, M2-199–M2-203

Right Angle Congruence Postulate, M2-174

Right cylinder, M4-56, M4-93

Right rectangular prism, M4-54, M4-93

Right Triangle Altitude/ Hypotenuse Theorem, M3-68, M3-113

Right Triangle Altitude/Leg Theorem, M3-68, M3-113

Right Triangle/Altitude Similarity Theorem, M3-67, M3-113

Right triangles
adjacent side, M3-124
constant ratios in, M3-123–M3-127
opposite side, M3-124
reference angle, M3-124
special, M2-126–M2-130
See also Triangle(s)

Right triangular prism, M4-52, M4-93

Rigid motion, M1-28–M1-29, M1-101
as functions, M1-203
geometric components of, M1-205–M1-210

Rotational symmetry, M1-204, M1-257–M1-263, M1-272

Rotation angle, M1-210, M1-268

Rotations, M1-101
defined, M1-245, M1-270
determining the center of, M1-248
as functions, M1-243–M1-249, M1-271

Rule of Compound Probability involving and, M5-34, M5-74

S

Same-Side Exterior Angles Converse Theorem, M2-176

Same-Side Exterior Angles Theorem, M2-91, M2-175

Same-Side Interior Angles Converse Theorem, M2-93, M2-176

Same-Side Interior Angles Theorem, M2-87, M2-175

Sample space
converse of the multiplication rule and, M5-84
defined, M5-8, M5-71
for pizza special, M5-10–M5-12
for student council election, M5-13–M5-14

Scale factor, dilating figures by, M3-9–M3-12

Secant (sec), M1-114, M1-194, M3-174, M3-217

Sector(s)
applications of, M4-34–M4-37
area of, M4-28–M4-30
of a circle, M4-26, M4-91

Segment
area of a, M4-31–M4-33
of a circle, M4-31

Segment Addition Postulate, M2-18, M2-52

Segment bisector, M1-20, M1-98
constructing, M1-99

Segment-Chord Theorem, M3-63

Set(s)
defined, M5-15, M5-73
disjoint, M5-15, M5-73
intersecting, M5-15, M5-73
union of, M5-15, M5-73

Shapes
classifying, on coordinate plane, M1-51–M1-65
volume and, M4-74

Side(s)
adjacent, M3-124, M3-199, M3-213

included, M2-32, M3-30, M3-111
opposite, M3-124, M3-199, M3-213

Side-angle-side congruence, M2-30–M2-31

Side-Angle-Side Congruence Theorem (SAS), M2-31, M2-54
on the coordinate plane, M2-44–M2-46
using to solve problems, M2-41–M2-43

Side-Angle-Side (SAS) Similarity criterion, M3-30–M3-31

Side-Angle-Side Similarity Theorem, M3-31, M3-111

Side-Side-Side Congruence Theorem (SSS), M2-28–M2-29, M2-29, M2-54
on the coordinate plane, M2-44–M2-46
using to solve problems, M2-41–M2-43

Side-Side-Side (SSS) Similarity criterion, M3-28–M3-29

Side-Side-Side Similarity Theorem, M3-29, M3-111

Similar figures, M3-12
defined, M3-109

Similar triangles, M3-16–M3-17. See also Triangle(s)
Angle-Angle (AA) Similarity criterion, M3-25–M3-27
application of, M3-79–M3-81
defined, M3-109
determining
height indirectly, M3-84–M3-85
width indirectly, M3-86–M3-88
geometric mean, M3-68–M3-70
indirect measurement, M3-81–M3-83
proving the Pythagorean Theorem with, M3-71–M3-72

Side-Angle-Side (SAS)
Similarity criterion,
M3-30–M3-31
Side-Side-Side (SSS)
Similarity criterion,
M3-28–M3-29
Sine (sin), M3-120, M3-216
Sine ratio, M3-157–M3-159,
M3-216
Sketching, geometric figure,
M1-9, M1-97
Slope(s)
connecting tangent and,
M3-119, M3-139–
M3-142
of perpendicular lines,
M1-40–M1-42
Solid, rigid motion to create,
M4-51–M4-54
Special right triangles,
M2-126–M2-130
Sphere, M4-79–M4-80
defined, M4-79, M4-95
diameter of, M4-79, M4-9
great circle of, M4-79, M4-95
hemisphere, M4-79, M4-95
radius of, M4-79, M4-95
Square(s), M1-9
constructing, M1-25–M1-27
perfect, M1-8
properties of, M2-204–
M2-205
Standard form
of the equation of a circle,
M4-121
of parabola, M4-166,
M4-234
Straightedge, M1-18, M1-98
A Study in Scarlet (Doyle),
M2-60
Surface area, M4-75–M4-78
formulas, M4-96
lateral, M4-75
solving problems using,
M4-81–M4-83
total, M4-75
Symmetry
identifying, M1-263
reflectional, M1-257–
M1-263, M1-272
rotational, M1-204,
M1-257–M1-263,
M1-272

T
Tables
contingency, M5-85,
M5-166
frequency, M5-83, M5-166
two-way, M5-81–M5-94
Tangent (tan), M1-194,
M3-120, M3-141,
M3-214
circumscribed angle and,
M1-120
connecting slope and,
M3-119, M3-139–
M3-142
defined, M1-120
inverse, M3-147–M3-148
problem solving with,
M3-143–M3-144
Tangent circles, M2-193,
M2-242
Tangent ratio, M3-214–
M3-215
generalizing, M3-145–
M3-146
Tangent segments, M2-184,
M2-191–M2-193,
M2-242
Tangent Segment Theorem,
M2-192, M2-242
Tangent to a Circle Theorem,
M2-159–M2-162,
M2-160, M2-179
Theorems, M2-6
defined, M1-121, M1-194,
M1-270, M2-16
of inscribed polygons,
M2-147–M2-149
parallel line, M2-83–M2-94
parallel line converse,
M2-92–M2-93
using to determine
unknown measures,
M2-76
See also specific theorems
30°-60°-90° angles, M1-165–
M1-168
30°-60°-90° Triangle
Theorem, M2-127,
M2-177
Three-dimensional figures
Cavalieri's Principle,
M4-57–M–60
in solids, M4-45–M4-64

transitioning to, M4-49–
M4-50
using rigid motions to
create, M4-51–M4-54
Total surface area, M4-75,
M4-95
Transformation, M1-28,
M1-268
defined, M1-6, M1-101
dilation as, M3-9, M3-109
using similarity to
demonstrate similarity,
M3-13–M3-15
Transitioning to three
dimensions, M4-49–
M4-50
Translations, M1-101
defined, M1-222, M1-268
determining congruence
using, M1-224–M1-225
as functions, M1-217–
M1-225
sequences of isometries
using, M1-237–M1-238
Transverse axis, M4-214,
M4-237
Trapezoid Midsegment
Theorem, M2-184,
M2-210, M2-243
Trapezoids
base angles of, M2-206,
M2-242
defined, M1-134, M2-183
isosceles, M1-134, M1-195
with one pair of parallel
sides, properties of,
M2-206–M2-210
Tree diagram, M5-10, M5-72
Triangle(s)
classifying, on coordinate
plane, M1-57–M1-59
conjectures about,
M1-161–M1-170
constant ratios in right,
M3-123–M3-127
equilateral, M1-155–
M1-156
heights of, M1-80–M1-84,
M1-105–M1-106
inequality and
midsegments, M1-169–
M1-170
median of, M3-56–M3-57

ratios in 30°-60°-90°, M3-128–M3-130
reference angle, M3-124
similar, M3-16–M3-17, M3-109
special right, M2-126–M2-130
sum, M1-165–M1-168
Triangle congruence, solving problem by, M2-39–M2-46
  ASA, M2-41–M2-43
  SAS, M2-41–M2-43
  SSS, M2-41–M2-43
Triangle congruence theorems, M2-131
  Angle-Angle-Side (AAS) Congruence Theorem, M2-131
  angle-side-angle congruence, M2-32
  applying, M2-189–M2-190
  congruent line segments by reflection, M2-25–M2-27
  Hypotenuse-Angle (HA) Congruence Theorem, M2-131
  non-examples of, M2-33
  side-angle-side congruence, M2-30–M2-31
  Side-Side-Side Congruence Theorem (SSS), M2-28–M2-29
Triangle Midsegment Theorem, M3-6, M3-53–M3-55, M3-112
Triangle Proportionality Theorem, M3-6, M3-48–M3-51, M3-111
  Converse of, M3-51, M3-112
Triangle similarity criteria
  Angle-Angle (AA) Similarity criterion, M3-25–M3-27

Side-Angle-Side (SAS) Similarity criterion, M3-30–M3-31
Side-Side-Side (SSS) Similarity criterion, M3-28–M3-29
Triangle Sum Theorem, M2-105–M2-106, M2-176
Triangular prism
  oblique, M4-52, M4-93
  right, M4-52, M4-93
Trigonometric laws, applying, M3-207–M3-208
Trigonometric ratios
  applying, M3-193–M3-194
  complementary relationships of, M3-190
Trigonometry
  constant ratios in right triangles, M3-123–M3-127
  cosine ratio, M3-174–M3-177
  inverse cosine (or arccosine), M3-178–M3-180
  inverse sine (or arcsine), M3-160–M3-162
  ratios in 30°-60°-90° triangles, M3-128–M3-130
  sine ratio, M3-157–M3-159
Truth table, M2-13, M2-52
Truth value, M2-10, M2-52
2-D shapes, rotating through space, M4-47–M4-48
Two-column proof, M2-69–M2-70, M2-173. See also Proof(s)
Two-dimensional cross-sections, M4-106–M4-108
Two-way frequency table, M5-85, M5-166
Two-way relative frequency table, M5-86, M5-167

Two-way table, M5-81–M5-94
  analyzing, M5-85–M5-89
  defined, M5-82, M5-165

U
Undefined terms, M1-208
Uniform probability model, M5-8, M5-72
Union of sets, M5-15, M5-73
Unknown measures
  using theorems to determine, M2-76

V
Value, expected, M5-149–M5-161
Velocity(ies)
  angular, M4-38, M4-92
  in circular motion, M4-38–M4-39
  linear, M4-38, M4-92
Venn diagram of quadrilaterals, M2-183
Vertex of parabola, M4-163, M4-234
Vertical Angle Theorem, M2-75, M2-174
  proofs of, M2-74–M2-75
Vertical lines, M1-43–M1-44
Vertices, M4-190, M4-235
Volume
  comparing shapes and, M4-74
  formula
    of cone, M4-72–M4-73
    of cylinder, M4-55–M4-56
    of pyramid, M4-68–M4-71
  solving problems using, M4-81–M4-83

W
Width, determining indirectly, M3-86–M3-88

Z
Zukei puzzle, M1-142